"I have found *Southern Forages* to be an
and farm advisors. It is user friendly and its
appealing to a diverse audience."

Dr. Jim Green, Extension Forage Specialist, N

MW00658614

"Page after page reveals keystone principles of applied forage information. From dashboards of trucks to libraries, this book will be dog-eared from regular use. I highly recommend *Southern Forages*."

Dr. Jimmy Henning, Extension Forage Specialist, University of Kentucky

"*Southern Forages* is a 'must read' for every livestock producer who uses pasture and hay or silage. I find it a rare blend of scientific and easy-to-read practical information. It is one of my most used references."

Mr. Earl Manning, Mid-South Editor (retired), Progressive Farmer magazine

"Any livestock producer who is planning a new forage program should read this book. Any livestock producer with an established forage program who reads this book will be stimulated to reevaluate and improve that program. It is very well organized, interesting, and easy to read."

Dr. John Moore, Animal Scientist/Nutritionist (retired), University of Florida

"I like the approach used in separating the various types of forages as well as the various types of livestock. Too often, information concerning forages and pastures for horses, sheep, and wildlife is omitted from traditional texts. I found the book easy to read and suitable as either a textbook for the classroom or a handbook for the producer."

Dr. Monte Rouquette, Jr., Forage Physiologist, Texas A&M University Agricultural Research and Extension Center, Overton

"There are three books that I couldn't do without: The *Bible*, *Progressive Fallow Deer Farming*, and *Southern Forages*."

Mr. Cleve Tedford, Deer Farmer, Tellico Plains, Tennessee

"At long last, a great book on how, when, what, and why to grow and use forages in the South has been written! A masterful job of blending complex scientific facts in everyday language."

Mr. Warren Thompson, National Forage Specialist, ABI Alfalfa, Lexington, Kentucky

"*Southern Forages* contains a unique combination of features not found in other texts. Examples are the full-color photographs which clearly illustrate characteristics of forage species and the appendix which serves as a valuable compendium, summarizing key forage-related information."

Dr. J.J. Volenec, Forage Researcher/Teacher, Purdue University

"Reference books are a necessity for any forage producer. No matter how large or how small your library is, *Southern Forages* is a must. Its unique format makes it simple enough for the beginner, yet comprehensive enough to keep the veteran producer on track. It's top shelf."

Mr. David Wright, Dairy Producer, Alexandria, Alabama

Dedication . . .

To Vonda, Pat, and Cheryl

SOUTHERN FORAGES Third Edition

Modern Concepts for Forage Crop Management

By D.M Ball, C.S. Hoveland, and G.D. Lacefield

Published by the Potash & Phosphate Institute (PPI)
and the Foundation for Agronomic Research (FAR)
655 Engineering Drive, Suite 110
Norcross, Georgia 30092-2837 USA
Phone: 770-447-0335
Fax: 770-448-0439
E-mail: ppi@ppi-far.org

Printed by Graphic Communications Corporation,
Lawrenceville, Georgia, USA

Order from:
Potash & Phosphate Institute (PPI)
655 Engineering Drive, Suite 110
Norcross, Georgia 30092-2837 USA
Phone: 770-825-8082
Fax: 770-448-0439
E-mail: circulation@ppi-far.org

Library of Congress Control Number: 2002103672

ISBN 0-9629598-3-9

Foreword

This Third Edition of *Southern Forages* is the end result of more than 10 years of critical review of the first and second editions by the authors and publishers. While you, our readers, have told us how much you like and use the book...and have backed up your sentiments by purchasing more than 20,000 copies...we've continued to look for ways to make it an even more valuable resource.

When you look through the Third Edition, we believe you will find that the efforts to improve the book have been successful. Some chapters were expanded or shortened, combined with others, or omitted. Important new chapters have been added to discuss forage ecology and minimizing stored feed requirements. An up-to-date treatment of the fescue endophyte problem and an artist's rendition of forage seed are but two of the advancements that set this *Southern Forages* edition apart from its two predecessors. Layout has been modernized to provide a more open, easy-to-read text. The appendix section has been expanded. There are new illustrations and photographs. More recent research data have been added where available.

With all the improvements, this edition of *Southern Forages* continues the tradition of presenting information that is widely adapted across geographic and climatic areas. This breadth of coverage has resulted in the book being used as a text in more than 50 colleges and universities in the U.S., and it continues to be discovered by readers throughout the world. Through cooperation with Purdue University, we supported the publication of a Polish version in 1996. In 2001, with the cooperation of the Oregon Seed Council, a Chinese language version was introduced. Some of our readers have suggested that with such global appeal, we should consider changing the name, but we don't want to lose our identity with *Southern Forages,* so the title remains the same.

As with the first two editions, we continue to be grateful to and respectful of the work of Drs. Ball, Hoveland, and Lacefield. Partnering with them to produce *Southern Forages* has been a fulfilling experience for all of us here at the Institute and Foundation. We sincerely hope that you, our readers, will appreciate their efforts as much as we do and that the book will be a valuable learning tool for you.

David W. Dibb, President
Potash & Phosphate Institute

Terry L. Roberts, President
Foundation for Agronomic Research

Acknowledgements

The authors gratefully acknowledge the extensive in-depth reviews of the initial manuscript for this book that were provided by: Dr. Henry Amos, Department of Animal and Dairy Science, University of Georgia; Dr. Pat Bagley, Department of Agricultural Science, Sam Houston State University; Dr. Roy Blaser, University Distinguished Professor Emeritus (retired), Virginia Tech University; Dr. Larry Grabau, University of Kentucky; Mr. Curtis Grissom, County Agent-Coordinator, Limestone County, Alabama; and Mr. Ken Rogers, Alabama Natural Resources Conservation Service (NRCS), State Office.

Other helpful suggestions regarding the initial manuscript were provided by: Dr. Glenn Burton, Research Geneticist (retired), Coastal Plain Experiment Station, Tifton, Georgia; Dr. Jimmy Henning, Dr. Monroe Rasnake, Dr. Roy Burris, and Dr. Duane Miksch (retired), University of Kentucky; Dr. Mark McCann, Virginia Tech University; Dr. Troy Johnson and Dr. Harold Brown (both retired), University of Georgia; Dr. Edgar Cabrera, Pioneer Hi-Bred International; Dr. Lowell Moser, University of Nebraska; Dr. Lee Stribling, Dr. David Bransby, and Dr. John Everest, Auburn University; Dr. Henry Fribourg (retired), Plant and Soil Science Department, University of Tennessee; Dr. G.W. Evers, Texas A&M University, Overton Research Station; Dr. Bill Griffith and Dr. Bob Thompson (both retired), Potash & Phosphate Institute; Dr. Larry Murphy, Fluid Fertilizer Foundation; Dr. Ron Haaland, The Haaland Company, Auburn, Alabama; Dr. Stewart Smith, LiphaTech Inc., Milwaukee, Wisconsin; Mr. William Green and Mr. George Kelley, county agents in Graves and Hopkins counties, respectively, in Kentucky; and Mr. Ken Johnson, NRCS, Monroe County, Kentucky.

Special thanks go to Dr. Thomas A. Powe, Jr. (retired), College of Veterinary Medicine, Auburn University, for consultation regarding poisonous plants. The typing of Ms. Thyrza Smith, Ms. Lynn Tidwell, Ms. Carolyn Hightower, and Ms. Christi Forsythe is also gratefully acknowledged.

Suggestions and/or assistance regarding the Third Edition were provided by numerous people, including: Dr. David Mays, Alabama A&M University; Dr. Billy Powell, Alabama Cattlemen's Association; Dr. George Bates, Alcorn State University; Dr. David Bransby, Dr. Bob Burdett, Mr. Mike Davis, Dr. John Everest, Dr. Cindy McCall, Dr. Mary Miller-Goodman, Dr. Jorge Mosjidis, and Ms. Carmalita Pollard, Auburn University; Mr. Curtis Avery, cattleman, Pine Mountain, Georgia; Mr. Billy Womack, cattleman, Ashford, Alabama; Dr. Bruce Pinkerton, Clemson University; Mr. Cleve Tedford, deer farmer, Tellico Plains, Tennessee; Mr. Hank Bendorf, Forage Genetics International; Dr. Bill Kunkle (deceased), Dr. Ken Quesenberry, and Dr. Lynn Sollenberger, University of Florida; Dr. Will Getz, Fort Valley State University; Dr. John Andrae, Dr. Roger Bates, Dr. Gary Hill, Dr. Nick Hill, and Dr. Julia McCann, University of Georgia; Dr. Mike Collins, Ms. Christi Forsythe, Dr. Jimmy Henning, Mr. John James, Dr. Monroe Rasnake, and

Ms. Sandie Waddell, University of Kentucky; Mr. Tim Sickman, journalist, Louisville, Kentucky; Dr. Brad Venuto, Louisiana State University; Dr. Charles Baskin (retired) and Dr. Malcolm Broome, Mississippi State University; Mr. Ken Johnson, NRCS, Monroe County, Kentucky; Mr. R.L. Dalrymple (retired) the Noble Foundation; Mr. Ken Rogers, NRCS State Office, Alabama; Dr. Cliff Snyder and Dr. Noble Usherwood (retired), Potash & Phosphate Institute; Dr. Gary Bates, Professor Joe Burns (retired), and Dr. Warren Gill, University of Tennessee; Dr. Mark McCann, Department of Animal Science, Virginia Tech University; Dr. Bill Young, Oregon State University; Dr. John Baylor (retired), Penn State University; Dr. Becky Greenwald, Pioneer Hi-Bred International; Dr. Wade Faw, Tennessee Tech University; Dr. G.W. Evers and Dr. David Forbes, Texas A&M University; Dr. Geoff Brink, USDA/ARS, Starkville, Mississippi; and Dr. Jeff Pedersen, USDA/ARS, Lincoln, Nebraska; Dr. Ed Rayburn, West Virginia University; and Dr. Dan Undersander, University of Wisconsin.

The authors also acknowledge the ongoing support and contributions of Dr. David W. Dibb, Dr. Bob Darst (retired), Dr. Terry Roberts, and others affiliated with the Potash & Phosphate Institute and the Foundation for Agronomic Research. The work of Mr. Bill Agerton, Potash & Phosphate Institute (retired), and Mr. Charles Hamilton (graphic consultant) in earlier editions was useful in this new edition. The dedicated efforts of editor Don Armstrong, Potash & Phosphate Institute, in all editions are greatly appreciated by the authors. Ms. Kathy Hefner worked on previous editions and deserves great credit for design, layout, and typesetting of the Third Edition. Ms. Katherine Griffin, Potash & Phosphate Institute, had key responsibility in coordinating the production schedule and the many revisions and improvements in this edition.

Photo/Art Credits: The cover photograph of dairy cattle was provided by Mr. Warren Thompson, ABI Alfalfa, Lexington, Kentucky. The deer photograph was supplied by Dr. Neil Waer, Consulting Wildlife Biologist, Auburn, Alabama. Mr. Todd Scott of Graphic Communications created the cover design, and many other individuals with the company were also involved in various phases of production. The drawings of forage crop seed shown in chapters 5, 6, 7, and 8, and certain other illustrations were done by Mr. Craig Adams. Other photographs, acknowledged at various points throughout the book, were provided by: Dr. G.W. Evers, Mr. Morris Gillespie, Dr. Jimmy Henning, Dr. Mike Patterson, Dr. Tom Powe, Dr. Monroe Rasnake, Dr. Ron Shumack, Mr. Warren Thompson, Dr. Neil Waer, Quail Unlimited, and the National Wild Turkey Federation. Photographs not acknowledged were supplied by the authors.

Preface

In the Preface to the First Edition of *Southern Forages*, we emphasized the great economic and environmental value of forages in the South. We mentioned the unrealized potential of forages, the opportunity for improvement that exists on most farms, and the need for a modern, practical book that contains basic information for successful forage production.

Our objective in writing *Southern Forages* was to provide a book on practical aspects of forage production that any forage producer or agricultural worker, regardless of his or her scientific training, can read and understand. Our editor and publisher encouraged us to use color photographs and diagrams to illustrate plant species and concepts. The result was an attractive and easy-to-read book.

The response to both the First Edition of *Southern Forages* as well as to the updated and expanded Second Edition has been gratifying. Both editions were widely accepted and used by livestock producers; seed, chemical, fertilizer, and equipment dealers; agricultural Extension and Natural Resources Conservation Service personnel; vocational agriculture teachers; and agricultural consultants. The book has been widely used in grazing schools and cattle producer short courses. Our hope that the book might be useful to students in college forage courses was certainly fulfilled as presently it is used as a text at over 50 colleges and universities. We also hoped that the book might have value outside the southern U.S. In this we were not disappointed as orders for the book have come from all over the U.S. and more than 30 other countries. The book has been translated into Polish and Chinese. Our wide readership suggests that many of the forage-livestock principles covered in *Southern Forages* have no geographic boundaries.

The Third Edition is a major revision of the book. Many chapters have been completely rewritten, updated, and expanded. Two new chapters, "Forage Ecology" and "Minimizing Stored Feed Requirements", have been added as well as many additional, useful tables in the popular Appendix section. Color drawings of forage seed and new diagrams also make the book more useful. The use of color throughout the book makes it more attractive.

The Third Edition of *Southern Forages* is the same practical, easy-to-understand book, but it provides additional information on forage production and management. We hope that it continues to meet the needs of forage producers, students, teachers, and others. We are grateful for the warm reception previous editions of our book has received and trust that this new edition will serve your needs well.

Don Ball
Carl Hoveland
Garry Lacefield

Contents

History of Southern Forage Crops

Prior to European settlement, the Southern U.S. was mainly forest interspersed with small patches of burned areas where Indian women grew crops of corn, beans and squash. Grazing animals consisted mainly of deer and bison that were hunted for meat.

During the late 1600s, some Indians began to raise cattle that they acquired from European colonists. There was some grazing of native grasses, but no hay was harvested. Later, Indians such as the Cherokee tribe adopted the European practice of raising cattle, sheep and horses on planted pastures.

European settlers in the region found big bluestem, indiangrass, and switchgrass growing on favorable soils. These grasses were generally nutritious and relished by livestock, but overgrazing soon reduced vigor and stands, probably resulting in replacement by less desirable grasses such as broomsedge and three-awn grasses. Most of the native grasses on leached, infertile soils common to much of the Southern U.S. were handicapped by low nutritive quality, low yield, short productive season, or intolerance to grazing. Thus, animal agriculture based on native grasses was at a distinct disadvantage in the South.

Forage production with improved species developed differently in the South than it did in other parts of the nation. In the Northeast and Midwest, commercial dairy, beef, and sheep production on European-introduced forage plants increased rapidly during the 1800s to supply the needs of large industrial cities and for export to Europe. Natural grasslands in the more arid West were exploited for beef cattle and sheep. In contrast, agriculture in

Bison such as these originally grazed the native grasses of the South.

the South consisted of cash crops such as cotton, with livestock being grown on only a limited scale to supply the local demands of small cities and rural areas.

Improved pastures and large-scale beef and dairy production did not occur in much of the South until the 1930s and 1940s. Since then, there has been a massive expansion of cattle production throughout the region, and forages have become an important agricultural commodity. Currently, there are over 60 million acres of perennial pasture in the South, making up about 75 percent of the total pasture acreage in the humid eastern U.S. In addition, there are about 19 million acres of annual pastures in the South.

European settlers in the Northeast introduced cool season species such as orchardgrass, perennial ryegrass, timothy, bluegrass, and white clover, which were productive there. As the settlers migrated west and south, they found these species were also adapted to the upper South. Farther south, they succeeded with these cool season forages in the mountains, but failed at lower elevations. Colonists at Savannah, Georgia, introduced alfalfa in 1736, but it failed. Virginia farmers were also disappointed with alfalfa, which performed poorly due to soil acidity and low fertility.

None of the improved forage species commonly grown in the South are native to the region or even to other areas of the U.S. Most Southern forage plants, like most of the nation's human population, were originally immigrants from other parts of the world (**Figure 1.1**).

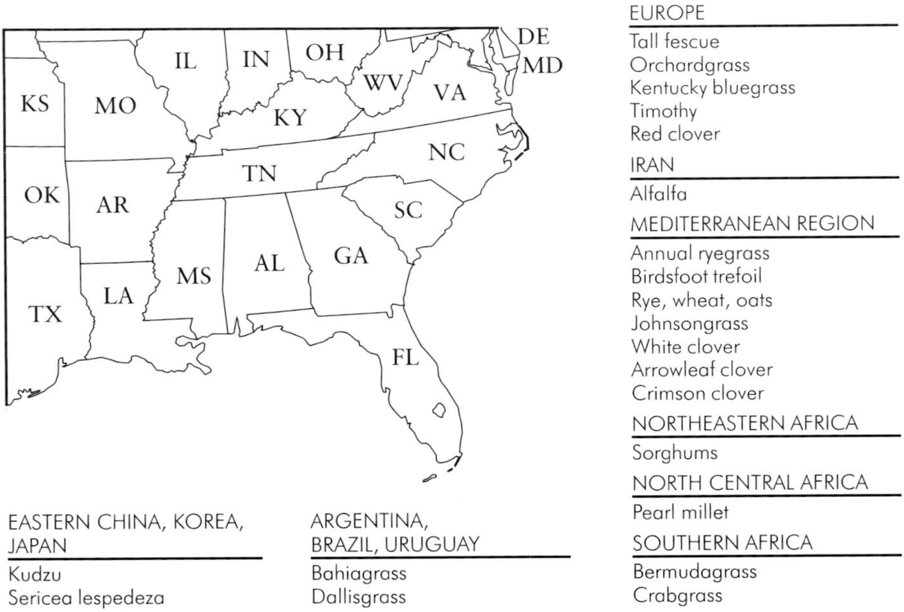

Figure 1.1. All major Southern forage grasses and legumes are immigrants from other parts of the world.

Bermudagrass was introduced from Africa, probably in the late 1600s, and soon became one of the most important grasses in the lower South. Dallisgrass, a native of Argentina and Brazil, was introduced accidentally through the port of New Orleans and grown in Louisiana in the early 1800s. Johnsongrass, native to the Mediterranean area, was introduced into South Carolina in the 1830s. In about 1840 it was planted by Colonel William Johnson on the black soils of central Alabama where it became a popular forage grass.

Common bahiagrass was first introduced from Brazil by the University of Florida in 1913. It was found to be well adapted but low yielding. E.H. Finlayson, an agricultural Extension agent, found a much more vigorous and productive bahiagrass growing near the ship docks at Pensacola, Florida, in 1935. It was eventually released by the University of Florida and the Soil Conservation Service (SCS) as the variety Pensacola, which now comprises the majority of the bahiagrass acreage in the U.S.

Tall fescue, the most widely grown cultivated pasture grass in the U.S., probably was originally introduced as a contaminant in other grass seed from Europe. It was found growing on a hill pasture in eastern Kentucky in 1931 by E.N. Fergus, a professor at the University of Kentucky. Tall fescue was growing on this farm when it was purchased by William M. Suiter in 1887. Tests revealed that it was a productive grass, and it was released in 1943 as the variety Kentucky 31. There was phenomenal acceptance and planting of this variety in the late 1940s and 1950s, as it was useful in a large

Kentucky 31 tall fescue originated from plants growing in this pasture on the William Suiter farm, Menifee County, Kentucky.

portion of the lower Midwest and upper South where other cool season perennial grasses were not well adapted. Later releases of Claire timothy and Boone orchardgrass by the University of Kentucky provided additional forage grasses for the upper South.

The cereal grasses—oats, wheat and rye—were grown as grain crops in the South from the time of the first European settlements. Later, they became important as high quality winter annual grazing crops. Annual ryegrass, native to the Mediterranean area, was also introduced into the South during the early years of European settlement and is now the most common component in winter annual pastures.

There was little selection or breeding of forage crops in the South until the 1930s. When G.W. Burton came to Tifton, Georgia, as a forage grass breeder in 1936, common bermudagrass was generally considered a weed in row crops. His remarkable breeding program soon resulted in release of the hybrid variety Coastal which was more drought-tolerant, frost-tolerant, and much higher yielding than common bermudagrass. At present, it is estimated that there are over 12 million acres of this variety in the South.

There have since been many notable achievements in developing improved forage varieties for the South. Dr. Burton's breeding program has released several additional improved bermuda hybrids that are more productive, more cold hardy, or more digestible. Other breeding work at Tifton by Dr. Burton and W.W. Hanna greatly improved the nutritive quality of pearl millet, a summer annual grass native to Africa. Another breeding achievement at Auburn University in Alabama resulted in the release of AU Triumph, the first winter-productive tall fescue variety for the lower South. The first novel (non-toxic) endophyte tall fescue variety was developed in 1999 at the University of Georgia by J.H. Bouton and G.C.M. Latch of Ag Research New Zealand.

Legumes have been less successful in the South, a result of low soil fertility, subsoil acidity, heat, drought, pest problems, and generally higher management requirements than grasses. Crimson clover, a winter annual from the Mediterranean region, was introduced into the U.S. in 1819, but did not become important until 1880. The long-term breeding work of W.E. Knight in Mississippi did much to improve this clover and resulted in release of the winter-productive variety Tibbee. Arrowleaf clover, a winter annual from Italy, was released in the early 1960s. In particular, the Auburn University-developed variety Yuchi became important due to its ability to extend the winter annual grazing season in the lower South.

A significant step in the acceptance and use of perennial clovers occurred in the late 1940s when E.N. Fergus released the variety Kenland red clover from the University of Kentucky. Continued red clover breeding in Kentucky by N.L. Taylor resulted in additional disease-resistant varieties for the South. The ladino white clover, Regal, developed at Auburn University by P.B. Gibson, E.D. Donnelly, and W.C. Johnson, and the intermediate white clover Louisiana S-1, released by C.R. Owen at Louisiana State University, have made important contributions to forage/livestock production.

Tall fescue-white clover-birdsfoot trefoil provides excellent pasture for beef cows and calves. (Tim and Peg Taylor farm in eastern Kentucky.)

Alfalfa, originally from Iran, was of little importance in the South until the development of better adapted, improved varieties and enhanced soil fertilization technology. Alfalfa acreage declined with the arrival of the alfalfa weevil, but recovered with new control measures. The development of grazing-tolerant varieties at the University of Georgia by Dr. Bouton in the late 1980s greatly increased the feasibility of using alfalfa as a pasture species.

Common annual (striate) lespedeza was introduced to Georgia from eastern Asia in 1846, later spreading throughout the region. Korean annual lespedeza (a separate species) was introduced in 1920 and became important in the upper South. Sericea, a perennial lespedeza, was introduced from Japan in the late 1890s, but did not become important until the 1920s and 1930s. Sericea is especially tolerant of low fertility and acid subsoils, but was considered a low-quality forage plant. Later, the breeding program of Dr. Donnelly at Auburn University developed fine-stemmed and low-tannin sericea varieties with improved palatability and nutritive quality.

Several other forage species have shown promise and some are being utilized. Berseem and rose clovers are valuable winter annuals in certain areas of the lower South. In portions of the Gulf Coast area and in peninsular Florida, perennial peanut is a valuable, high-quality hay plant. In the upper South, there is greater use of warm season perennial grasses such as big bluestem, caucasian bluestem, switchgrass, and indiangrass.

Introduction of improved forage plants, together with advances in fertilization and weed control, has greatly increased productivity of pastures and hay areas. Pasture renovation that has included establishing legumes in grass sods has improved yield and quality of pastures and hayfields. Along with forage improvement, there have been great advances in animal breeding, control of animal breeding season, and animal health care.

Grazing research by scientists such as Roy Blaser in Virginia and G.C. Mott in Florida has shown the great potential of well-managed pasture for livestock production in the South. Probably the least progress has been made by Southern livestock producers in managing pastures and hay fields for high forage quality. Improper grazing often results in surplus grass of reduced quality, and the resultant shading prevents development of new tillers and leaves. Most hay is cut when it is too mature and stored outside, reducing digestible energy and protein and wasting forage.

Forage production in the South has come a long way, mainly through improved plants, farm equipment inventions, and fertilization. **Table 1.1** lists some significant dates.

The primary challenges for the future are better management of existing grasses and legumes for improved nutritive quality, and matching animal nutrient requirements with the available forages. Adoption of these skills will result in continued progress in the efficiency and profitability of Southern forage/livestock systems. SF

Table 1.1. Some significant events affecting Southern forage/livestock production.

1701	Grain drill invented by Jethro Tull.
1733	J.E. Oglethorpe established an experimental garden for foreign plant introductions at Savannah, Georgia.
1833	Obed Hussey developed the first successful reciprocating cutter bar hay mower.
1837	John Deere produced the first steel moldboard plow.
1840	Wire-toothed hay dump rake developed.
1840	Justus von Liebig, Germany, founded the science of modern plant nutrition.
1841	Edmund Ruffin, Virginia, increased the yield of crops such as alfalfa with lime.
1843	First fertilizer research on grassland began at Rothamsted, England.
1850	Invention of corn planter.
1862	Morrill Act created the Land Grant University System in the U.S.
1866	Gregor Mendel of Moravia hybridized peas and laid the basis for modern genetics and breeding.
1870	Disk harrow first produced.
1872	First horizontal continual action hay press.
1873	First silo constructed in U.S.
1874	Barbed wire patented for fence.
1886	Hellriegel and Wilfarth, Germany, discovered that legumes fix nitrogen in nodules of roots.

1887	Hatch Act approved, providing funding of U.S. Agricultural Experiment Station system.
1890	Side-delivery hay rake and hay loader developed.
1903	C.W. Hart and C.H. Parr began manufacture of the first gasoline-powered tractors in Iowa.
1908	G.H. Shull discovered the concept of hybrid vigor in corn.
1914	Smith-Lever Act established the Cooperative Extension Service in the U.S.
1918	D.F. Jones developed the double-cross procedure, making production of hybrid corn seed practical.
1919	First grassland plant breeding station in the world started by R.G. Stapledon at Aberystwyth, Wales.
1933	Agricultural Adjustment Act created a county committee system that became the Agricultural Stabilization and Conservation Service in 1954.
1935	Release of Pensacola bahiagrass in Florida.
1935	Soil Conservation Act created the SCS, now called the Natural Resources Conservation Service (NCRS).
1940	Self-tying hay baler developed.
1940	Southern Pasture and Forage Crop Improvement Association founded, Tifton, Georgia.
1943	Release of Kentucky 31 tall fescue and Coastal bermudagrass.
1944	Joint Committee on Grassland Farming organized at Rutgers University in New Jersey, becoming the American Grassland Council in 1957 and the American Forage and Grassland Council in 1968.
1945	Introduction and use of anhydrous ammonia as a fertilizer.
1948	Society for Range Management organized in Salt Lake City, Utah.
1953	Certified Alfalfa Seed Council (now Alfalfa Council) organized.
1958	Development of hay baler for large round bales.
1960s	Development of no-till drill for seeding in grass sods.
1975	Development of high-voltage electric fence in New Zealand.
1976	Near infrared reflectance spectroscopy described as a method for predicting forage quality.
1980s	Discovery of the effects of the tall fescue fungal endophyte on livestock and the grass plant.
1990	Release of the first grazing-tolerant alfalfa variety adapted in the South.
1990	Round bale silage (haylage) became popular.
1994	First National Alfalfa Grazing Conference held in Nashville, Tennessee.
1999	Release of stress-tolerant tall fescue with a novel (non-toxic) fungal endophyte.

Developing a Forage Program

Within a particular community or area of the South, the basic forage production resources may be quite similar on many farms. Yet, there are vast differences in the levels of production, efficiency, and profitability of forage/livestock programs.

Actually, many factors influence the success of a forage/livestock operation, and the approaches taken in developing a forage program rank high on the list. In turn, the approaches taken are influenced by the concepts and attitudes of the producer.

There is no one plan or program that fits all forage production situations. Prior to making forage plantings, many factors need to be considered, including: available soil types, topography, other farm enterprises, availability of capital, labor resources, type of livestock operation, and objectives of the producer. Consequently, there is no one right or wrong forage program. There are numerous options available and the producer must make careful selections.

Forage/livestock production is complex. Thus, development of a good program requires thought and planning. In fact, a written plan is best because it helps clarify objectives, identify problems or limiting factors, and define needs and opportunities.

Without question, a producer's overall forage production philosophy has an important influence on the type of forage program developed. This chapter introduces several characteristics of outstanding grasslanders. These might be considered basic concepts, and certainly they deserve consideration by any producer who wants to develop and maintain a good forage program. Several are discussed in greater detail in later chapters.

Concepts and attitudes of the producer are critically important in forage/livestock production.

The Basic Commodity Is Forage

The U.S. has a livestock industry of which we can justly be proud, but some parts of the world out-produce us and often do so more efficiently. Climatic differences may explain part of this, but management philosophy is a major difference often noted among forage-based livestock farms in the U.S. and the highly efficient livestock farms in New Zealand, Argentina, Australia, and some other regions.

This difference in philosophy is that most U.S. producers see themselves basically as **livestock managers** who run their animals on pasture; in other parts of the world where there is outstanding forage/livestock production, the operators see themselves as **forage producers** who are using livestock to harvest their crop. This subtle difference in philosophy likely accounts for a substantial portion of the success of these competing areas.

While good animal management and breeding are of critical importance, it appears there are far more American producers who have excellent animal management skills and outstanding breeding stock, but who have poor forage management knowledge (or willingness to apply knowledge), than vice versa. In most cases, profitable livestock production is largely dependent on a producer's ability to efficiently convert forage (hay, pasture, and/or silage) into meat, wool or milk.

Inadequate digestible energy in the diet is the primary limiting factor in most Southern livestock operations. The solution to this problem on a majority of farms is development of a forage program that increases the digestible energy content of consumed forages.

Use of Reliable Information

It is not unusual for an inexperienced, but highly motivated, person to start a cattle operation and quickly develop a more efficient and profitable business than more experienced neighbors. Likewise, some horse producers or wildlife enthusiasts who are inexperienced with making forage plantings have great success while others, perhaps more experienced, do not.

Such occurrences are not beginner's luck; they result from the enthusiastic application of technology. Though initially not knowledgeable, such producers find and utilize sources of reliable information.

Producers need to pay attention to research-based recommendations, particularly those from universities. Agriculturally-oriented universities are in the business of doing scientific research and have the facilities and trained personnel. They are therefore an excellent source of unbiased information.

Great care and precision are required to accurately evaluate forage crops. There are variables that enter into the evaluation that are not relevant to other crop species. For example, total pasture yield may be less important than seasonal production and forage quality. In animal feeding, the primary emphasis should be on the total pounds of available nutrients produced and the economics of animal performance obtained from those nutrients.

It is especially difficult to accurately determine animal performance on

pasture through observation of on-farm situations. Livestock prefer certain forage species or varieties, but these may not be the best nutritionally. Differences in palatability may be associated with higher forage quality of the preferred crop, but not always. Grazing animals may perform equally well on a less-preferred forage when it is all that is available. Slight differences among fields with regard to soil type, slope, drainage, or fertility can also affect forage growth and animal preference.

The Cooperative Extension Service is the organization primarily responsible for disseminating research-based agricultural information from land grant universities. This is done through farm demonstrations, local meetings, publications, the Internet, and mass media. Extension personnel can also visit individual farms, evaluate an operation, and suggest specific practices that might be implemented to advantage.

Local Extension offices should thus be a prime source of information, but other excellent sources also exist. The Natural Resources Conservation Service (NRCS), vocational agricultural departments, Farm Service Agency offices, and many state Departments of Agriculture offer agricultural information and advice that can be of great help to forage producers. Some non-land grant universities also have faculty who provide agricultural information to producers as a service function.

Much of this information is localized and therefore particularly useful. For example, the general recommendations set forth in this book are subject to alteration depending on local conditions. Local agricultural workers should be able to adapt research findings or other information to practical on-farm situations suitable to the financial and management skills of individual producers.

Industry is another important source of information. As agricultural technology becomes more complex, it is increasingly difficult for universities to work in all research areas. Many seed, equipment, fertilizer, chemical, and other companies have research departments with highly trained and competent personnel. Their contributions are immense and valuable.

Regardless of the source of research data, it is rare that a particular new technology or product is applicable on every farm. The best approach is to first try a new approach or product on a small scale, then expand its use once it has been proven beneficial.

Timeliness

Some producers develop superb forage programs while others of similar intelligence, resources, and experience have little success. It appears that in many cases the ability to get things done when they need to be done accounts for the difference.

Timely action can be important in virtually any aspect of forage production, but is especially critical in establishment. For example, different crops have differing optimum planting times, often a period of only a few weeks. Weather and soil conditions sometimes interfere with timely planting, but often late planting is simply the result of a producer not being ready at the right time. This is particularly unfortunate because missing the optimum planting time often results in a poor or failed stand. Timely planting costs no more, but the return on investment can be much greater.

Timely action can also make a big difference in productivity once a forage crop is established. Timely fertilization can influence forage yield and quality. Timely herbicide application is more likely to effectively reduce weed populations. Most importantly, timely adjustment of pasture stocking rates or timely cutting of a crop for hay or silage can make a great difference in quality, stand composition, forage utilization, and animal performance.

Eliminating procrastination is essentially a matter of setting priorities. Producers who want a good forage program that will improve their livestock production, efficiency, and profits need to place a high priority on timeliness.

Use of Adapted Species and Varieties

This is an elementary point, yet many forage plantings fail or perform poorly simply because the crop is not adapted to the site or area. Forage crop adaptation is limited by soil type, climate, and drainage. Therefore, it is important to consider all of the major species that are adapted for each field (see Chapters 5 through 8).

A soil map, available free of charge from the NRCS in most areas, is a valuable resource in deciding which forage species are most suitable for a particular site. Observing plants that are already growing successfully or volunteering in an area, as well as consulting with persons who have experience and knowledge regarding matching forages to particular fields, may also be helpful. These approaches can help a producer understand potential forage options on a field-by-field basis.

Matching Crops to Needs

Once the forage options for each field have been determined, the best choice(s) for each field should be made in accordance with the objectives of the producer. One consideration should be the nutritional needs of the species and classes of livestock to be grazed or fed forage harvested from each field. For example, a dairy producer would want to plant high quality forage crops in fields that are to provide feed for lactating animals. Lower-quality species might be suitable in areas that are to be used for dry cows. Thus, it is important to know the usual range of quality in forage produced by various species to allow choosing those that will best meet animal requirements (see Chapters 16 and 17).

Other needs should also be considered. For example, a horse producer might want to plant alfalfa in one field to provide high quality hay and grow orchardgrass and white clover in another for pasture. In a holding lot where there will be a great deal of trampling, common bermudagrass or tall fescue might be the best choice. Minimizing erosion is always important, but especially in deciding the location of annual pastures that will require frequent soil tillage. Soil survey information can be helpful in planning.

Maximizing the Length of the Grazing Season

A basic goal of any grazing program should be to grow several forage crops that will provide good grazing over an extended period of time, thus reducing stored feed requirements. In general, grazed forages cost only about one-third to one-half as much as stored feed due to the costs associated with hay or silage production and feeding.

It is less expensive and less trouble to allow animals to harvest the forage whenever possible. This philosophy should be reflected in the planting and management decisions made for different fields on a livestock farm. Strategies for minimizing stored feed needs are discussed in Chapter 21.

Soil Testing and Fertility

Proper fertilization and liming normally result in more dramatic increases in forage production than any other single practice. They are management tools that deserve special attention.

It is highly desirable to keep a record of the soil fertility and pH status of each field. One good approach is to make a file for each field in which to keep soil test reports as well as a record of lime and fertilizer applications. Soil testing is a simple step, but one that is quite important, both agronomically and economically.

Fertilizing and liming at the proper times and rates recommended on soil test reports are basic to good pasture management. For most forage

Photo courtesy of Mr. Morris Gillespie

In many areas, soil survey documents are available free of charge from NRCS.

species, certain minimum levels of fertilization and liming are necessary just to maintain a forage stand. However, heavy fertilization is much more feasible when stocking rates are high than when they are low. Detailed information regarding soil testing, fertilization, and liming is provided in Chapter 9.

Use of Legumes

Growing legumes with grasses may be more profitable than growing grass alone. Although legumes are usually more difficult to manage, their advantages often out-weigh their disadvantages. Not every acre of forage crops should include legumes, but it is worthwhile for a producer to consider whether the introduction of legumes would be of benefit and be feasible. Chapters 7, 8, and 13 provide additional information on forage legumes.

Stored Feed

Even though the South has a long growing season and high rainfall relative to many other parts of the U.S., most livestock producers will need to make some provisions for stored feed to use during periods when pasture is not available. In developing or evaluating a forage program, factors such as amount and quality of stored feed needed and convenient location of hay fields should be considered.

The cost of storing feed for livestock has risen steadily. Therefore, the best interests of livestock producers are served by striving to maximize production in fields devoted to the production of stored feed. This is true with regard to both yield and quality.

Typically, around 30 percent of the costs associated with hay production are fixed costs (i.e. purchase of hay baler, tractor, rake, etc.). These costs will be essentially the same regardless of yield. Therefore, increasing yield is beneficial even if it involves an increase in variable costs (i.e. labor, fuel) of 10 to 20 percent or more. It is important to carefully consider whether the size of the operation warrants the purchase of hay equipment. Many small producers are better off buying hay or having it custom baled.

Usually it is desirable to produce the best quality hay or silage possible. In feeding livestock, it is the pounds of nutrients consumed and not the pounds of feed they receive that determine performance. Chapters 18, 19, and 20 provide additional information regarding the production and utilization of hay and silage. Chapter 21 provides a discussion of ways to minimize stored feed requirements.

Grazing Methods

A final consideration in developing or evaluating a forage program is how to best utilize the forage produced. Most livestock producers use continuous stocking (continuous grazing; see Chapter 25). While this is most convenient, it may or may not be the most efficient, feasible, or profitable.

Fencing, water, and labor costs will normally be higher with rotational stocking (rotational grazing). Production and net returns may or may not be higher, depending on the situation.

However, grazing management can have many important impacts, both short term and long term. Depending on the forage species and the situation, it can affect pasture botanical composition, stand density, forage quality, the efficiency of nutrient recycling, and the environmental soundness of an operation.

When evaluating or planning a forage program, a producer should give careful consideration to what will be the most suitable and convenient way to utilize pastures. The decisions may influence fencing patterns, fertilization practices, labor requirements, and even species selection.

Summary

Development of a good forage program requires time and thought, but is worth the effort. Having basic concepts and principles in mind throughout the planning process is important. Keeping accurate written records also greatly facilitates proper management and wise decision making. **Good forage programs don't just happen, they are planned.** SF

Climate and Soils Areas

Climatic conditions largely determine the adaptation of forage species. From the standpoint of plant survival and growth, the most critical aspects of climate are generally temperature and the distribution and amount of rainfall. Climate extremes are more likely to determine adaptation than are average conditions. While local conditions are of primary concern to individual producers, an assessment of the forage/livestock potential of the region is made easier by taking a broader view.

The Southern U.S. from eastern Texas and Oklahoma to the Atlantic Coast is described as a humid or high rainfall area. Total rainfall varies substantially in the region, increasing from 40 inches in northern Kentucky and Virginia to 65 inches along the Gulf Coast of Louisiana, Mississippi, Alabama, and Florida. It declines from 50 inches in western Louisiana and Arkansas to 40 inches in eastern Oklahoma and Texas.

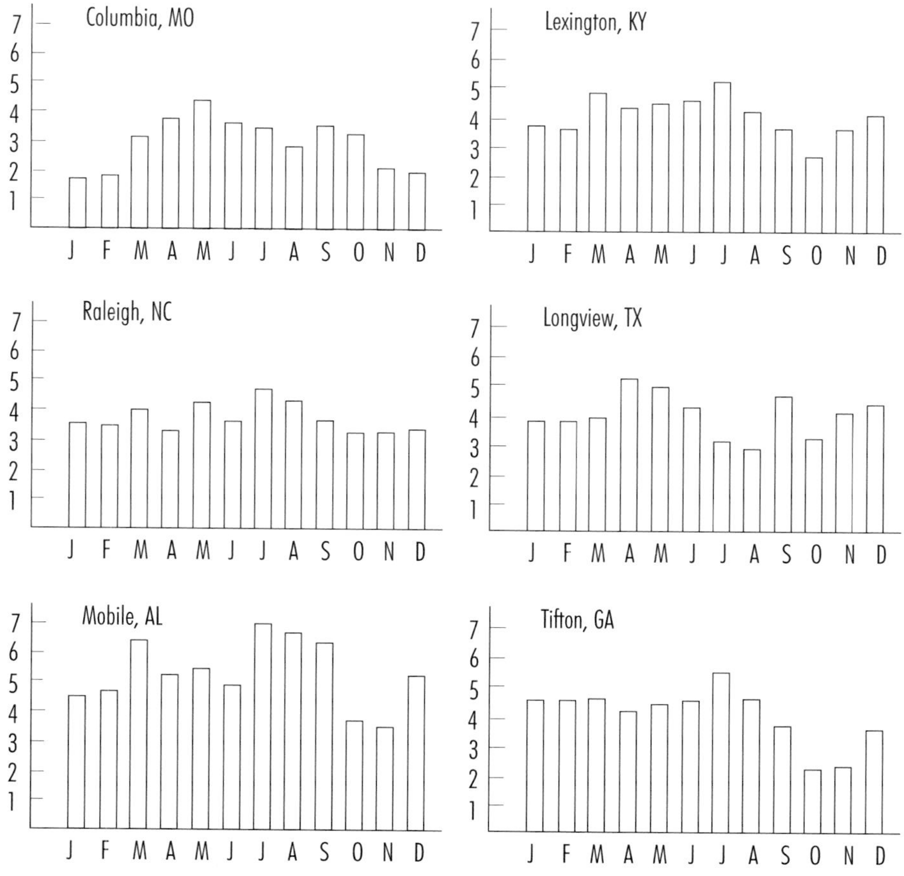

Figure 3.1. Average monthly rainfall distribution (inches) at six locations.

Generally, rainfall in the South is distributed reasonably well throughout the year (**Figure 3.1**). However, there are periods of the year when amounts are low or undependable, thus creating problems for forage production in certain areas. In Missouri, rainfall is highest in spring with occasional droughts in late summer, reducing summer production of cool season perennial grasses. Farther east in North Carolina, rainfall is usually adequate during the year except for a drier period in October when autumn production is reduced.

East Texas normally has good rainfall from autumn through spring, creating excellent conditions for winter annual pastures. However, hot summers with low and poorly distributed rainfall may reduce output of warm season grasses. Adequate amounts typically occur all year in the Gulf Coast area (Mobile, Alabama). With mild winter temperatures, forage growth in this area is excellent, but pasture flooding and leaching of soil nutrients may be problems.

Farther east in south Georgia, autumn droughts are common and often make it difficult to establish winter annuals. Soils with low water-holding capacity accentuate the effects of drought. In each case, local rainfall distribution and soils must be taken into account when selecting species, deciding on stocking rates, and planning for amount of stored forage.

Summer rainfall at lower elevations in the South originates from convectional storms, often accompanied by thunder and lightning. The South has more thunderstorms than any other part of the U.S. The storms are intense and often of short duration, dropping large amounts of water on the

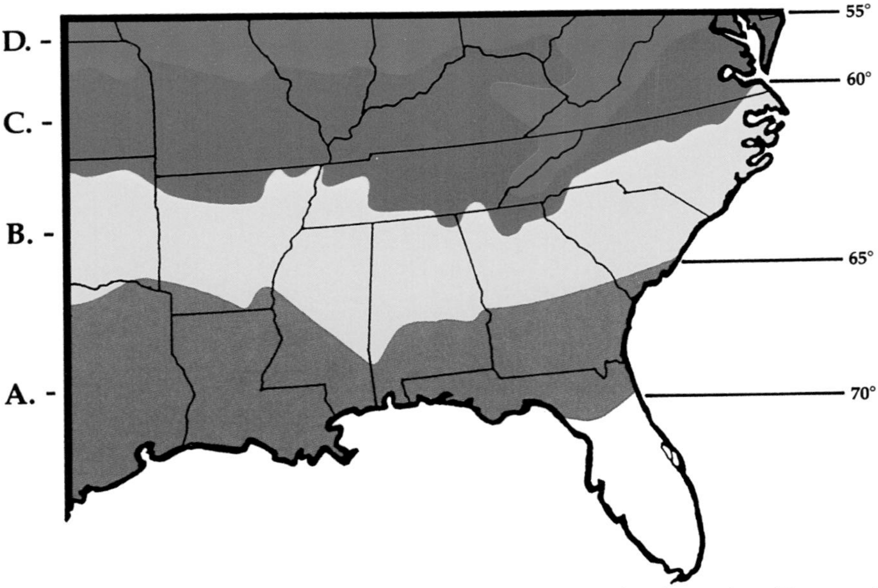

Figure 3.2. Mean annual air temperatures, °F, and adaptation Zones, A, B, C, D.

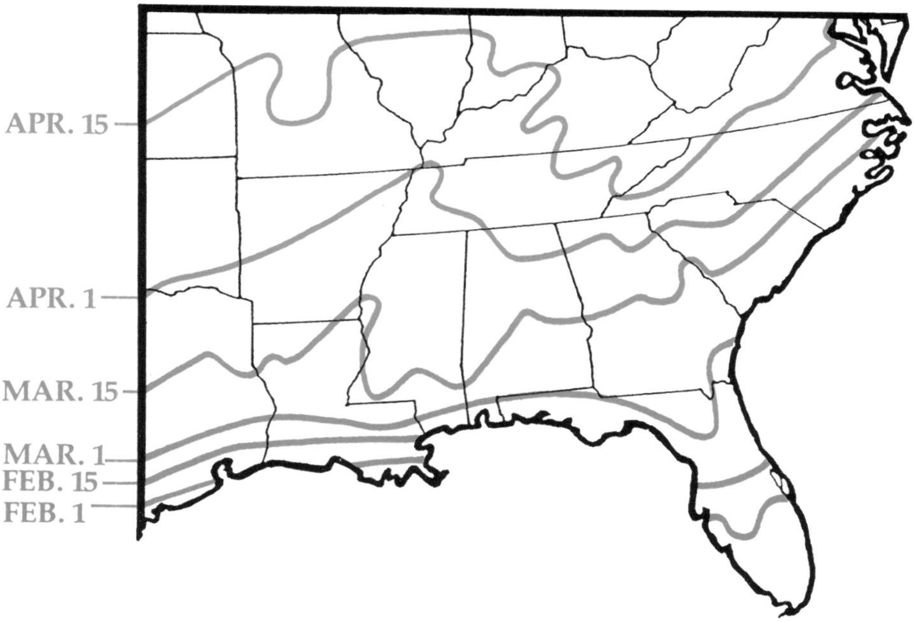

Figure 3.3. Fifty percent chance that temperature will fall to 32°F in spring. Based on average elevation for area. Dates shift as elevation changes.

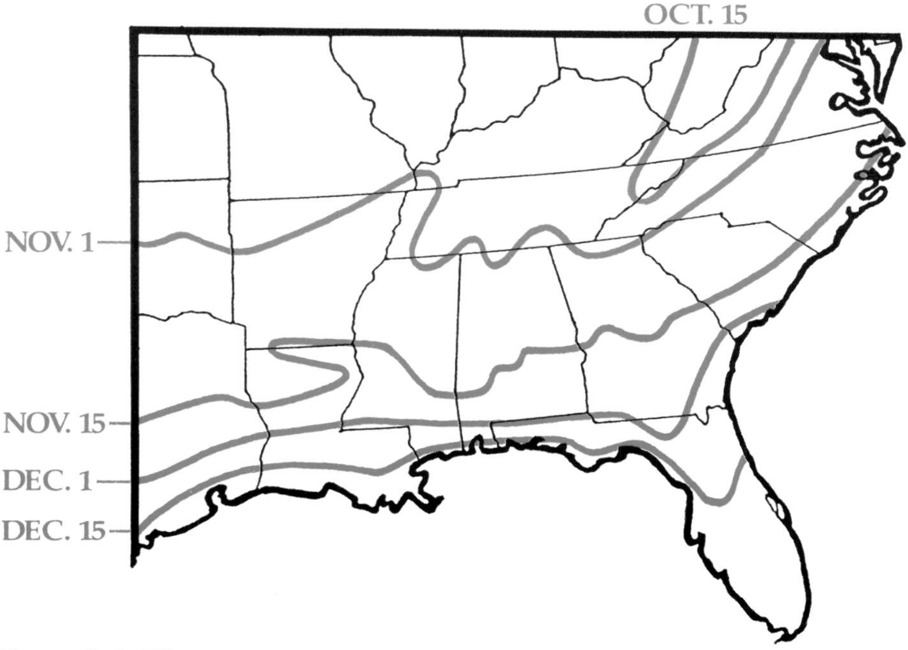

Figure 3.4. Fifty percent chance that temperature will fall to 32°F in autumn. Based on average elevation for area. Dates shift as elevation changes.

land, exceeding potential soil infiltration rates, and resulting in rapid runoff of water. Thus, although the total amount of measured rainfall is high, available water to plants may be low. This problem is even more serious on clay than on sandy soils because infiltration rates are higher on sandy land.

Days are hot and sultry in summer. Nights can be oppressive. The humid atmosphere prevents rapid loss of heat that takes place in the drier climates and clearer air of the western U.S. In addition, there is often little air movement as the southern U.S. is the least windy part of the country. This combination of high temperatures and humidity with little air movement favors disease development on susceptible forage varieties. In addition, the summer climate makes haymaking of legumes difficult and favors the use of rapid-drying grasses for hay. Hurricanes during late summer and autumn, although infrequent, can dump large quantities of water over extended areas and cause flooding of pastures and hay fields.

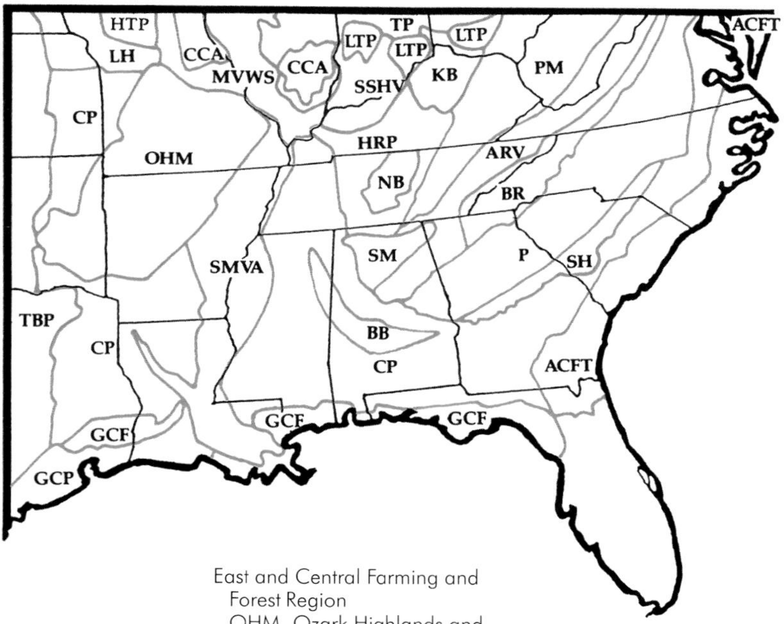

Mississippi Delta Region
- SMVA Southern Mississippi Valley Alluvium

South Atlantic and Gulf Slope
- CP Coastal Plain
- BB Black Belt
- P Piedmont
- SH Sand Hills

Atlantic and Gulf Coast Lowland
- GCP Gulf Coast Prairies
- ACFT Atlantic Coast Flat-woods and Tidewater

East and Central Farming and Forest Region
- OHM Ozark Highlands and Mountains
- SSHV Sandstone and Shale Hills and Valleys
- KB Kentucky Bluegrass
- HRP Highland Rim and Pennyroyal
- NB Nashville Basin
- PM Plateau and Mountains
- ARV Appalachian Ridges and Valleys
- SM Sand Mountain
- BR Blue Ridge

Southwestern Prairies
- TBP Texas Blackland Prairie

Central Feed Grains and Livestock Region
- LH Loess Hills
- HTP Heavy Till Plain
- CP Cherokee Prairies
- CCA Central Claypan Areas
- LTP Loess and Till Plain
- TP Till Plain
- MVWS Mississippi Valley Wooded Slopes

Figure 3.5. Land use (physiographic) areas of the South.

Winter rainfall is of frontal origin where humid, warm Gulf air meets cool polar air and is forced upward, resulting in persistent cloud cover and rains that may fall steadily for many hours and sometimes several days. The wet cool winters favor growth of cool season forages, especially in the lower South. Snow may fall, but it rarely stays on the ground for more than a few days except in the upper South and mountain areas.

Average annual temperatures increase from north to south in the region (**Figure 3.2**). Even though temperatures are generally moderate in the South, the continental effect of the North American landmass exerts a strong effect on winter temperatures. Outbreaks of polar air occasionally cause sharp drops in temperature. These occasional severe cold waves determine survival and adaptation of many forage species. Summers are long and hot, especially in the southern and western parts of the region, resulting in the use of warm season perennial grasses followed by cool season annuals. Higher elevations in the Appalachian Mountains have moderate summer temperatures and frequent thundershowers, favoring cool season species such as tall fescue, Kentucky bluegrass, orchardgrass, timothy, and clovers.

To illustrate general areas of forage adaptation, the region has been divided into four major temperature zones designated as A, B, C, and D (**Figure 3.2**). Moving northward or to higher elevations, the length of the frost-free season decreases, with frosts occurring later in spring and earlier in autumn (**Figures 3.3 and 3.4**).

The Southern U.S. can be divided into different land use areas based on soils, natural vegetation, and agriculture (**Figure 3.5**). Reference will be made to these areas in describing adaptation and use of various forage species.

Because of the diversity of soils within the South, it is not feasible to describe the soils in each part of the region in this book. In general, sandy soils predominate in the Coastal Plain while clay, loam, or shaley soils are found farther north. Local descriptions of soils in a particular area can be obtained from the Natural Resources Conservation Service or the Cooperative Extension Service.

Soils often modify the effects of climate, as they differ greatly in water and nutrient-holding capacity, native fertility, and potential for pests such as nematodes. This often has a major effect on adaptation and productivity of particular grasses and legumes.

Generally, soils throughout much of the region tend to be acid and low in nutrients. Acid subsoils that cause aluminum or manganese toxicity are a problem in the Piedmont, Coastal Plain, and Flatwoods areas and limit adaptation of some forage species. Certain soils of chalk or limestone origin in the Alabama-Mississippi Black Belt, Nashville Basin of central Tennessee, Kentucky Bluegrass region, and western parts of the South are alkaline or have near neutral pH, favoring growth of lime-loving legumes. Soil tests are essential to determine lime and fertilizer needs on all soils. SF

Overview of Southern Forages

More than 40 species of forage crops are routinely grown in the South, although many can be successfully grown only in certain areas. At least 20 others frequently volunteer or are at least occasionally planted. These crops differ widely in their characteristics, potential uses and value. However, putting them into various categories makes it easier to understand the potential for using them.

The three criteria normally used to categorize forage crops are: 1) grasses or legumes; 2) annuals or perennials; and 3) warm season or cool season plants. **Table 4.1** gives a general classification of Southern forage crops. Brief definitions follow.

Grasses–Botanically speaking, a grass is any member of the *Poaceae* plant family. Grasses are generally herbaceous (not woody), they have parallel leaf veins, fibrous root systems, and bear seed on an elongated seed stalk (see **Figure 4.1**). Grasses may have one of three different types of seed heads.

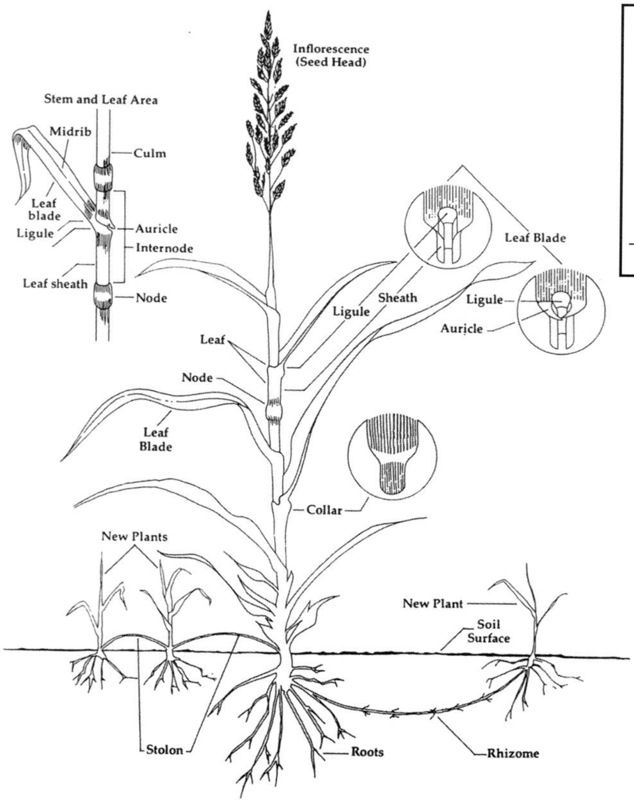

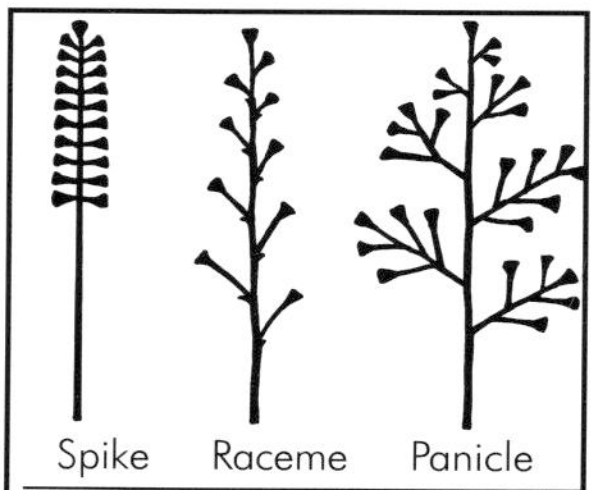

Types of grass seed heads.

Figure 4.1. Parts of a grass plant. Generalized illustration–not a particular species.

Table 4.1. **A general classification of forage crops frequently grown or found in the South.**

GRASSES			
Perennials		Annuals	
Warm season perennial grasses	Cool season perennial grasses	Warm season annual grasses	Cool season annual grasses
Bahiagrass	Kentucky bluegrass	Browntop millet	Barley
Bermudagrass[1]	Orchardgrass	Corn	Oats
Big bluestem	Perennial ryegrass	Crabgrass	Rescuegrass[2]
Carpetgrass		Forage sorghum	Rye
Caucasian bluestem	Reed canarygrass	Foxtail millet	Annual ryegrass
Dallisgrass	Smooth bromegrass	Grain sorghum	Triticale
Eastern gamagrass	Tall fescue	Pearl millet	Wheat
Indiangrass	Timothy	Sorghum-sudan hybrids	
Johnsongrass			
Switchgrass		Sudangrass	
LEGUMES			
Perennials		Annuals	
Warm season perennial legumes	Cool season perennial legumes	Warm season annual legumes	Cool season annual legumes
Kudzu	Alfalfa	Alyceclover	Arrowleaf clover
Perennial peanut[1]	Alsike clover	Cowpea	Ball clover
Sericea lespedeza	Birdsfoot trefoil	Korean lespedeza	Berseem clover
	Red clover[2]	Soybean	Bigflower vetch
	White clover	Striate lespedeza	Black medic
		Velvetbean	Burclover[3]
			Button clover
			Caleypea
			Common vetch
			Crimson clover
			Hairy vetch
			Hop clover[3]
			Lappa clover
			Persian clover
			Rose clover
			Subterranean clover
			Sweetclover[2,3]
			Winter pea

[1]Frequently or exclusively vegetatively propagated.
[2]This plant may act as an annual, or as a biennial, or a weak perennial. One species of sweetclover is a true annual, while two others are biennials.
[3]More than one species is present in the South.

Grasses are monocots (produce only one seed leaf), but should not be confused with sedges and rushes, which are also monocots.

Legumes–Members of the *Fabaceae* plant family. Legumes are dicots (produce two seed leaves), produce seed in a pod, have netted leaf venation, and usually have a taproot type of root system (**Figure 4.2**). Most legumes have the ability to interact with bacteria of the genus *Rhizobium* to fix nitrogen in

Some typical legume leaf types:

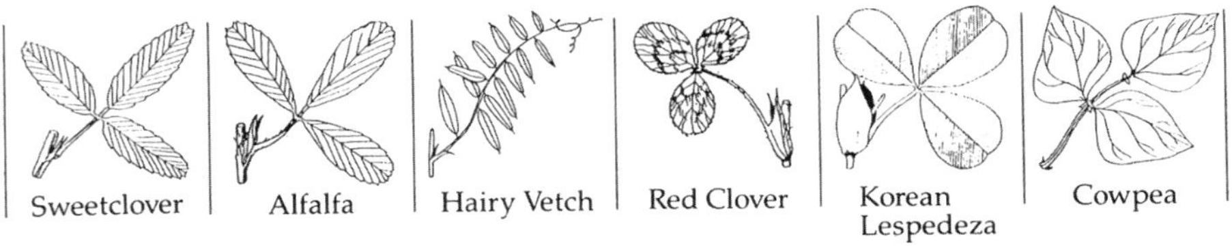

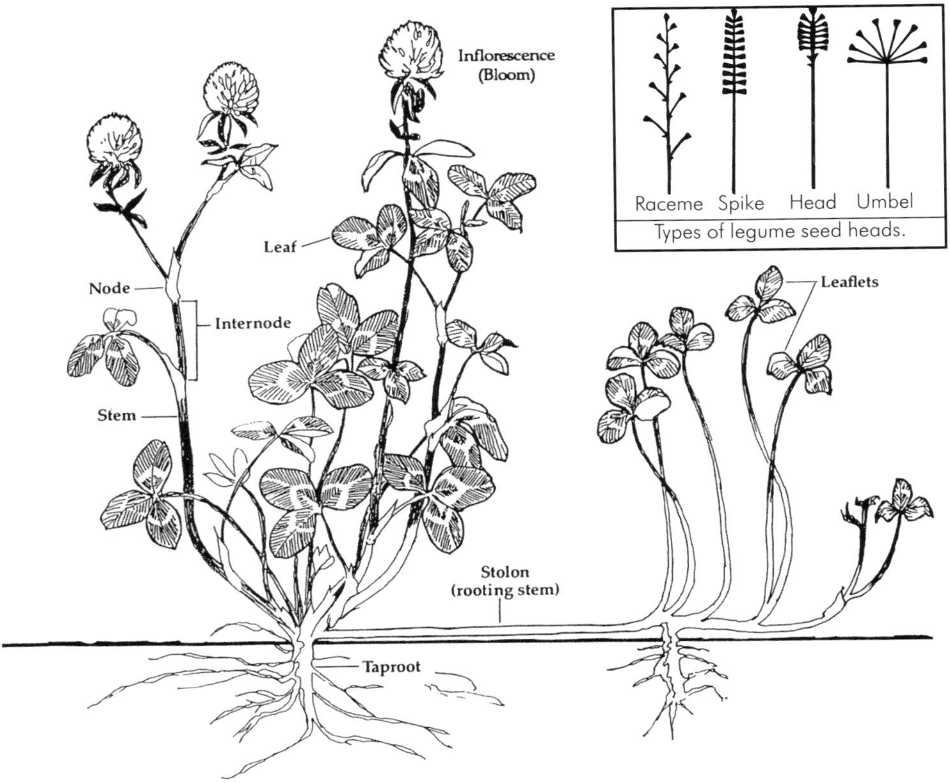

Figure 4.2. Characteristics of some forage legumes. Generalized illustration–not a particular species.

nodules on their roots. Legumes may have one of four different types of seed heads.

Annual–A plant that germinates, grows, reproduces, and dies in one year's time or one growing season. Annuals reproduce only by seed.

Perennial–A plant that, under suitable conditions, has the ability to live for more than one year. A perennial may appear to die back or become dormant at certain times of the year, but can recover from tubers, rhizomes, or stolons in succeeding years. Perennials may reproduce by seed as well as vegetatively. A few plants are biennials. Some plants are weak perennials and may die after the second or third growing season.

Warm Season Plants–In general, warm season species begin growth and/or

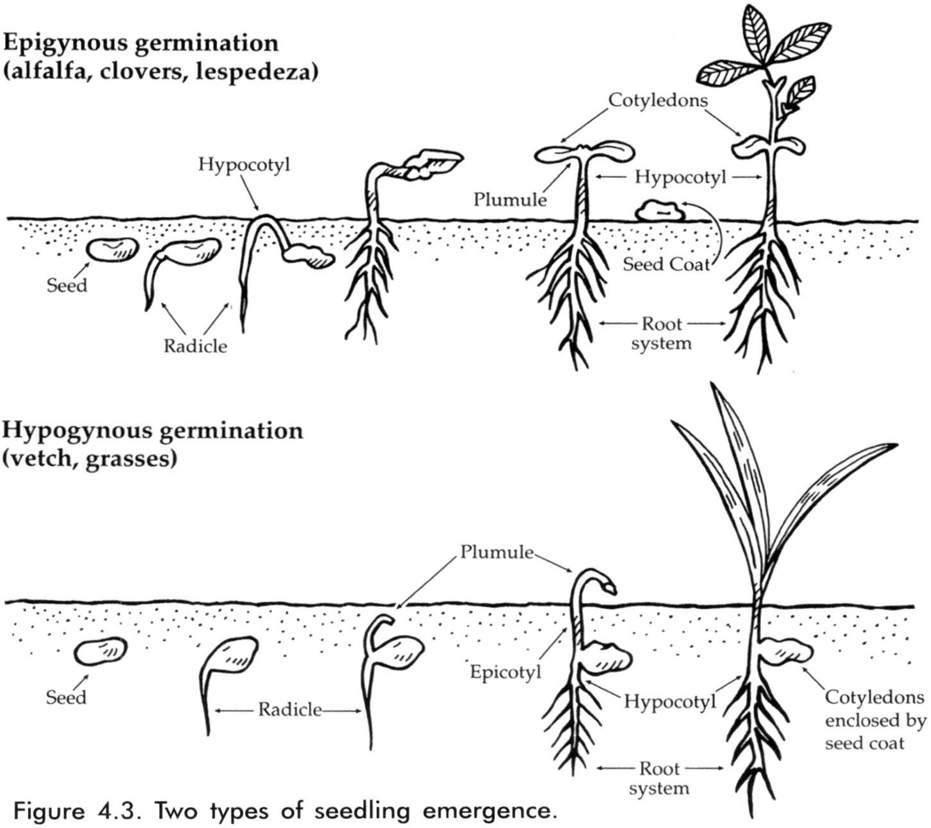

Figure 4.3. Two types of seedling emergence.

are planted in the spring or early summer and make most of their growth during the warmest months of the year.

Cool Season Plants–In general, cool season species begin growth and/or are planted in the autumn or sometimes late winter or early spring and make most of their growth during the coolest months of the year, except for the coldest periods during winter. **Figure 4.3** shows types of seedling emergence.

Distribution of Growth

The distribution of forage growth varies greatly among species and is extremely important in planning a grazing program. Examples of the approximate growing season of a few commonly-used species are shown in **Figures 4.4 through 4.7** for Zones A, B, C, and D (see also **Figure 3.2**).

It should be emphasized that these illustrations are only rough approximations. The actual growing season will vary with rainfall, timing and amount of fertilization, temperature, variety, and other factors. Furthermore, these illustrations are less accurate with regard to depicting total forage yield than showing usual seasonal distribution of growth. Therefore, comparison of total growth of various species as indicated by the illustrations could be misleading. SF

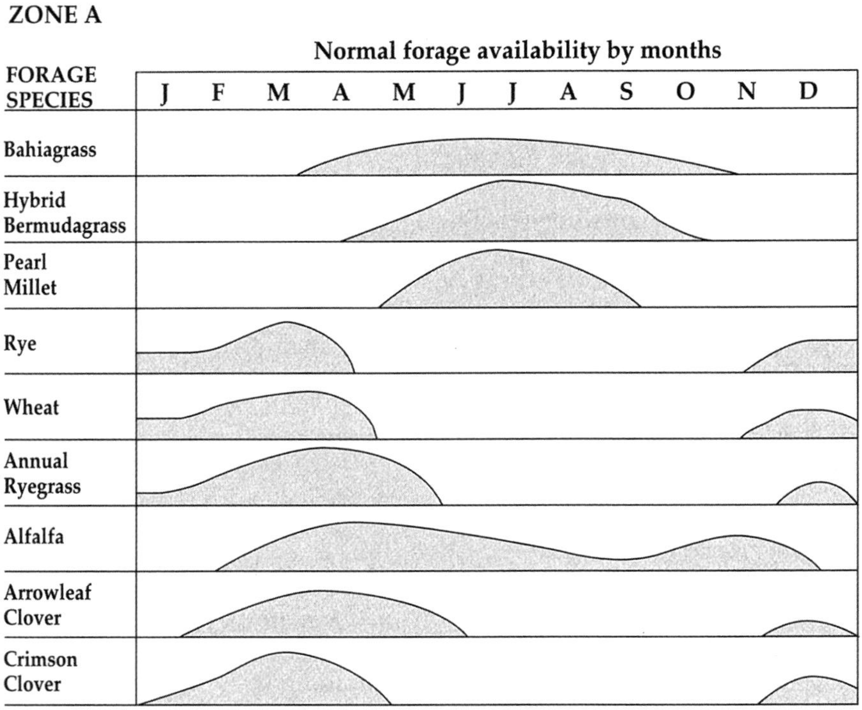

Figure 4.4. Seasonal forage availability of common forage species in Zone A.

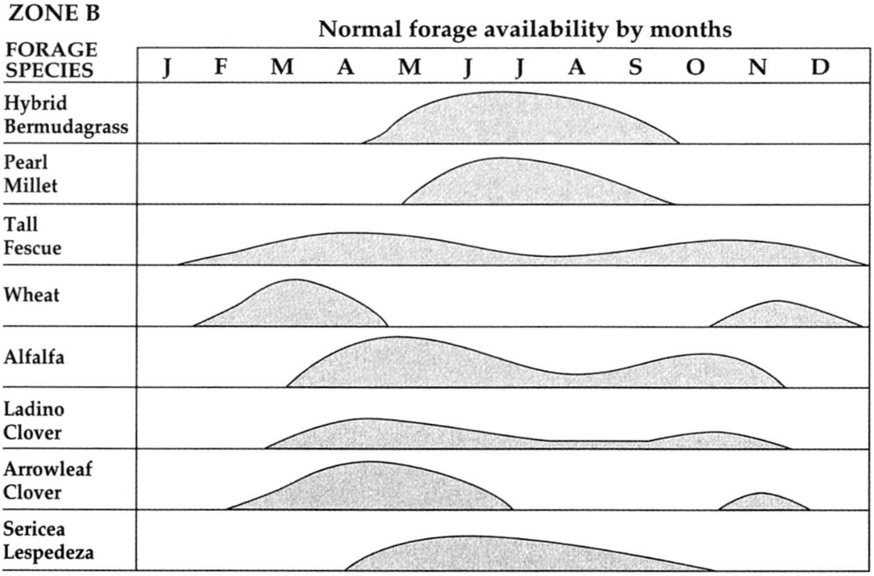

Figure 4.5. Seasonal forage availability of common forage species in Zone B.

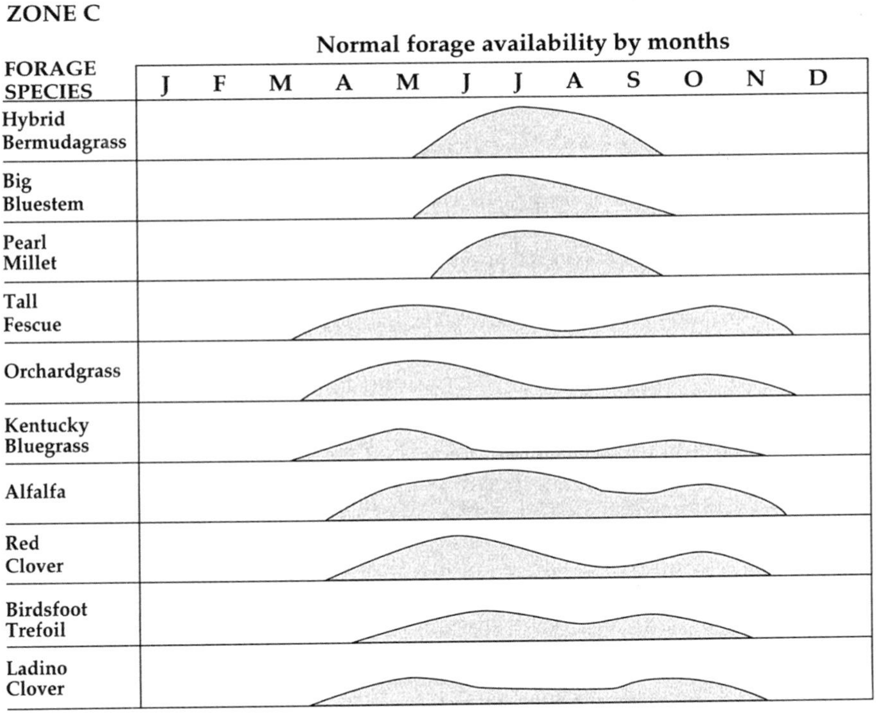

Figure 4.6. Seasonal forage availability of common forage species in Zone C.

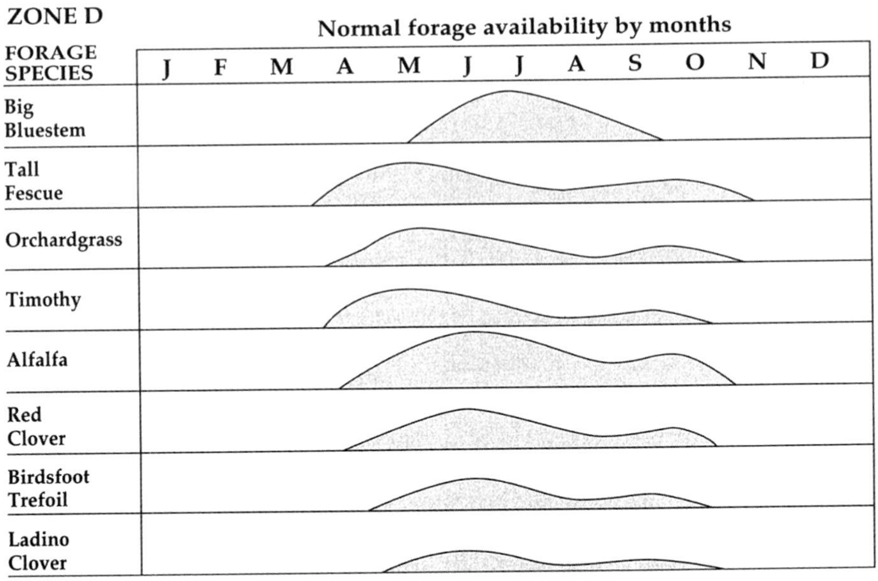

Figure 4.7. Seasonal forage availability of common forage species in Zone D.

Warm Season Grasses

Warm season grasses grown in the Southern region are of tropical origin and grow mainly during late spring, summer, and early autumn. Frost kills warm season annual grasses, while warm season perennial grasses become dormant and remain unproductive during the winter months. The productive season of warm season grasses can be as little as three months in the northern part of the region (Zones C and D) but may be seven or eight months in the Gulf Coast area (lower part of Zone A). Adaptation zones are provided in **Figure 3.2.**

Some of these grasses have the potential for very high forage yields with good fertilization. Unfortunately, forage quality (see Chapter 16) of warm season grasses, especially perennials, is generally much lower than that of cool season grasses. Plant breeding has resulted in significant improvements in forage quality of some warm season grasses. Winterkilling is a problem with some species or varieties of perennial warm season grasses, especially in northern parts of the region.

Bahiagrass

Rhizome

Bahiagrass *(Paspalum notatum)*

Origin: Argentina, Brazil, Uruguay, Paraguay.

Description: Perennial. Spreads by J-shaped purplish rhizomes and seed. Seed head two or three spikes. Forms a dense sod. Very aggressive. Deep rooted. Grows 12 to 20 inches tall.

Primary Adaptation: Zone A and lower part of Zone B. Best adapted on sandy soils. Tolerant of drought and poor drainage.

Major Uses: Pasture, hay, erosion control.

Establishment: Plant seed at 15 to 20 lb/A in March or April.

Fertilization: Very tolerant of low fertility and soil acidity. Responds to nitrogen and potassium.

Seasonal Production: April-October.

Management: Best used for pasture. Close grazing is desirable. Overseed with winter annuals if desired.

Pests: Usually not a problem.

Note: Drawings of seed in Chapters 5, 6, 7, and 8 show an enlarged view to help illustrate shape and color. The smaller silhouette shows actual seed size.

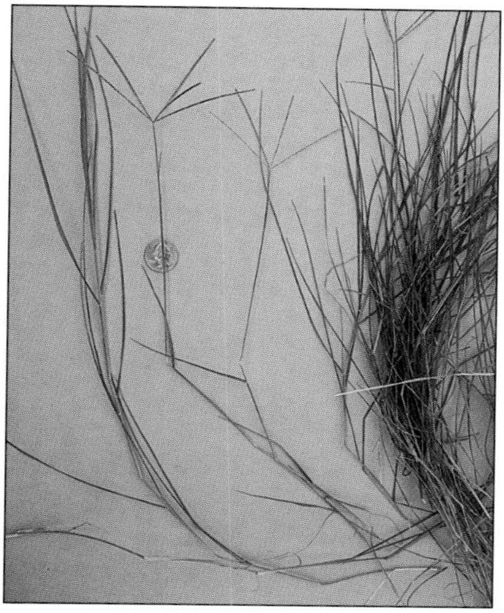

Bermudagrass

Bermudagrass field scene.

Bermudagrass *(Cynodon dactylon)*

Origin: Southeastern Africa.

Description: Perennial. Spreads by rhizomes, stolons, and (in some types) by seed. Hairy ligule. Seed head three to five slender spikes. Hybrids are deep-rooted. Grows 15 to 24 inches tall.

Primary Adaptation: Best in Zone A, but certain varieties are cold-hardy in Zones B and C. Best adapted on sandy soils. Extremely drought-tolerant.

Major Uses: Pasture and hay.

Establishment: Hulled seed of common bermudagrass or other seed-propagated varieties or types should be planted at 5 to 10 lb/A in spring. Hybrids are planted in March-April with sprigs at 10 bu/A in rows or broadcast at 25 to 40 bu/A and covered.

Fertilization: Highly responsive to nitrogen. Total requirements for nitrogen and potassium are similar. Inadequate fertilization with potassium is by far the most common reason for stand declines.

Seasonal Production: May-October in Zone A, late May-September in Zone B.

Management: Hay should be harvested at four to six week intervals. With good management, hay yields of 5 to 7 tons/A can be obtained. Should be closely grazed to maintain quality. Annual clovers, small grains, and ryegrass should be overseeded in autumn if winter-spring production is desired.

Pests: Armyworms and spittlebug. Leafspot may occur, especially when soil potassium levels are low.

Big Bluestem

Big Bluestem *(Andropogon gerardii)*

Origin: Great Plains and eastern U.S.
Description: Perennial bunchgrass, sometimes having rhizomes. Medium-size ligule, leaf sheath compressed, rough leaf edges. Seed head three to six spikes with twisted awns. Deep-rooted. Grows 3 to 6 feet tall. More drought-tolerant than most warm season grasses.
Primary Adaptation: Western parts of Zones B, C, and D.
Major Uses: Pasture, hay. It remains palatable and nutritious over a longer time than switchgrass.
Establishment: Slow seedling establishment. Seed should be planted at 5 to 10 lb/A pure live seed in April-May.
Fertilization: Responsive to nitrogen.
Seasonal Production: June-August.
Management: Will not tolerate close, continuous grazing.
Pests: Usually not a problem.

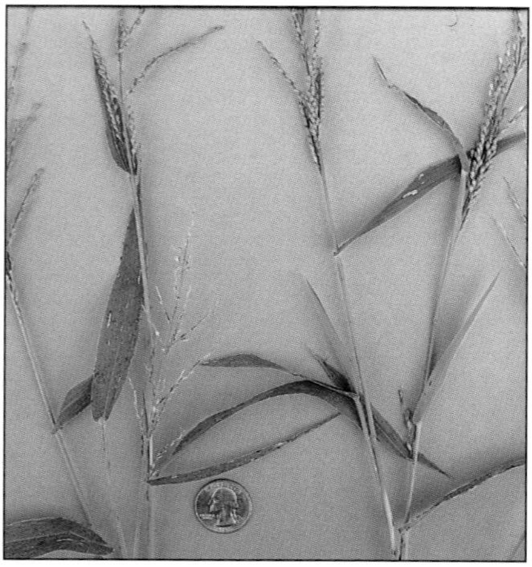

Browntop Millet

Browntop Millet *(Panicum ramosum)*

Origin: Southeast Asia.
Description: Annual. Erect, 2 to 3 feet tall. Leafy, fine-stemmed. Seed head a yellow to brown panicle.
Primary Adaptation: Zones A, B, and C. Does not produce well on calcareous soils.
Major Uses: Pasture and hay.
Establishment: Seed drilled at 15 to 20 lb/A or broadcast at 25 to 30 lb/A in April-August. Growing season about 60 days.
Fertilization: Responsive to nitrogen. Very tolerant of soil acidity.
Seasonal Production: June-August. Much less productive than pearl millet or sorghum-sudan hybrids.
Management: Hay should be cut at heading. Usually a one-cut crop.
Pests. Armyworms.

Carpetgrass

Carpetgrass *(Axonopus affinis)*

Origin: Central America and West Indies.

Description: Perennial. Low-growing. Spread by stolons and seed. Collar and ligule hairy, leaf blades short. Seed head two to five spikes. Forms a dense sod. Grows 6 to 10 inches tall.

Primary Adaptation: Zone A, low soil fertility, often on wet sites.

Major Uses: Pasture. Low nutritive quality. Low yield.

Establishment: Seed.

Fertilization: Not very responsive to fertilization.

Seasonal Production: May-August.

Management: Close grazing.

Pests: Usually not a problem.

Caucasian Bluestem

Caucasian Bluestem *(Bothriocloa caucasica)*

Origin: Russia.

Description: Perennial bunchgrass. Leafy with fine stems. Seed head an open, pink panicle. Deep-rooted and drought-tolerant. Grows 2 to 4 feet tall.

Primary Adaptation: Western parts of Zones B, C, and D. Best on loam and clay soils.

Major Uses: Pasture and hay. Less palatable than big bluestem.

Establishment: Seed planted at 2 to 3 lb/A in May or June.

Fertilization: Responsive to nitrogen.

Seasonal Production: Late May-August.

Management: Stock heavily in early summer when quality is best. Nutritive quality declines with maturity.

Pests: Usually not a problem.

Corn

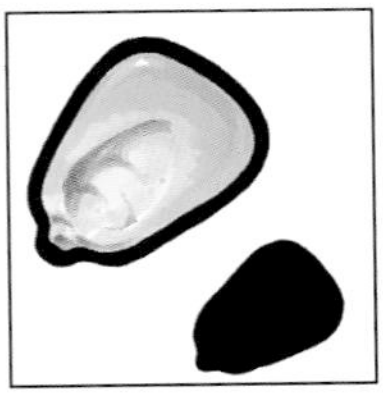

Corn *(Zea mays)*

Origin: Southern Mexico.

Description: Annual. Erect, thick-stemmed. Leafy. Eight to 10 feet tall. High forage digestibility.

Primary Adaptation: Zones A, B, C, and D. Best adapted on loam soils with good water-holding capacity or irrigation.

Major Use: Silage and grain.

Establishment: Seed drilled in wide rows at 12 to 20 lb/A in March-May.

Fertilization: High fertility. Very responsive to nitrogen, phosphorus and potassium. Needs lime on very acid soils.

Seasonal Production: Harvested July-October.

Management: Harvested for silage when kernels are in early dent stage.

Pests: Corn borer, corn rootworm, and corn smut.

Crabgrass

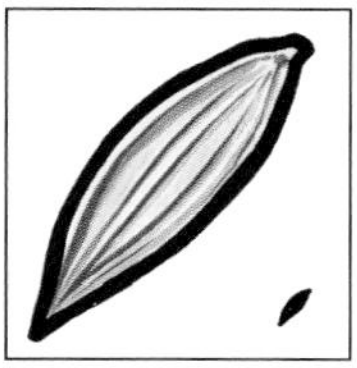

Crabgrass *(Digitaria sanguinalis)*

Origin: Southern Africa.

Description: Annual. Creeping-type growth with long stolons. Very leafy. Tall ligule. Leaves sparsely hairy. Long hairs at collar. Seed head three or more spikes. Grows 2 to 4 feet tall.

Primary Adaptation: Zones A, B, C, and D. Particularly productive in the Gulf Coast area.

Major Uses: Considered a weed in many farming situations. Useful for pasture and hay. Nutritive quality is superior to warm season perennial grasses.

Establishment: Plant seed at 4 to 6 lb/A in March-May. Reseeds well. Large crabgrass (*D. sanguinalis*) is most commonly planted for forage, but other crabgrass species exist. Volunteer stands are often a mixture of two or more species.

Fertilization: Highly responsive to nitrogen.

Seasonal Production: May-September.

Management: With adequate fertilization, will support good stocking rates. Often volunteers after winter annuals.

Pests: Armyworms.

Dallisgrass

Dallisgrass *(Paspalum dilatatum)*

Origin: Argentina, Uruguay, Brazil.

Description: Perennial bunchgrass. Short rhizomes. Tall ligule. Leaf edges rough, sparse hairs near base. Seed head three to six spikes, often drooping. Grows 10 to 20 inches tall. Very leafy.

Primary Adaptation: Zone A, lower part of Zone B. Best adapted on clay and loam soils in areas of good summer moisture.

Major Uses: Pasture, but can be harvested for hay. Better nutritive quality than bermudagrass.

Establishment: Seed germination is low, and establishment is slow. About 10 to 15 lb/A of pure live seed should be broadcast in March or April.

Fertilization: Moderately responsive to nitrogen.

Seasonal Production: April-October.

Management: Best grown with white or red clover. Seed heads can be clipped to eliminate ergot problem if it develops.

Pests: Ergot reduces seed set and can cause toxicity (usually mild) in cattle. Sugarcane borer.

Dallisgrass field scene.

Eastern Gamagrass

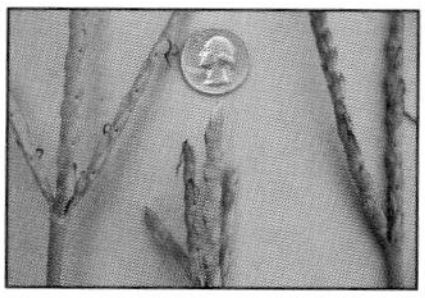

Seed head

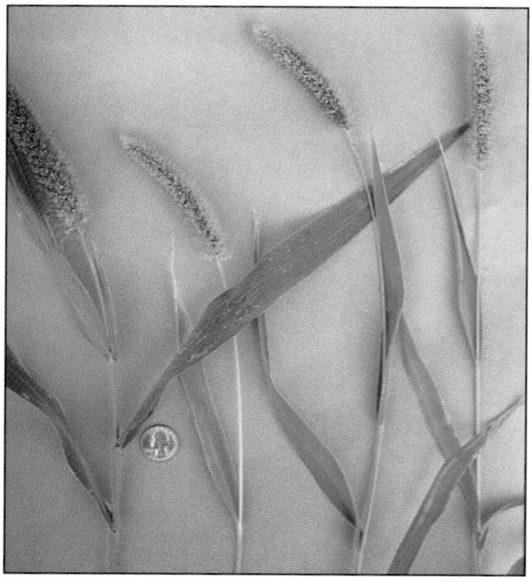

Foxtail Millet

Eastern Gamagrass
(Tripsacum dactyloides)

Origin: Eastern Great Plains and eastern U.S.

Description: Perennial bunchgrass. Wide leaves, rough edges. Seed head one to three spikes with large seed. Short rhizomes. Grows 3 to 8 feet tall.

Primary Adaptation: Western parts of Zones B, C, and D. Loam to clay soils. Especially well-suited to sites with good moisture availability.

Major Uses: Pasture and hay. Good nutritive quality. Little is planted.

Establishment: Seed production and establishment are difficult. Plant 8 lb/A of pure live seed in April-May

Fertilization: High fertility requirement.

Seasonal Production: June-August.

Management: Rotational stocking.

Pests: Usually not a problem.

Foxtail Millet *(Setaria italica)*

Origin: Southern Asia.

Description: Annual. Erect, 3 to 4 feet tall. Leafy. Fine-stemmed. Seed head a cylindrical bristled panicle.

Primary Adaptation: Well-drained soils in Zones A, B, C, and D. Fairly drought tolerant.

Major Uses: Hay. Infrequently grown.

Establishment: Seed can be drilled at 15 to 20 lb/A or broadcast at 20 to 30 lb/A in May-July.

Fertilization: Responds to nitrogen.

Seasonal Production: Most varieties are ready to be harvested in 60 to 70 days. Less productive than pearl millet or sorghum-sudan hybrids. One cutting only.

Management: Should be cut for hay near seed head emergence. Not recommended for horse hay because of a toxin that can cause kidney and joint problems.

Pests: Usually not a problem.

Indiangrass

Indiangrass *(Sorghastrum nutans)*

Origin: Native to tall grass prairie of eastern Great Plains and eastern U.S.

Description: Perennial bunchgrass. Spreads by rhizomes and seed. Deep rooted. Grows 3 to 6 feet tall. Auricles on leaf sheath. Yellow panicles are 6 to 12 inches long.

Primary Adaptation: Zones B, C, and D. Little is planted in the South at present. Well-drained, fertile clay soils. Heat and drought-tolerant.

Major Uses: Pasture, but can be harvested for hay. Nutritive quality is generally better than most other warm season perennial grasses.

Establishment: Seedlings grow slowly and compete poorly with weeds. Should be planted at 6 to 10 lb/A pure live seed during April-May.

Fertilization: Nitrogen is the most important fertilizer nutrient. Response to other nutrients is generally lower than for cool season grasses.

Seasonal Production: Late June-September.

Management: Rotational stocking is essential if grazed below 6 inches. Can be continuously stocked if stubble is maintained between 10 to 16 inches. Very light grazing after September 1.

Pests: Usually not a problem.

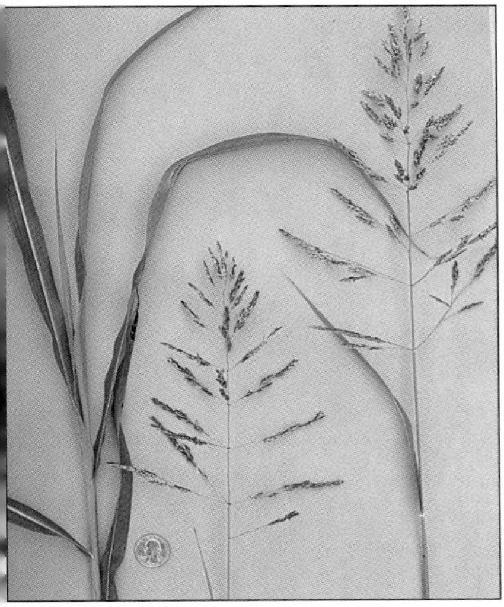

Johnsongrass

Johnsongrass *(Sorghum halepense)*

Origin: Mediterranean region.

Description: Perennial. Erect, 3 to 6 feet tall. Leaves have a white midrib. Very tall ligule. Seed head an open brown panicle. Spreads by rhizomes and seed. Drought-tolerant. Can be a serious pest in crops.

Primary Adaptation: Zones A, B, C, and D. Best on clay soils.

Major Uses: Best used for hay. Can be grazed with good management.

Establishment: Plant seed in April at 20 to 30 lb/A broadcast or 10 to 15 lb/A drilled.

Fertilization: Responds well to nitrogen.

Seasonal Production: May-September.

Management: Hay should be harvested at heading. If used for pasture, rotational stocking is needed to maintain stands. Close continuous grazing will reduce vigor and stands. Prussic acid potential (see Chapter 22).

Pests: Usually not a problem.

Johnsongrass field scene.

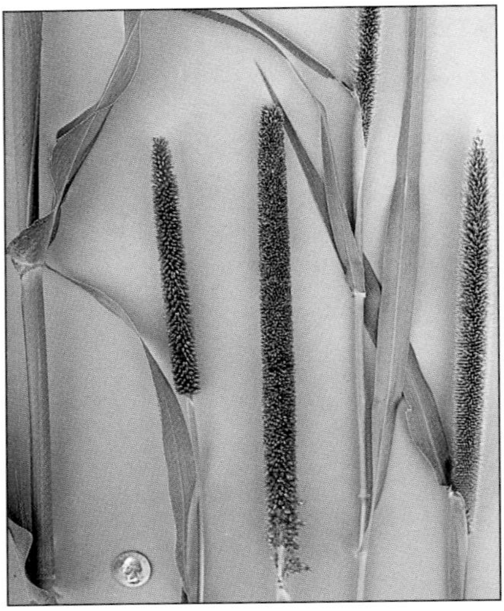

Pearl Millet

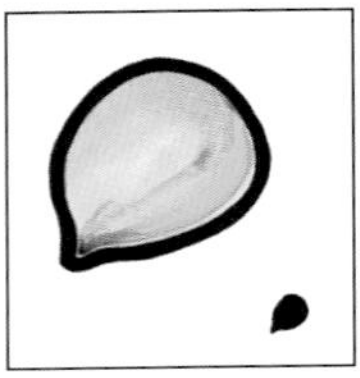

Pearl Millet *(Pennisetum glaucum)*

Origin: Northcentral Africa.

Description: Annual. Erect, 3 to 8 feet tall. Leafy. Very wide leaves serrated at margins; hairy ligule. Seed head a large cylindrical spike.

Primary Adaptation: Zones A, B, C, and D. Best adapted on sandy soils. Does not do well on calcareous soils. Tolerant of drought and soil acidity.

Major Uses: Pasture and silage. Difficult to make hay because of thick stems. High nutritive quality if harvested at immature stage. Nitrate accumulation can cause toxicity under some circumstances (see Chapter 22).

Establishment: Seed are drilled at 12 to 15 lb/A or broadcast at 25 to 30 lb/A in April-June.

Fertilization: Much more tolerant of soil acidity than sorghum. Responsive to nitrogen.

Seasonal Production: Very productive over a short season, generally from June-September.

Management: Requires high stocking rate, preferably with rotational stocking. Stems may need to be mowed after grazing. Should be cut for hay when plants are 30 to 40 inches tall.

Pests: Armyworms, chinch bugs.

Sorghum

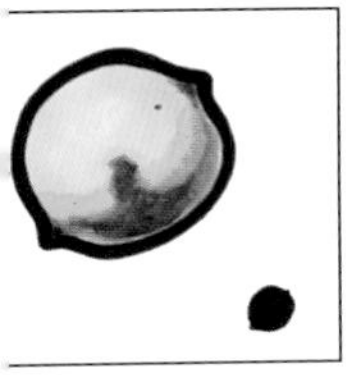

Sorghum *(Sorghum bicolor)*

Origin: Northeast Africa.

Description: Coarse-stemmed. Erect annual, 4 to 15 feet tall. Grain types are short with large seed heads. Forage types are tall with small seed heads.

Primary Adaptation: Zones A, B, C, and D. Very drought-tolerant. Not tolerant of highly acid soils.

Major Uses: Silage. Nutritive value is 85 to 90 percent of corn silage. Nitrate accumulation or prussic acid can cause toxicity under some circumstances (see Chapter 22).

Establishment: Seed are drilled in wide rows at 4 to 6 lb/A or broadcast at 15 to 20 lb/A in May-June.

Fertilization: Moderate fertility requirement.

Seasonal Production: Harvested July-September. Ratoon crop (second harvest) is possible in Zone A.

Management: Harvested for silage when seed are in early dough stage.

Pests: Leafspots, lesser cornstalk borer, sorghum midge.

Sorghum is a drought-tolerant crop that can be harvested for high-energy silage.

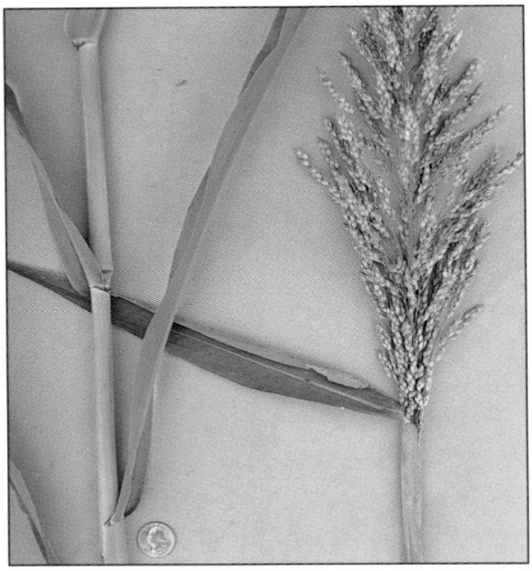

Sorghum-Sudan Hybrid

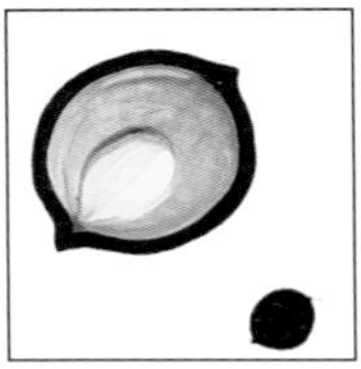

Sudangrass

Sorghum-Sudan Hybrids and Sudangrass *(Sorghum bicolor)*

Origin: Northeast Africa.

Description: Annual. Erect, 4 to 8 feet tall. Leafy. Seed head an open panicle.

Primary Adaptation: Zones A, B, C, and D. Drought-tolerant. Not tolerant of highly acid soils.

Major Uses: Pasture, hay, and silage. High quality if harvested at immature stage. Difficult to make hay because of thick stems. Nitrate accumulation or prussic acid can cause toxicity under some circumstances (see Chapter 22).

Establishment: Seed are drilled at 20 to 25 lb/A or broadcast at 30 to 35 lb/A in May or June.

Fertilization: Very responsive to nitrogen. Needs lime on highly acid soils.

Seasonal Production: Quite productive over a short season, June-September.

Management: Requires high stocking rate, preferably grazed rotationally, to utilize rapid growth and maintain high quality. Thin-stemmed varieties recover more rapidly after cutting or grazing than thick-stemmed varieties. Stems may need to be mowed after grazing. Hay and silage should be cut when plants are 30 to 40 inches tall.

Pests: Armyworms.

Switchgrass

Switchgrass *(Panicum virgatum)*

Origin: Native to Great Plains and most of eastern U.S.

Description: Perennial bunchgrass. Hairy near base of leaf. Seed head an open panicle. Spreads by rhizomes and seed. Deep-rooted. Grows 3 to 7 feet tall.

Primary Adaptation: Zones A, B, C, and D. Drought-tolerant. Will tolerate poorly drained soils.

Major Uses: Pasture and hay. Develops stems several weeks earlier than other warm season grasses so may become stemmy and unpalatable early in summer. Improved varieties have higher yields and nutritive quality.

Establishment: Slow seedling establishment. Plant at 5 to 6 lb/A pure live seed in April-May.

Fertilization: Responsive to nitrogen.

Seasonal Production: Late May-July.

Management: Should be stocked heavily and rotationally stocked with four to six weeks rest between grazings to maintain quality and stands.

Pests: Usually not a problem. SF

Cool Season Grasses

Cool season perennial grasses are the main pasture and hay species in regions north of Zone A (see **Figure 3.2**). They are generally of higher nutritive value and have a longer productive season than warm season perennial grasses. Cool season annual grasses are widely grown in Zones A and B where they provide high quality grazing when warm season grasses are dormant.

Kentucky Bluegrass

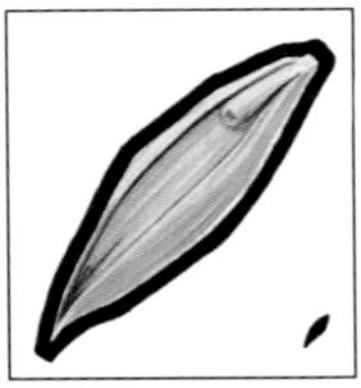

Kentucky Bluegrass *(Poa pratensis)*

Origin: Europe.

Description: Perennial. Narrow leaves with boat-shaped tips. Seed head an open, pyramid-shaped panicle. Rhizomes produce a dense sod. Grows 1 to 3 feet tall.

Primary Adaptation: Upper part of Zone C and Zone D. Intolerant of drought and high temperature.

Major Uses: Pasture, limited use for hay. High nutritive value.

Establishment: Seed are planted at 10 to 15 lb/A in August-September or sometimes in February-March.

Fertilization: Not highly productive unless well fertilized or grown with a legume.

Seasonal Production: April-October. Limited production in July and August.

Management: Tolerates close and frequent grazing better than many grasses. Grazing to a height of 1 to 2 inches favors productivity and maintains a dense sod. Pasture is much more productive when clover is grown with it.

Pests: Grubs, bluegrass billbug, sod webworms, chinch bugs, frit fly, and the greenbug aphid can be serious pests that lower production or even reduce stands.

Note: Drawings of seed in Chapters 5, 6, 7, and 8 show an enlarged view to help illustrate shape and color. The smaller silhouette shows actual seed size.

Orchardgrass

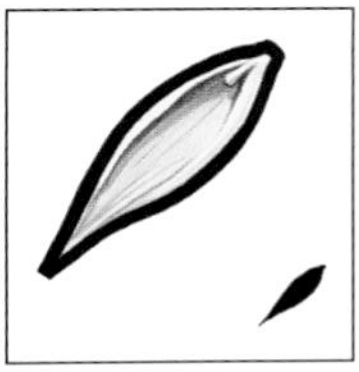

Orchardgrass *(Dactylis glomerata)*

Origin: Europe.

Description: Perennial bunchgrass. Leaf sheath flattened, tall ligule, blue-green blades with v-shape in cross section. Seed head an open panicle. Grows 2 to 3 feet tall.

Primary Adaptation: Upper part of Zone B and Zones C and D. Less tolerant of drought and poor drainage than tall fescue. More shade-tolerant than most grasses. In the lower South, stands do not generally persist more than two to four years.

Major Uses: Pasture, hay. Forage quality is high under good management.

Establishment: Seed should be planted in August-September at 15 to 20 lb/A. In the upper part of Zone C and Zone D, plantings are sometimes made in early spring.

Fertilization: Requires higher fertility than tall fescue. Responds well to nitrogen.

Seasonal Production: March-June or July. Production during September-November is much less than tall fescue.

Management: Requires better management than endophyte-infected tall fescue. Close continuous grazing will weaken stands. Moderate stocking is best. Less competitive than tall fescue, so adapted legumes persist better in association with it. The first hay harvest of the season should be in the boot to early bloom stage, with subsequent harvests as growth permits.

Pests: Armyworms, rust and leafspot diseases. Nematodes are very serious in sandy soils.

Reed Canarygrass

Reed Canarygrass *(Phalaris arundinacea)*

Origin: Europe.

Description: Leaves wide with rough edges and a sharp point. Seed head is a panicle. Coarse, sod-forming perennial with short rhizomes. Two to 6 feet tall. Deep-rooted.

Primary Adaptation: Upper part of Zone C and Zone D. Extremely tolerant of flooding and poorly drained soils. Also drought-tolerant. Tolerates a soil pH range of 5 to 8.

Major Uses: Pasture, hay, silage. Common reed canarygrass contains alkaloids that reduce palatibility. Low-alkaloid varieties are much more palatable to livestock.

Establishment: Seedling vigor is poor, so establishment is slow. A seeding rate of 5 to 8 lb/A planted during April-May in Zone D or August-September in Zone C should give satisfactory stands.

Fertilization: Highly responsive to nitrogen.

Seasonal Production: April-September, limited in July and August.

Management: Rotational stocking.

Pests: Tawny blotch, *Helminthosporium* leafspot, and frit fly.

Annual Ryegrass

Ryegrass, Annual *(Lolium multiflorum)*

Origin: Europe.

Description: Annual bunchgrass. Leaves dark and shiny with smooth edges. Soft, clasping auricles. Seed head is a spike with awned seeds. Grows 2 to 3 feet tall (see **Figure 6.1**).

Primary Adaptation: Zones A, B, and some areas of C. Tolerates wet, poorly drained soil. Less winter-hardy than tall fescue or orchardgrass. High moisture requirement.

Major Uses: Mainly pasture, although sometimes used for hay or silage. High nutritive quality.

Establishment: Seeding rate, 10 to 15 lb/A in mixtures, or 20 to 30 lb/A alone. September or early October are generally the best months to plant, but November overseeding of warm season grasses can be done along the Gulf Coast. Natural reseeding is common.

Fertilization: Responsive to nitrogen. Tolerant of moderate soil acidity.

Seasonal Production: In high rainfall areas of the Gulf Coast, high production can be expected through the winter from November to May. Farther north, most production is concentrated from late February or March through May. Under favorable conditions, high forage production and excellent animal gains can be achieved.

Management: May be seeded alone in the Gulf Coast area. Farther north, it is usually seeded with a small grain (rye, wheat, or oats) and/or a clover. Will tolerate close, continuous grazing.

Pests: Armyworms. Rust disease attacks some varieties, especially within 100 miles of the Gulf of Mexico.

Differences in Annual and Perennial Ryegrass

Annual ryegrass can be distinguished from perennial ryegrass by observing differences in some plant parts. For example, annual ryegrass seeds are smaller than perennial ryegrass seeds. Perennial ryegrass usually has no awns on the seed. Annual ryegrass plants have long, clasping auricles, while perennial ryegrass plants have short, non-clasping auricles.

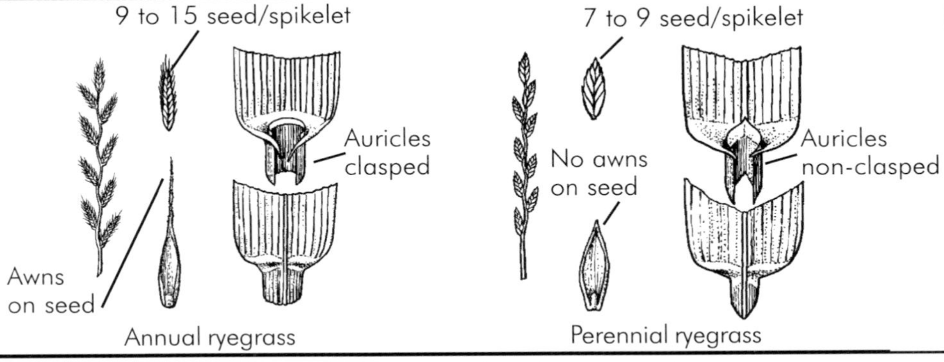

Figure 6.1. Identifying differences in annual and perennial ryegrass.

Ryegrass, Perennial (*Lolium perenne*)

Origin: Europe.

Description: Perennial bunchgrass. Leaves shiny, smooth edges. Soft, short, non-clasping auricles. No awns on spike seed head. Seed are twice the size of annual ryegrass. Grows 2 to 3 feet tall.

Primary Adaptation: Upper Zone C and Zone D. Well drained soils with good moisture. Less tolerant of drought and heat than tall fescue or orchardgrass.

Major Uses: Pasture, hay, silage. High nutritive quality. If infected with fungal endophyte, can cause staggers syndrome in sheep and cattle.

Establishment: Seeding rate, 5 to 8 lb/A in mixtures, or 14 to 18 lb/A alone in spring or late summer.

Fertilization: Very responsive to nitrogen. Tolerant of moderate soil acidity.

Seasonal Production: Main production in spring and early summer. Less autumn production than tall fescue.

Management: Rotational stocking best. Will tolerate close grazing. Does not stockpile well.

Pests: Usually not a problem.

Rye

Oats

Small Grains

Rye *(Secale cereale)*
Oats *(Avena sativa)*
Wheat *(Triticum aestivum)*
Barley *(Hordeum vulgare)*
Triticale *(Triticum secale)*

Origin: Iraq, Turkey, Europe.

Description: Annual bunchgrasses 2 to 4 feet tall. Seed heads are spikes on all except oats, which has a panicle (see **Figure 6.2**).

Primary Adaptation: Rye and wheat—Zones A, B, C, and D. Oats—Zone A. Rye is more tolerant of soil acidity than wheat or oats. Wheat is more tolerant of heavy, wet soils than rye or oats. Although varieties differ, oats are generally more cold sensitive than other small grains and can be winterkilled in some years.

Major Uses: Rye—pasture; barley, wheat, oats—pasture, hay, silage; triticale—hay, silage.

Establishment: Seed are usually planted in September or October. In mixtures, 60 to 90 lb/A are recommended, but 90 to 120 lb/A if planted alone.

Fertilization: All the small grains are highly responsive to nitrogen and require adequate amounts of phosphorus and potassium.

Seasonal Production: Zone A–November to April; Zone B–November to December and February to April; Zones C and D–March to June.

Management: Stocking rate should be adequate to utilize forage and to allow new leaf growth. An annual legume such as arrowleaf clover that produces growth in late spring can be planted as a companion crop to extend the production season and maintain spring forage quality. If cut for hay or silage, harvest should be made in the boot to early heading stage.

Pests: Armyworms, Hessian fly.

Wheat

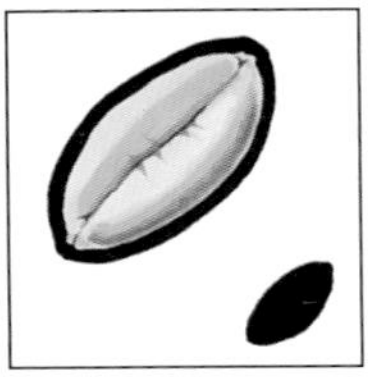

Triticale

Barley

Vegetative Identification of Small Grains

Identification of the vegetative growth of small grains can be difficult, but the leaf collar of most varieties of a given species exhibits unique characteristics. Triticale tends to be more variable than the other small grains.

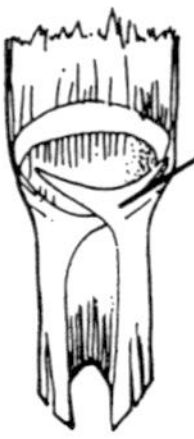

Barley

Barley has large auricles which tend to clasp or overlap.

Rye

Rye has small or medium-sized auricles which are not hairy.

Leaf sheaths usually are hairy.

Leaf color is more blue-green and leaves are less erect than other small grains. Rye seedlings sometimes are red tinted if stressed.

Wheat

Wheat has small or medium-sized auricles which are hairy.

The leaf sheath is not hairy.

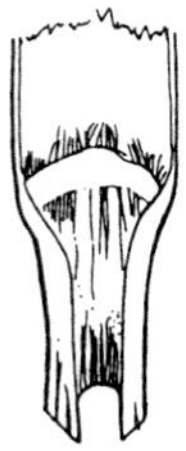

Oats

Oats have no auricles. Leaves of most varieties are wider than those of other small grains.

Figure 6.2. Vegetative identification of small grains.

Smooth Bromegrass

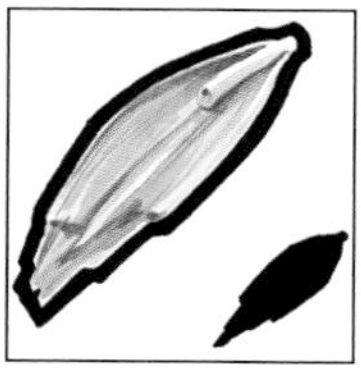

Smooth Bromegrass
(Bromus inermis)

Origin: Russia.

Description: Perennial, cool season grass. Blades narrow, smooth, often constricted to form a W or M. Leafy. Seed head an erect panicle. Deep rooted. Sod forming. Grows 2 to 3 feet tall. Spreads by rhizomes. Grows best on well drained silt-loam or clay-loam soils.

Primary Adaptation: Upper part of Zone C and Zone D.

Major Uses: Pasture, hay, and silage. Often grown with a legume such as alfalfa. Grows well alone when adequate nitrogen is applied.

Establishment: Seeds are planted at 15 to 20 lb/A in August–September or February–April.

Fertilization: Requires higher fertility than tall fescue. Responds well to nitrogen. Often grown with legumes. Grows best at a soil pH of 6.0 to 7.0.

Seasonal Production: April to October. Production limited in July-August.

Management: Close continuous stocking will weaken stands. Moderate rotational stocking is best. The first hay harvest should be taken in the boot to early bloom stage with subsequent harvests as growth permits.

Pests: Armyworms and grasshoppers. Foliar diseases more prevalent in humid areas.

Tall Fescue

Tall Fescue *(Festuca arundinacea)*

Origin: Europe.

Description: Perennial long-lived bunchgrass with short rhizomes. Leaves slightly shiny, dark green, prominent veins, rough edges. Seed head a compressed panicle. Deep rooted. Grows 2 to 4 feet tall.

Primary Adaptation: Zones B, C, and D. Best adapted in clay or loam soils. Tolerant of soil acidity and poor drainage. Relatively tolerant of drought.

Major Uses: Pasture, hay, erosion control. High forage quality if free of fungal endophyte toxins (see Chapter 24).

Establishment: Seed drilled at 15 to 20 lb/A or broadcast at 20 to 25 lb/A in August-September or October. In Zones C and D, planting can be done in early spring.

Fertilization: Tolerant of low fertility and acid soils, but responds well to fertilization.

Seasonal Production: September–December, March–June or July.

Management: If endophyte-infected, will tolerate grazing abuse better than most grasses. Endophyte-free tall fescue should not be grazed closer than 3 inches and should not be overgrazed during summer. Can be grown with white clover, red clover, or alfalfa. The first harvest of hay should be cut in the late boot stage for high quality. Subsequent harvests can be made as growth permits. Autumn stockpiling works well with this grass.

Pests: Wild strains of the fungal endophyte *Neotyphodium coenophiadum* can drastically reduce the performance of animals consuming pasture or hay (see Chapter 24). Only non-toxic endophyte seed or endophyte-free seed should be planted if high animal performance is desired. Nematodes are a serious problem on sandy soils.

Timothy

Timothy *(Phleum pratense)*

Origin: Northern Europe.

Description: Bluish-green perennial bunchgrass. Leaf blades narrow, sharp pointed. Large ligule. Seed head a dense cylindrical spike. Bulb-like corms at plant base. Grows 2 to 4 feet tall.

Primary Adaptation: Upper part of Zone C and Zone D. Cool, humid conditions without drought. When planted in warmer zones, stands weaken and disappear quickly.

Major Use: Primarily as a hay plant, but also used for pasture. Popular as a hay crop for horses although other grasses are equally satisfactory.

Establishment: Seed planted at 6 to 8 lb/A in August-September or sometimes in early spring.

Fertilization: Tolerant of low fertility, but responds well to fertilization.

Seasonal Production: April-October with low production in August-October.

Management: Hay should be cut at the boot to early bloom stage to obtain best quality. Late-cut hay is of low quality.

Pests: No serious pest problems when grown in area of adaptation.

SF

Warm Season Legumes

There is a great need in Southern livestock production for persistent perennial legumes, especially warm season species, that provide good quality forage and fix nitrogen over an extended period of the year. Two of the most useful in the South, alfalfa (a cool season species that grows throughout the summer) and improved sericea lespedeza, have quite different adaptation requirements and uses. Both are grown on a relatively small but increasing acreage as producers recognize their valuable characteristics. Perennial peanut is also an excellent warm season perennial forage legume. However, its potential is limited by adaptation only to the lower Coastal Plain, and it is very slow to establish. Adaptation zones are provided in **Figure 3.2**, page 16.

Alyceclover

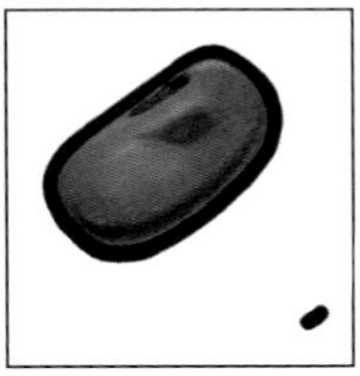

Alyceclover *(Alysicarpus vaginalis)*

Origin: Tropical areas of the Orient.

Description: Annual. Erect, thin-stemmed, rounded leaves, pink flowers in a spike, 12 to 24 inches tall. Not a true clover.

Primary Adaptation: Zone A. Grows best in Gulf Coast area with high summer rainfall.

Major Uses: Pasture and hay. High nutritive quality. Maintains quality well in late summer.

Establishment: Seed are planted at 15 to 20 lb/A in May-June. Establishment is slow, and weed competition may be a problem.

Fertilization: Tolerant of soil acidity, but responds to phosphorus fertilization.

Seasonal Production: July-September.

Management: Best adapted to well-drained, sandy soils. Grazing should begin at 12 to 15 inches. Hay should be cut at 18 to 24 inches. A second cutting of hay is possible under favorable growing conditions. Reseeding is not dependable.

Pests: Susceptible to nematodes. Not competitive with weeds in seedling stage.

Note: Drawings of seed in Chapters 5, 6, 7, and 8 show an enlarged view to help illustrate shape and color. The smaller silhouette shows actual seed size.

Striate Lespedeza

Korean Lespedeza

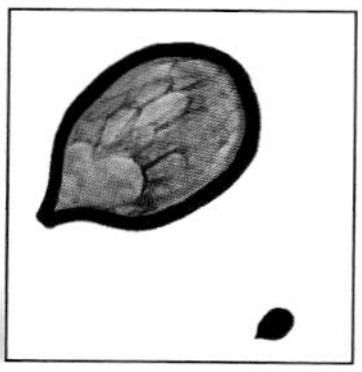

Annual Lespedeza

Striate *(Lespedeza striata)* and Korean *(Lespedeza stipulacea)*

Origin: Eastern China, Korea, Japan.

Description: Annuals. Both species are fine-stemmed, leafy, and have shallow taproots. Leaflets of striate are narrower than Korean. Hairs on stems extend downward on striate, but upward on Korean. Both have pink flowers. Seed of striate are in leaf axils while seed of Korean are borne in clusters at tips of branches. Both species reseed easily.

Primary Adaptation: Korean in Zones B, C, and D; striate in Zones B and C.

Major Uses: Pasture, hay, erosion control. High nutritive quality, furnishing excellent quality pasture in late summer. Relatively low yield, especially in southern zones.

Establishment: Seed are planted at 25 to 35 lb/A in February-March.

Fertilization: Tolerant of acidity and low soil phosphorus. Under high fertility, annual lespedezas are often crowded out by more vigorous and higher yielding grasses and legumes.

Seasonal Production: July-September.

Management: High fertilization of a grass/lespedeza mixture reduces potential growth of lespedeza. Light grazing will allow some seed production for natural reseeding. Hay should be cut at early bloom stage.

Pests: Bacterial wilt, tar spot, powdery mildew, and southern blight can reduce yield and stands (striate is more resistant to these diseases than Korean). Insect damage is slight.

Cowpea

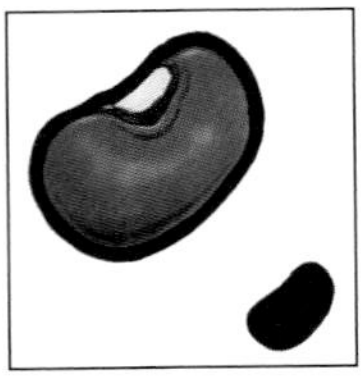

Cowpea *(Vigna unguiculata)*

Origin: Ethiopia.
Description: Annual. Viney, weak stems, three large leaflets, single white flowers, and curved pods.
Primary Adaptation: Zones A, B, and C. Tolerant of drought. Needs good drainage.
Major Uses: Pasture, hay. Forage quality is good.
Establishment: Seed are planted in rows at 30 to 40 lb/A, or 100 to 120 lb/A broadcast in May to early June.
Fertilization: Tolerant of low fertility and soil acidity.
Seasonal Production: June-August.
Management: Similar to soybeans.
Pests: Grasshoppers, curculio weevil, Southern cornstalk borer, and armyworms can be serious insect pests. Rusts and leafspots.

Kudzu

Note: Kudzu does not usually produce mature seed. It is propagated vegetatively from crowns.

Kudzu *(Pueraria lobata)*

Origin: Japan, Korea, eastern China.
Description: Perennial. Hairy, large leaves on long, twining vines arising from heavy woody crowns. Racemes with reddish purple flowers rarely make seed before frost. Spreads rapidly. Deep-rooted and drought-tolerant.
Primary Adaptation: Zones A, B, and C. Rarely planted, but volunteers in many parts of the South.
Major Uses: Erosion control, pasture, hay. Good nutritive quality. Can be a pest where not grazed or otherwise controlled.
Establishment: Usually vegetative from crowns.
Fertilization: Tolerant of soil acidity and low fertility.
Seasonal Production: May-October.
Management: Usually only one hay

cutting can be made per season. If pastured, rotational stocking should be used to maintain crown and root food reserves. Continuous close grazing will weaken plants, reduce productivity, and eventually eliminate stands.

Pests: Usually not a problem.

Perennial Peanut *(Arachis glabrata)*

Perennial Peanut

Note: Perennial peanut is also an excellent warm season perennial forage legume, but its potential is limited by adaptation only to the lower Coastal Plain. It is very slow to establish.

Origin: Brazil.

Description: Perennial, long-lived, leafy, 12 to 16 inches tall, spreading by rhizomes, single yellow or orange flowers.

Primary Adaptation: Lower part of Zone A. Can survive temperatures down to 15°F, but a long cool season greatly reduces potential production. Grows best on well-drained sandy soils. Will not tolerate poor drainage.

Major Uses: Pasture, hay. High nutritive quality.

Establishment: Rhizomes are planted on prepared land at 60 to 80 bu/A from December to early March. Irrigation greatly facilitates establishment.

Fertilization: Low fertility requirement. Calcium application generally necessary.

Seasonal Production: April-October.

Management: Rotational stocking that allows at least a three-week rest between grazing periods of 10 days or less is best, but continuous stocking to maintain a height of at least 4 inches can be used. Two to three hay cuts can be obtained per year. No cutting should be made five to six weeks before killing frost to allow replacement of rhizome food reserves.

Pests: Usually not a problem.

Sericea Lespedeza

Sericea Lespedeza
(Lespedeza cuneata)

Origin: Eastern China, Korea, Japan.

Description: Perennial. Erect-growing, leafy, with fine stems in improved varieties. Long, narrow leaflets are rounded at end, with a sharp tip. Grows 18 to 40 inches tall. Deep-rooted and drought-tolerant. Single white to pink flowers borne in leaf axils.

Primary Adaptation: Zones B, C, and D. Best on clay or loam soils. Very tolerant of acid soils high in aluminum. Not adapted on calcareous soils. Grows well on low-fertility soils where most other legumes do not thrive.

Major Uses: Hay, erosion control, pasture. Most varieties have high levels of tannin that reduce digestibility, but low-tannin varieties are available. Non-bloating.

Establishment: Ideally, seed are planted at 20 to 30 lb/A with a pre-plant herbicide during late March-May. Establishment is slow. Post-emergence herbicide treatments may also be required.

Fertilization: Very tolerant of low fertility and acid soils. May respond to potassium on some soils.

Seasonal Production: April to September.

Management: Hay harvests that leave a 4-inch stubble height should be made when plants are 15 to 24 inches tall, obtaining two to three cuttings per year. High-tannin sericea forage has nutritive value similar to bermudagrass. Low-tannin types have better nutritive value. The tannin level of forage drops sharply in hay, improving palatability and digestibility. Vigor and yield of low-tannin sericea tend to be somewhat less than for high-tannin types. Grazing of sericea should begin when plants are 8 to 15 inches tall. Should not be grazed lower than 4 inches. Removal of forage by grazing or hay production between late August or early September and the first killing frost should be avoided, as this is a period when food reserves are building in the roots. Tall fescue or orchardgrass can be seeded into sericea to provide a longer productive season than sericea alone. Winter annuals such as cereals, crimson clover, or vetch can also be drilled into sericea in October to provide late winter forage. Grasses seeded into sericea should be fertilized with nitrogen.

Pests: Relatively free of insects and diseases. Dodder, a parasitic plant, can be a serious problem in hay or seed fields, so it is important to plant dodder-free seed and kill any volunteer dodder plants with a herbicide.

Soybean (Laredo variety)

Soybean *(Glycine max)*

Origin: China.
Description: Annual. Bushy, with groups of three hairy leaflets.
Primary Adaptation: Zones A, B, C, and D. Raceme with white to pink flowers. Tolerates drought when grown for forage. Well-drained soil.
Major Uses: Most varieties were developed for oil seed production, but can be used for high quality short-season grazing or hay with yields of 2 to 5 tons/A. New hay varieties are higher yielding. Hay should be harvested when pods are 75 percent filled.
Establishment: Seed are planted at 60 to 100 lb/A in May or June.
Fertilization: Intolerant of soil acidity and low fertility.
Seasonal Production: July-August.
Management: One hay cut can be made. Hay is difficult to cure and requires a hay conditioner. If grazed, the season will be short as no regrowth can be expected.
Pests: Armyworms.

Velvetbean

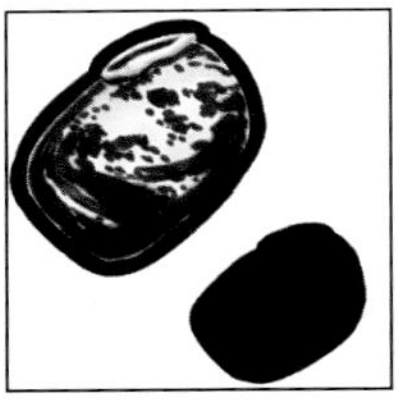

Velvetbean *(Mucana pruriens)*

Origin: India.
Description: Viney annual, extending 20 to 40 feet. Groups of three large leaflets. White to purple flowers in clusters. Hairs on 2- to 6-inch pods can irritate human skin.
Primary Adaptation: Zone A. Sandy soils.
Major Uses: Pasture, green manure.
Establishment: Seed planted at 30 lb/A after all danger of frost is past.
Fertilization: Tolerant of soil acidity and low fertility.
Seasonal Production: May-August.
Management: Moderate grazing to allow regrowth.
Pests: Velvetbean caterpillar. SF

Cool Season Legumes

Cool season legumes make most of their growth in late winter-early spring and in autumn when temperatures and rainfall are generally favorable. Perennial legumes, which usually do not persist more than two or three years in the South, are generally restricted to Zones B, C, and D (see **Figure 3.2**), except for some areas in Zone A where there are soils with good moisture availability during summer.

Annual legumes are most commonly grown in Zone A and the lower part of Zone B. Annuals have the disadvantage of needing to be reestablished each autumn. The seedling stage is the most hazardous period of development when plants are subject to damage from insects, diseases and drought. Thus, dependability is increased by using perennial legumes whenever possible. White clover and red clover are the perennial legumes most commonly grown in association with perennial grasses such as tall fescue, orchardgrass, or dallisgrass. Annual legumes are usually grown with annual grasses (a small grain and/or annual ryegrass) and may be planted on a prepared seedbed in early autumn or overseeded in bermudagrass or bahiagrass during autumn.

Alfalfa

Alfalfa *(Medicago sativa)*

Origin: Iran and central Asia.

Description: Perennial. Erect-growing with many leafy stems arising from large crowns at the soil surface. Grows 24 to 36 inches tall. Trifoliate leaves with long narrow leaflets serrated at the tips. Flowers of the varieties grown in the South are normally some shade of purple. Drought-tolerant, long taproot.

Primary Adaptation: Zones B, C, and D, with a few varieties adapted to Zone A. Requires well-drained soils. Alfalfa planted on land having a very acid subsoil with large amounts of toxic aluminum will have shallow root development and lower yield.

Major Uses: Hay, haylage and pasture. Good quality hay has high nutritive value and is in high demand, particularly for horses and dairy cattle.

Establishment: A seeding rate of 15 to 20

Note: Drawings of seed in Chapters 5, 6, 7, and 8 show an enlarged view to help illustrate shape and color. The smaller silhouette shows actual seed size.

lb/A should be used. A cultipacker-seeder is the best planting equipment for prepared seedbeds. A firm seedbed is critically important. For sod-seeding, a no-till drill is needed. In Zones A and B, September-October is the best time to plant. Autumn planting on prepared land should be done in August to early September in Zones C and D. Winter-spring seeding can be done in February to April in Zones C, D, and the upper part of Zone B.

Fertilization: Sensitive to soil acidity; pH values 6.5 or above are required for high yields. Where subsoils are very acid and high in aluminum, it may be possible to offset the toxic subsoil syndrome and promote deeper root development through deep incorporation of lime or surface application of gypsum at a rate of about 2 ton/A. Potassium, phosphorus, sulfur, and boron are the nutrients that usually need to be applied in order to obtain good alfalfa production. Requires large amounts of potassium. Annual soil tests are critical in monitoring soil nutrient levels. Nitrogen fertilization is not needed. Large amounts of nitrogen are fixed if seed are properly inoculated.

Seasonal Production: March-November in Zone A, April-October in Zones B, C, and D. Has the longest productive season of any Southern-adapted legume.

Management: Successful production requires a higher level of management than other forage crops. For hay production, four to seven cuttings can be made each year, depending on location. In the extreme southern portion of Zone A, it may even be possible to obtain eight or nine harvests in some years. Harvesting at the early bloom stage is the best compromise for obtaining acceptable forage and nutrient yields with good stand persistence. In Zones B, C, and D, stand life is often three to five years, but stands may persist for eight years or more if adequately fertilized and cut at the proper stage of growth. In Zone A, stands on sandy Coastal Plain soils may remain productive for only two to four years. Continuous stocking of hay-type varieties will deplete food reserves in the roots and cause rapid stand loss. Grazing-tolerant varieties can be continuously stocked, but production will be higher and less weed encroachment will occur if rotational stocking with 20 to 35-day rest period is used. In the upper South, allow four weeks of growth in late summer to replenish root reserves. This may be grazed in late autumn.

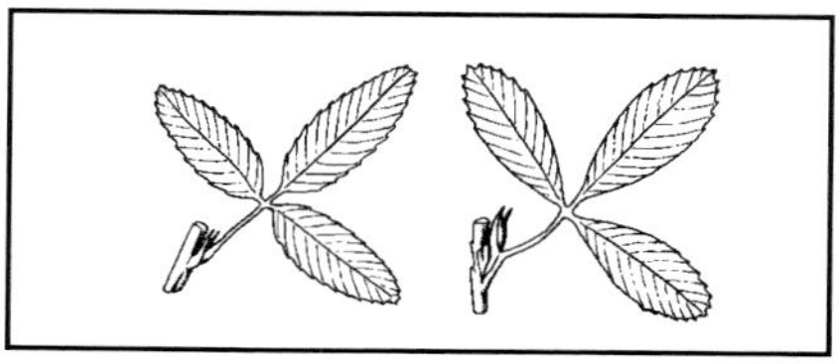

Leaflets of sweetclover (left) and alfalfa (right) appear to be similar. However, leaflets of sweetclover are serrated around the entire leaf margin. Alfalfa leaflets are serrated on only the upper part of the leaf margin.

Pests: Adapted varieties are fairly resistant to diseases. *Sclerotinia* crown and stem rot can be a problem in the establishment year when autumn-seeded. The most important insect problem is the alfalfa weevil, which can be controlled by spraying with an insecticide in the spring and/or early cutting or grazing. Leafhoppers may be a problem in summer, but can be controlled by spraying with an insecticide. A good, well-fertilized stand is strongly competitive, but weeds can be a problem in thin stands. Nematodes are a serious problem on non-resistant varieties in the sandy Coastal Plain of Zone A.

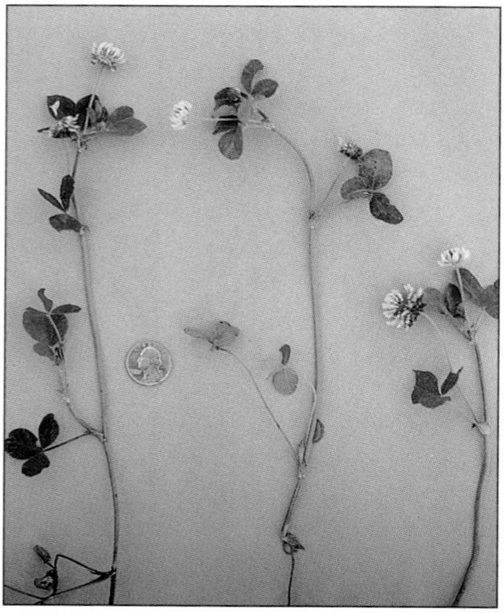

Alsike Clover

Alsike Clover *(Trifolium hybridum)*

Origin: Northern Europe.

Description: Semi-erect, short-lived perennial. From 1 to 3 feet tall. Small, dull green oval leaflets with fine serrated margins. Non-hairy. Pink and white flowers.

Primary Adaptation: Cool climates and wet soils in Zones C and D. Tolerates more flooding and soil acidity than most clovers.

Major Uses: Pasture and hay.

Establishment: Seed are broadcast at 4 to 6 lb/A.

Fertilization: Responds to phosphorus and potassium.

Seasonal Production: May-September.

Management: Stock heavy enough to prevent shading by grasses.

Pests: Powdery mildew, anthracnose, and several virus diseases.

Arrowleaf Clover

Arrowleaf Clover
(*Trifolium vesiculosum*)

Origin: Mediterranean region.

Description: Late season winter annual. Long, branching, hollow stems 2 to 4 feet long. Non-hairy arrow-shaped leaves generally have a large white V mark. The predominately white, but pink- and purple-tinged flower heads are large, often 3 inches long, maturing from bottom to top. Flowering and seed production occur over a long period in late spring and early summer. The seed are about twice the size of white clover seed, and over 70 percent have very hard seed coats, requiring scarification for satisfactory germination.

Primary Adaptation: Zone A and lower part of B. Not adapted on calcareous soils or wet areas.

Major Uses: Pasture and hay. Forage quality is high with digestibility generally superior to crimson clover at all stages of maturity. Bloat is rarely a problem.

Establishment: Scarified seed are planted broadcast at 5 to 10 lb/A in September to early November. Requires a special seed inoculant. Seed will germinate at lower temperatures than crimson clover. Reseeds easily.

Fertilization: Not very tolerant of soil acidity or low fertility. Optimum pH range is 5.8 to 6.5. Responds well to phosphorus and potassium fertilization.

Seasonal Production: March-early July in Zone B, February-early June in Zone A.

Management: Will continue to develop new leaves and remain productive longer in the spring when grazed to a height of 2 to 4 inches than where large amounts of forage accumulate. Where hay is desired, clover should be grazed until early to mid-April, then harvested at early to mid-bloom in May. No regrowth can be expected after cutting hay.

Pests: Crown and stem rot may occur during warm, wet winter weather, especially on loam or clay soils. Grazing to remove surplus growth and to permit light penetration and air movement in the sward will reduce disease losses. Nematodes and virus diseases can be problems as with most clovers. Leaves turn a distinctive purplish-red color in response to stress, whether caused by disease, nutritional imbalances, pest damage, or climatic conditions.

Ball Clover

Ball Clover *(Trifolium nigrescens)*

Origin: Mediterranean region.

Description: Winter annual. Prostrate to partially erect stems that reach a length of up to 3 feet tall. Non-hairy oval leaflets with toothed margins. Fragrant white flowers in small heads. Seed are smaller than white clover. Hard seed and prolific seed production can result in good natural reseeding.

Primary Adaptation: Zone A and lower part of B. Loam to clay soils. Tolerates poor drainage.

Major Uses: Pasture and honey production. Bloat can be a problem.

Establishment: Seed broadcast at 2 to 3 lb/A in September-October. Will germinate at lower temperatures than most annual clovers.

Fertilization: Similar to white clover. More tolerant of soil acidity than crimson clover.

Seasonal Production: Short season during late March to early May.

Management: Tolerates heavy grazing and will produce seed heads close to the ground. If grown with perennial grasses, close grazing in autumn favors reseeded stands.

Pests: Clover head weevil may reduce seed production.

Berseem Clover

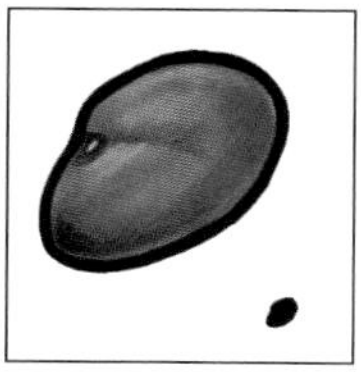

Berseem Clover
(Trifolium alexandrinum)

Origin: Mediterranean region.

Description: Winter annual. Resembles alfalfa. Hollow stems grow erect to a height of 2 feet or more. Non-hairy elongated leaflets. White flowers form small heads.

Primary Adaptation: Most varieties not winterhardy in the southeastern U.S. A winter-hardy variety can be grown in Zone A and the lower part of Zone B. Tolerant of alkaline soil. More tolerant of wet soil than most annuals. Particularly well-suited for use in non-acid Black Belt soils and in high rainfall areas near the Gulf Coast.

Major Uses: Pasture and hay. High quality. Rarely causes bloat.

Establishment: Seed planted broadcast at 20 lb/A or drilled at 10 to 15 lb/A in September.

Fertilization: Best on loam soils of pH 6 or above. Requires high fertility, including boron.

Seasonal Production: November-December and March-June.

Management: Grazing should begin when forage is 10 inches tall and the stubble maintained at 3 to 4 inches to encourage new leaf production. Rotational stocking is most successful. The winter-hardy variety produces hard seed and can reseed, though not as dependable as some annual clovers.

Pests: Crown rot can be a problem if excess forage is present during freezing temperatures.

Birdsfoot Trefoil

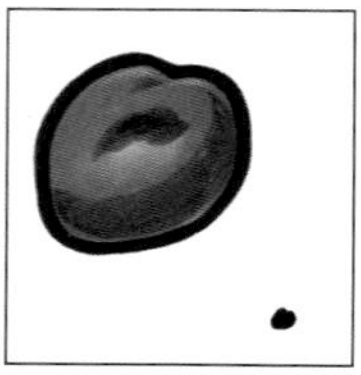

Birdsfoot Trefoil
(*Lotus corniculatus*)

Origin: Mediterranean region.

Description: Deep-rooted, shortlived perennial, having finer stems and more leaves than alfalfa. Grows 12 to 30 inches tall, depending on whether it is a prostrate or erect variety. Five oval leaflets, non-hairy. Flowers are bright yellow. Brown to purple seed pods radiate from the stem branch, resembling a bird's foot. Reseeds under proper management.

Primary Adaptation: Zones C and D. Well-drained soils. Tolerant of drought, moderate soil acidity. Grows well in association with Kentucky bluegrass, orchardgrass, and tall fescue. Will not compete with bermudagrass or bahiagrass.

Major Uses: Pasture and erosion control. High quality forage. Non-bloating legume.

Establishment: Seed planted at 4 to 6 lb/A with cool season perennial grasses using a cultipacker-seeder in late August-September.

Fertilization: Lime if soil pH is below 5.5. Responds well to phosphorus and potassium.

Seasonal Production: April-early October.

Management: Practical grazing management should leave 3 to 4 inches of leaf tissue to maintain root carbohydrates and assure vigorous regrowth. Natural reseeding is essential for maintaining stands and productivity. Plants should be allowed to produce some seed each year.

Pests: Crown and root rots are serious diseases that weaken or kill plants, requiring natural reseeding to maintain stands. Nematodes are a major problem on sandy soils.

Black Medic

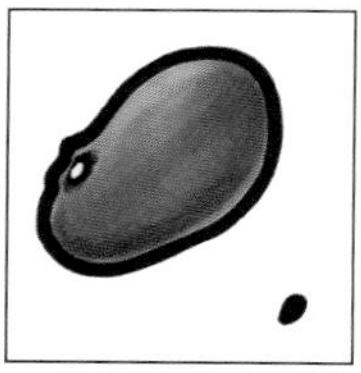

Black Medic *(Medicago lupulina)*

Origin: Mediterranean region.
Description: Winter annual with prostrate stems. Usually not over 6 to 8 inches tall. Heart shaped, hairy leaflets with toothed margins. Small yellow flowers develop coiled seed pods.
Primary Adaptation: Zones A, B, C, D.
Major Uses: Pasture.
Establishment: Volunteers in many areas. Seed broadcast at 10 to 12 lb/A in September-October. Seed not readily available.
Fertilization: Grows on moderately acid soil, but is most productive on calcareous soils.
Seasonal Production: Low yields, occurring mainly in April and early May.
Management: Should be quickly utilized due to short productive season.
Pests: Not usually a problem.

Button Clover

Button Clover *(Medicago orbicularis)*

Origin: Mediterranean region.
Description: Winter annual with leafy decumbent stems 2 to 3 feet long. Smooth, oval non-hairy leaflets with toothed margins. Orange-yellow flowers that develop with flat, coiled seed pods that lack the spines of other burclovers.
Primary Adaptation: Zones A, B, and C on loam or clay soils. Best growth on limestone soils.
Major Uses: Pasture and hay.
Establishment: Seed broadcast at 10 lb/A in September-October. Seed not readily available.
Fertilization: Lime needed if soil is below pH 6.
Seasonal Production: March-May.
Management: If cut for hay, only one harvest can be obtained.
Pests: Not usually a problem.

Caleypea, Roughpea, or Singletary Pea

Caleypea, Roughpea, or Singletary Pea *(Lathyrus hirsutus)*

Origin: Mediterranean region.

Description: Winter annual with thin-winged spreading stems up to 3 feet long. Long non-hairy paired leaflets. Small red and blue flowers that form small seedpods. Hard seed coats can result in good reseeding.

Primary Adaptation: Zone A or lower part of Zone B on loam and clay soils. Grows on soils too wet for most clovers. Does well on both acid and calcareous soils.

Major Uses: Pasture. Seed are mildly toxic to livestock.

Establishment: Scarified seed broadcast at 50 to 55 lb/A in September-October.

Fertilization: Phosphorus and potassium are required.

Seasonal Production: March-May.

Management: Grazing should be discontinued in late spring when seedpods are forming to avoid toxicity and to permit seed production for natural reseeding.

Pests: Aphids.

Crimson Clover

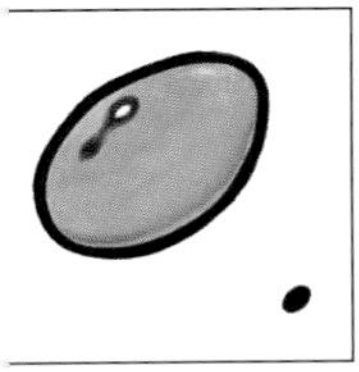

Crimson clover field scene.

Crimson Clover
(Trifolium incarnatum)

Origin: Mediterranean region.

Description: Winter annual. Plants have dark green oval leaflets without a V mark. Dense hairs on leaves and stems. Grows to a height of 1 to 3 feet. Brilliant crimson flowers. Long heads, maturing from bottom to top. Yellow rounded seed about 2.5 times the size of arrowleaf clover seed. Combine-harvested seed do not need scarification.

Primary Adaptation: Mainly Zones A and B, limited use in Zone C. Does not tolerate calcareous or poorly drained soils.

Major Uses: Pasture, hay, green manure, field or roadside beautification. Will produce more forage at low temperatures than other clovers.

Establishment: Seed broadcast at 20 to 30 lb/A in late August-October.

Fertilization: Fairly tolerant of soil acidity.

Seasonal Production: Late November-December, February-early April in Zone A; November, March-April in Zone B.

Management: Can be grazed throughout winter, but if hay is desired, cattle must be removed by mid-March.

Pests: Clover head weevils often cause heavy seed losses, resulting in poor natural reseeding. Cool, wet weather in winter often results in crown and stem rot, especially where there is a thick layer of leaves. Moderate stocking in winter reduces the problem.

Lappa Clover

Lappa Clover (*Trifolium lappaceum*)

Origin: Mediterranean region.
Description: Dense growth habit, growing to 2 feet. Leaves and stems very hairy. Pink-white flowers in small heads.
Primary Adaptation: Zone A and lower part of Zone B. Loam to clay soils. Tolerates poor drainage.
Major Uses: Pasture.
Establishment: Seed broadcast at 10 to 15 lb/A in September-October. Seed not readily available commercially.
Fertilization: Grows best on calcareous soils.
Seasonal Production: April and May.
Management: Should be quickly utilized due to short productive period.
Pests: Not usually a problem.

Large Hop Clover

Large Hop Clover (*Trifolium campestre*) and Small Hop Clover (*Trifolium dubium*)

Origin: Mediterranean region.
Description: Low-growing winter annuals. Yellow flowers in small heads.
Primary Adaptation: Zones A, B, C, and D.
Major uses: Pasture.
Establishment: Volunteers throughout the South. Seed broadcast at 4 to 8 lb/A in September. Seed not commercially available.
Fertilizer: Tolerant of acid soils with low fertility.
Seasonal Production: Low yield over a short season in April and May.
Management: Should be quickly utilized due to short productive period.
Pests: Not usually a problem.

Persian Clover

Persian Clover
(Trifolium resupinatum)

Origin: Mediterranean region.

Description: Winter annual. Stems may reach a height of 2 to 3 feet. Non-hairy, oval leaflets with toothed margins. Small pink flowers. Seed are olive green to purple. Hard seed coats favor good reseeding.

Primary Adaptation: Zone A and lower part of Zone B. Loam to clay soils. Tolerates poor drainage.

Major Uses: Pasture, hay, green manure. Bloat can be a problem.

Establishment: Seed broadcast at 3 to 5 lb/A in September-October.

Fertilization: Requires soil pH 6 or above.

Seasonal Production: Very productive in March-April.

Management: Close grazing.

Pests: Not usually a problem.

Rose Clover

Rose Clover *(Trifolium hirtum)*

Origin: Mediterranean area of Europe and north Africa.

Description: Winter annual. Very hairy gray-green oval leaflets. Rose-colored flowers.

Primary Adaptation: Zone A and lower part of Zone B. Tolerant of drought and low soil fertility.

Major Uses: Pasture. High quality.

Establishment: Seed broadcast 15 to 20 lb/A in September-October. Good natural reseeding. Many seed are quite hard and can volunteer over many years.

Fertilization: Responds to phosphorus and potassium where these nutrients are deficient. Best adapted to soil pH 6 to 7.

Seasonal Production: California varieties are low yielders and mature in April in the South. A long-season improved variety is available.

Management: Can be grazed continuously until maturity, but livestock must be removed by mid-April if natural reseeding is desired.

Pests: Not usually a problem.

Red Clover

Red Clover
(Trifolium pratense)

Origin: Southeastern Europe and Turkey.

Description: Short-lived perennial, usually two years in the South, except where it is an annual. Erect-growing, leafy plants 2 to 3 feet tall. Oval leaflets hairy and marked with a white V. Flowers are clustered into large pinkish-violet heads.

Primary Adaptation: Best in Zones C and D, but with good management will perenniate in Zone B. Grows as a winter annual in Zone A. Fairly drought-tolerant. Tolerates more soil acidity and poorer soil drainage than alfalfa. Less tolerant of extremely wet conditions than white clover. Due to a long growing season, red clover is the best yielding clover in areas where well adapted. Well suited for hay, silage, and grazing with tall fescue, orchardgrass, timothy, dallisgrass, or johnsongrass.

Major Uses: Hay and pasture.

Establishment: Seed planted on prepared land at 6 to 8 lb/A in drill rows or 12 to 15 lb/A broadcast during September-October in Zones A, B, C, and D and February-March in Zones B, C, and D. Established grass pastures should be overseeded in October-November or February-March. Seedling vigor is better than any other clover. Especially well suited for seeding into cool season perennial grass sods or into dallisgrass or johnsongrass.

Fertilizer: If soil pH is below 5.5, lime should be applied. Responsive to phosphorus and potassium.

Seasonal Production: April-October in Zones C and D, March-June in Zone B.

Management: Hay should be cut in early bloom stage. Red clover will provide more grazing than white clover during summer. Unlike white clover, red clover will not tolerate continuous close grazing over long periods of time.

Pests: Many diseases such as powdery mildew, northern and southern anthracnose, and bean yellow mosaic virus attack red clover. Varieties have been developed with resistance to one or more of these diseases.

Spotted or Southern Burclover

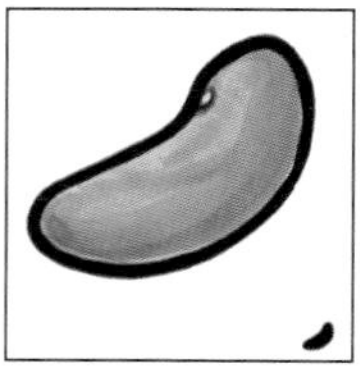

Spotted or Southern Burclover
(Medicago arabica)

Origin: Mediterranean region.
Description: Winter annual with decumbent branches up to 2 feet long. Nonhairy heart-shaped leaflets usually with a dark spot in center. Large stipules. Small yellow flowers form small burs.
Primary Adaptation: Zones A and B.
Major Uses: Pasture.
Establishment: Volunteers in many areas. Seed broadcast at 10 to 15 lb/A in September-October. Seed not readily available.
Fertilization: Grows best in calcareous soils with pH above 6.
Seasonal Production: March and April. Relatively low yield.
Management: Should be quickly utilized due to short season.
Pests: Not usually a problem.

Subterranean Clover

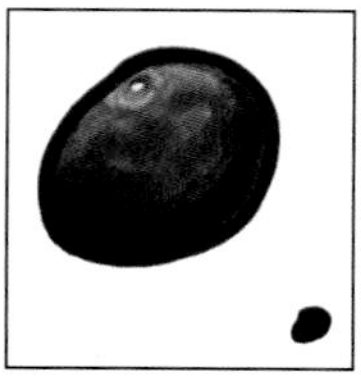

Subterranean Clover
(Trifolium subterraneum)

Origin: Mediterranean region.
Description: Dense, low-growing winter annual clover. Heart-shaped leaflets; dark green, hairy, with a black spot. Large stipules. Small, mainly white flowers form a small bur that is forced into the surface of the soil. Good reseeding possible. Seed are large and either black or tan.
Primary Adaptation: Zone A and lower part of Zone B. Well-drained soil.
Major Uses: Pasture. Lower-yielding than crimson or arrowleaf clovers.
Establishment: Seed broadcast at 10 to 20 lb/A. Special inoculant required.
Fertilization: Fairly acid tolerant. Requires adequate phosphorus and potassium for growth.
Seasonal Production: November-

Sweetclover

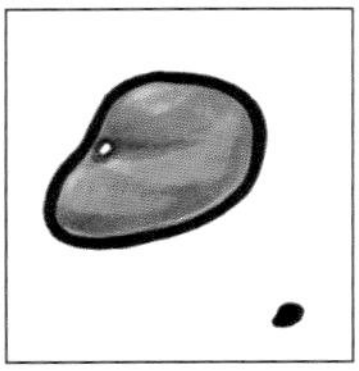

Hairy Vetch

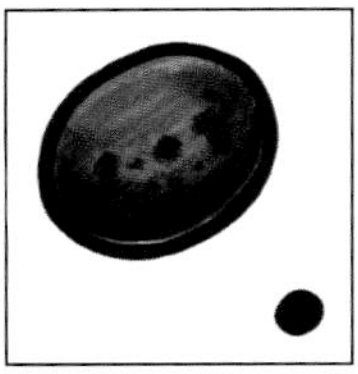

December and March-May.
Management: Tolerates close continuous stocking. Tolerates shade better than most clovers.
Pests: Relatively free of pests.

Sweetclover
Yellow (*Melilotus officinalis*)
White (*Melilotus alba*)

Origin: Europe and central Asia.
Description: Biennial, erect, coarse stems, 4 to 8 feet tall. Leaflets serrated margins. Deep taproot. Yellow or white flowers in racemes. Not a true clover.
Primary Adaptation: Zones A, B, C, and D. Clay or loam soils. Drought tolerant and winterhardy, but intolerant of soil acidity.
Major Uses: Pasture. Coumarin in forage reduces palatability to livestock. Low-coumarin varieties are available.
Establishment: Seed can be planted in spring or autumn at 10 to 15 lb/A.
Fertilization: Requires soil pH near neutral, similar to alfalfa.
Seasonal Production: May-August.
Management: New growth comes from stem buds. Overgrazing should be avoided during the first year.
Pests: Sweetclover weevil.

Vetch
Hairy (*Vicia villosa*)
Common (*Vicia sativa*)
Bigflower (*Vicia grandiflora*)

Origin: Mediterranean region.
Description: Viney winter annuals with stems 2 to 4 feet in length. Leaves compound with narrow leaflets. White, purple, or pale yellow flowers borne in racemes.
Primary Adaptation: Hairy vetch and bigflower vetch in Zones A, B, C, and

Common (Cahaba White) Vetch

Bigflower Vetch

D; common vetch in Zone A and lower part of Zone B. Vetches need well-drained soil.

Major Uses: Pasture, hay, silage (with small grain companion), and green manure.

Establishment: Hairy and bigflower vetch seed broadcast at 20 to 25 lb/A and common vetch at 30 to 40 lb/A in September-October.

Fertilization: Tolerant of soil acidity, but vetches have a relatively high phosphorus requirement.

Seasonal Production: April-May in Zone C, March-May in Zone B, and November-December and February-April in Zone A.

Management: Grazing should not begin until plants are at least 6 inches tall. Close grazing will destroy buds needed for regrowth. Should be cut for hay in the early bloom stage. A small grain seeded at 60 lb/A makes a good companion crop for vetch grown for hay or silage.

Pests: The vetch bruchid often attacks hairy vetch pods and destroys the seed, reducing reseeding.

White or Ladino Clover

White or Ladino Clover
(Trifolium repens)

Origin: Mediterranean region.

Description: Fairly long-lived perennial in upper South. Short-lived perennial or annual in lower South. Very leafy plants 8 to 12 inches tall. Spreads by stolons (runners) and forms shallow roots at nodes. Oval leaflets, non-hairy and usually marked with a white V. White flowers clustered into heads. Seed extremely small. Intermediate types can be expected to reseed naturally while giant or ladino types usually do not reseed well in the lower South.

Primary Adaptation: Zones A, B, C, and D. Not productive on droughty soils, but will survive considerable dry weather. Tolerant of moderate soil acidity and wetter soils. Grows well in association with cool season perennial grasses and dallisgrass, but generally not with bermudagrass and bahiagrass.

Major Use: Pasture. Very high quality grazing plant. Bloat can be a problem.

Establishment: Seed broadcast at 2 to 3 lb/A with tall fescue, orchardgrass, or Kentucky bluegrass in September-October. Under favorable growing conditions, can shade out seedling grasses. May be necessary to graze the clover to reduce competition. Established grass pastures can be overseeded in October-November or February-March.

Fertilization: Soil should be limed if pH is below 6. Highly responsive to potassium.

Seasonal Production: April-October in Zones C and D, March-June and October-November in Zones A and B if soil moisture is favorable.

Management: Grass competition from undergrazing is a major problem in maintaining productive stands. Grass can be planted in wide rows and clover broadcast to reduce competition. Adequate potassium and phosphorus are important for good production. Grazing should be sufficient to maintain forage height at 1 to 4 inches, preventing shading of clover by the grass.

Pests: A number of leaf and root diseases. Close grazing allows light and air penetration to reduce the likelihood of these problems. Virus diseases are the most serious problem. Normally plants are infected, weaken, and die after two to three years. Since no virus-resistant varieties are available, the only solution is to replant the pasture with clover every two to three years. Various insect pests attack white clover, but no practical control is available.

Winter Pea

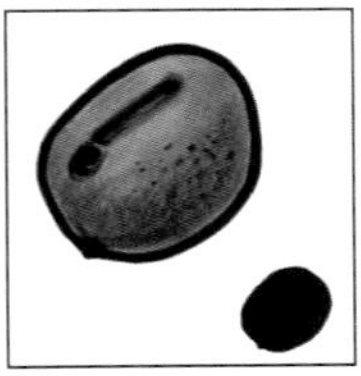

Winter Pea or Austrian Winter Pea
(Pisum sativum subsp. arvense)

Origin: Mediterranean region.

Description: Viney winter annual with stems 2 to 4 feet long. Alternate leaflets with toothed margins. Flowers pink, purple, or white.

Primary Adaptation: Zones A, B, and C. Well-drained loam or sandy loam soil.

Major Uses: Silage and green manure. High nutritive quality.

Establishment: Seed are planted in September-October at 30 to 40 lb/A if grown alone or 20 to 30 lb/A if sown with small grain.

Fertilization: Responds well to phosphorus and potassium. Intolerant of highly acid soil.

Seasonal Production: Can be cut for silage in April.

Management: Not well adapted for pasture because plants are easily damaged by trampling. Best used for silage as the crop is difficult to cure for hay.

Pests: Downy mildew can be quite destructive during warm, wet winters. Virus diseases can be a problem. Pea weevil, aphids, and nematodes also can cause considerable damage.

Chicory

Leafy chicory forage in bermudagrass pasture. Chicory is a short-lived perennial forb.

Chicory *(Cichorium intybus)*

Note: Chicory is a forb, not a legume. It is included here due to its potential as a pasture crop in some areas.

Origin: Europe.

Description: Short-lived (two to four years) perennial forb (neither grass or legume) with a rosette of broad crinkled prostrate leaves. Deep taproot. Pale purple flowers are borne on stems 4 to 5 feet tall.

Primary Adaptation: Zones A, B, C, and D. Very tolerant of drought and soil acidity. Competes well with tall fescue or bermudagrass when rotationally stocked.

Major Use: Pasture. High nutritive quality. Very palatable to livestock. Not suitable for hay because of high forage water content.

Establishment: Drill 3 to 4 lb/A on prepared land or grass sod in September-October in Zones A, B, and C; April-May in Zone D. Grass suppression desirable on sod.

Fertilization: High fertility requirement. Apply nitrogen in spring, summer and autumn.

Seasonal Production: March-October with peak in April-May. Good growth in summer.

Management: Rotational stocking. Mowing, especially in late spring, is needed to remove seedstalks and maintain good leaf growth.

Pests: Not known. SF

Soil Testing and Fertility

Periodic soil testing, followed by liming and fertilization according to soil test recommendations, is critically important to achieve good forage production and maintain forage stands. On most livestock farms in the South, no management practice will have more long-term influence on meat or milk production per acre.

The majority of land producing forage in the South and other regions is not regularly soil tested. Furthermore, most of the land that is tested is found to be in need of lime and/or fertilizer, yet most pastures and a significant portion of the hay acreage do not receive annual fertilization. Data in **Table 9.1** show that forage producers are missing a great opportunity for increasing profits by not following a good lime and fertilizer program. The only way to know how much fertilizer or lime is needed to produce high forage yields is to soil test. Perennial pastures should be tested at least once every two to three years. Fields used for hay production, overseeded in winter, or tilled and planted to annual forage crops should be tested each year.

The process of physically taking soil samples offers the greatest opportunity for error in the testing process. A pound or less of soil in the sample will represent millions of pounds of soil in the pasture or meadow, so it should be representative of the entire area. To help assure good sampling techniques, select a reputable soil testing laboratory...university run or privately managed...and carefully follow sampling, handling, and shipping instructions. This procedure will assure the most reliable results and help in the development of an efficient, profitable nutrient management system, based on research-proven soil test recommendations. Without question, soil testing and fertilization offer great opportunities for improving forage production.

Soil test recommendations are based on the assumption that the forage produced will be utilized. Thus, it is important for a producer to adjust stocking rates and grazing management as necessary to ensure that the forage produced is used. This is essential to obtain the maximum or near maximum benefit from the investment in fertilizer.

Table 9.1. Summary of soil test results and forage crop fertilization practices in the South.[1]

Item	Range of responses, %	Average, %
Forage land that is soil tested	5-50	21
Tested land that is below pH 6.0	30-80	52
Tested land that is low in phosphorus	25-70	46
Tested land that is low in potassium	10-60	33
Pasture land receiving fertilizer annually	10-50	28
Hay land receiving fertilizer annually	20-95	66

[1]Based on a survey of university agronomists in 10 Southern states.
Source: Monroe Rasnake and Garry D. Lacefield, University of Kentucky.

The primary source of error in soil testing is the sampling process.

The Major Nutrients

In forage production, as is the case for most crops, the major nutrients... nitrogen, phosphorus, and potassium...are of greatest concern because their deficiencies are most common. (See **Appendix A.7** for chemical symbols and ionic forms taken up by crops.) Each of these nutrients must be available in substantial quantities to obtain profitable, environmentally friendly forage production.

Nitrogen

Nitrogen is the nutrient that normally produces the most dramatic growth response in forage grasses. It is a component of chlorophyll, which is critical in the process of photosynthesis. Without photosynthesis, there would be no life.

The Earth's atmosphere is almost 80 percent nitrogen, and some nitrogen is furnished to the soil as a result of electrical storms and various other atmospheric reactions. In addition, nitrogen is released by the breakdown of soil organic matter as well as plant and animal residues. However, the major source of nitrogen for forage grasses is manufactured nitrogen fertilizer. Because nitrogen is required by forage grasses in fairly large quantities and because it leaches readily, it should usually be supplied in two or more applications during the growing season of a forage grass.

Plants have the ability to use nitrogen either as ammonium or as nitrate. The ammonium form is attracted to, and held by, soil particles, but may be converted to the nitrate form by a microbial process called nitrification. In this form, it can move down through the soil, out of the reach of plant roots, and can potentially pollute groundwater. Therefore, it is important to time nitrogen fertilization as closely to crop use as possible.

It is not necessary to apply nitrogen to forage legumes. It is also generally recommended that no nitrogen be applied to grass-legume mixtures if the legume comprises a substantial portion (usually 30 percent or more) of the stand because legumes have the ability to fix significant amounts of atmospheric nitrogen (see **Table 12.4**, page 102). One exception to this rule

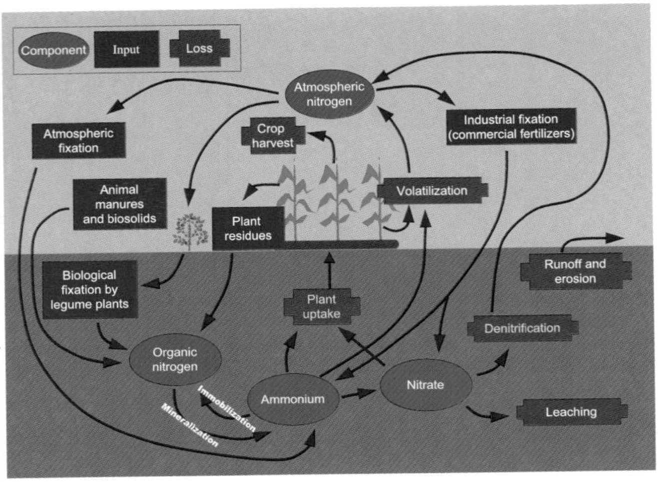

Source: Potash & Phosphate Institute (www.ppi-ppic.org)

Figure 9.1. The nitrogen cycle.

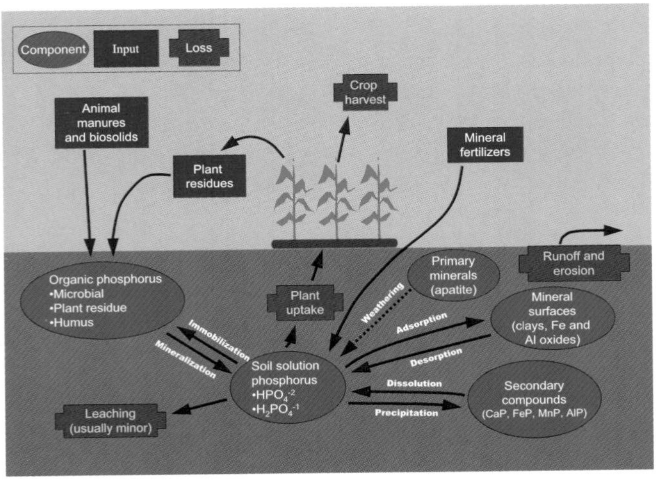

Source: Potash & Phosphate Institute (www.ppi-ppic.org)

Figure 9.2. The phosphorus cycle.

is sericea lespedeza/grass mixtures. Although sericea fixes enough nitrogen for its own needs, it provides little extra for grasses growing in association with it. However, even in this case, there is some benefit provided to the grass as a result of nitrogen from sericea forage being recycled in dung and urine.

There are several ways by which nitrogen applied to grassland can be lost. The most common of these is leaching, which is merely the movement of nitrogen (as nitrate-nitrogen) by water to depths at which plant roots cannot reach it. Heavy rainfall can cause substantial leaching losses in a short period of time, particularly on sandy soils. Also, nitrogen can be removed by water flowing over the soil surface.

Denitrification, which results in the gaseous loss of nitrogen into the atmosphere as nitrous oxide, nitric oxide, or nitrogen gases, is caused by microorganisms. This sometimes occurs when there are wet soil conditions for an extended period. The potential for denitrification losses is highest on clay soils that have a high water-holding capacity. This type of loss is associated with waterlogged soil conditions, which are most likely to occur during the

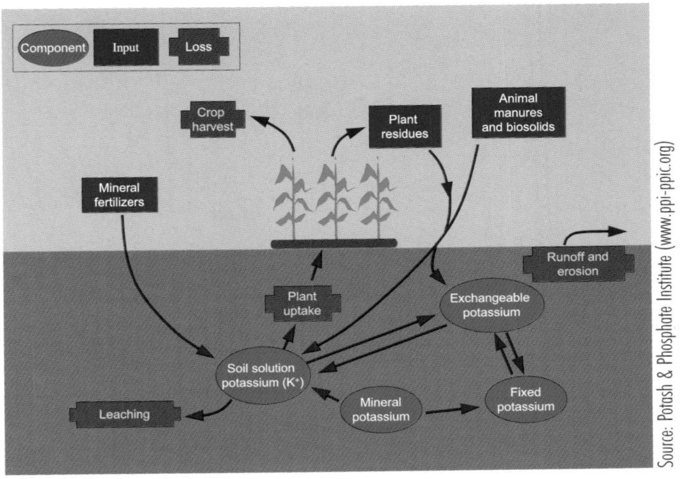

Figure 9.3. The potassium cycle.

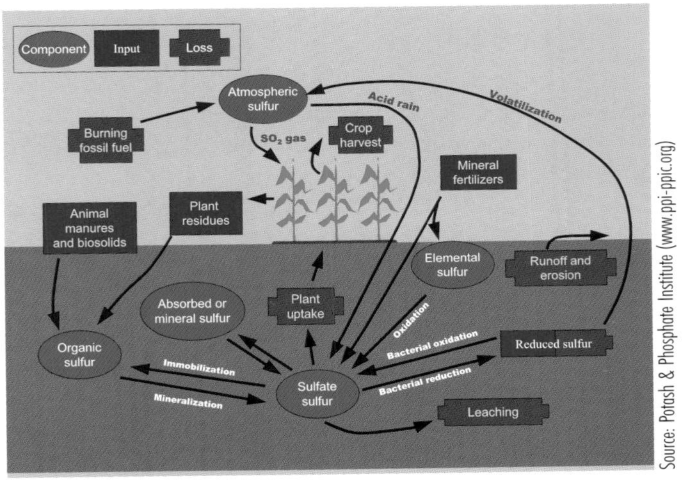

Figure 9.4. The sulfur cycle.

wettest months of the year.

The other type of gaseous nitrogen loss is volatilization, the release of nitrogen into the atmosphere as ammonia. Volatilization is caused by a chemical reaction that sometimes occurs with surface-applied fertilizers or urine from grazing animals. The nitrogen fertilizer source most likely to volatilize is urea, although in many situations, little or no loss will occur even with this product.

Several factors affect the amount of ammonia volatilization from nitrogen fertilizer containing urea. Temperature has a big influence, making summer applications risky. Also, because an enzyme (urease) in plant tissue promotes the volatilization reaction, the more plant material present, the more likely it is that substantial losses will occur. Volatilization losses are higher and more likely in alkaline soils (pH > 7.0). Surface applications of other types of nitrogen fertilizer do not usually result in significant volatilization losses.

Nitrogen cycle is a term used to encompass all the ways nitrogen can be added to, or removed from, the soil. A simplified schematic of this important process is shown in **Figure 9.1**.

Phosphorus

Phosphorus is important in helping plants manufacture food by using sunlight as a source of energy. It is needed for seed and fruit formation and for proper root growth, and it increases the survival and growth of seedlings. Fortunately, phosphate is not usually leached from the soil. Phosphate applied but unused one year will be available for plant growth in subsequent years, although in some soil types it may be tightly bound or fixed and slowly released over a period of years. Phosphate fertilizer can be applied as a single annual application or, if economics justify, rates sufficient for several years of production can be applied at one time. The phosphorus cycle is shown in **Figure 9.2**.

Potassium

Potassium is needed by plants in relatively large amounts. In some forages, more potassium than nitrogen is removed per unit of yield. This nutrient should be present in adequate amounts at all times, but is particularly important in areas where cold hardiness is a factor in forage stand persistence. Even where there is no cold stress, potassium is of major importance to stand longevity of legumes and rhizome production of bermudagrass.

Potash has also been shown to be important in reducing the susceptibility of bermudagrass to leafspot diseases as well as winterkill, and for enhancing root growth and development of many species. With regard to movement in the soil, potassium is intermediate between nitrogen and phosphorus. On sandy soils, two or more applications of potassium may be needed annually in order to minimize leaching losses and to meet crop demands. The potassium cycle is shown in **Figure 9.3**.

Application of fertilizer according to soil test recommendations is of basic importance in forage production.

Other Nutrients

Several other nutrients are essential for plant growth, but are required in smaller amounts and are less likely to limit crop growth. Calcium, magnesium, and sulfur are referred to as secondary nutrients. (See **Appendix A.7** for chemical symbols and ionic forms taken up by crops.) Soils limed according to soil test should contain adequate calcium. Magnesium is also important in plant nutrition because it is at the center of the chlorophyll molecule and thus essential for photosynthesis. It can be applied in products such as sulfate of potash magnesia. Magnesium can also be supplied through application of dolomitic lime.

Concern for the environment has resulted in changes in manufacturing processes that have reduced emissions of sulfur into the air and thus have reduced atmospheric contributions of sulfur to the soil in many areas. Sulfur was also once an incidental component in many fertilizers, but today most high analysis fertilizers contain little or no sulfur. Thus, sulfur deficiency is more common than it once was. Also, forage crops in which yields have been increased by plant breeding are removing more sulfur from the soil than in the past. Sulfur fertilization has been shown to increase yield and boost nitrogen use efficiency in bermudagrass. Recommendations for sulfur vary from state to state, primarily due to differences in soil texture and organic matter content of soils. Deficiencies are most common on low organic matter, sandy soils, and with shallow-rooted annual forages. The sulfur cycle is shown in **Figure 9.4.**

The micronutrients include manganese, iron, boron, copper, molybdenum, chloride, zinc, and nickel. (See **Appendix A.7** for chemical symbols and ionic forms taken up by crops.) In most areas of the South and with most Southern forage crops, there is usually no response to addition of these nutrients. An exception is boron, which is required at a rate of around 1.5 lb/A/yr for good clover seed production and at around 3 lb/A annually for alfalfa. Some of the other micronutrients, particularly copper, are showing up as a deficiency in animals grazing on nutrient-deficient forages. A list of the elements known to be essential to plant and animal growth is provided in **Appendix A.22.**

When dung and urine spots become readily apparent, pastures are nutrient deficient.

Table 9.2. **Percent nitrogen in various fertilizers and amounts of these materials required to supply various levels of nitrogen per acre.**

Fertilizer material	Nitrogen in fertilizer, %	Pounds of nitrogen desired per acre					
		30	60	90	120	150	180
Anhydrous ammonia	82	40	75	110	150	180	220
Urea	46	60	130	200	260	320	390
Ammonium nitrate	33.5	90	180	270	360	450	540
Ammonium sulfate	21	140	280	430	570	710	860
Nitrate of soda[1]	16	190	380	560	750	940	1,120
Calcium nitrate[1]	15	200	400	600	800	1,000	1,200
		Gallons of liquid per acre					
Anhydrous ammonia	82	7	14	21	28	35	42
Solutions	32	9	17	26	34	43	52
	21	13	27	40	53	66	79

[1]May not be readily available commercially.

Fertilizers

Soil test results often indicate that the level of one or more nutrients is low. When this is the case, the soil test report normally provides a recommendation to apply enough fertilizer to eliminate the deficiency. The appropriate type and amount of fertilizer to apply will depend on which nutrients are deficient and to what extent.

Fertilizers are sold in many different formulations, usually expressed as ratios. A ratio is merely a convenient method of expressing the percentage of nitrogen (N), phosphate (P_2O_5), and potash (K_2O) in a particular type or blend of fertilizer. For example, triple 13 (13-13-13) fertilizer is a fertilizer having a ratio of $N:P_2O_5:K_2O$ of 13:13:13. Each 100 lb of the material contains 13 lb of nitrogen, 13 lb of P_2O_5, and 13 lb of K_2O.

Table 9.3. **Approximate nutrient content of common phosphorus and potassium fertilizers.**

Material	P_2O_5, %
Triple superphosphate (TSP)	45
Monoammonium phosphate (MAP)	52
Diammonium phosphate (DAP)	46
Basic slag[1]	10
Bone meal[1]	24
Material	**K_2O, %**
Muriate of potash	60
Sulfate of potash	50
Sulfate of potash magnesia	22
Potassium nitrate	44

[1]May not be readily available commercially.

Fertilizers such as mentioned in the previous example and that contain nitrogen, phosphate, and potash are referred to as complete fertilizers. They are used when all three of the major nutrients need to be applied. In other cases, soil test reports will indicate that only one or two nutrients are deficient. Therefore, a fertilizer that provides only these nutrients is needed. Nutrient contents of various nitrogen, phosphorus and potassium fertilizers are shown in **Tables 9.2 and 9.3**.

Most commercially available forms of nitrogen tend to increase soil acidity, particularly at high application rates, eventually reducing yields because of low soil pH if lime is not applied periodically. Other factors, such as leaching, runoff, and removal of calcium and magnesium by crops, also tend to increase acidity. Soil pH should be checked by a soil test and lime applied as needed to neutralize soil acidity.

Livestock manures are another source of nutrients for forage crops. Their use is common in the South and should be encouraged. However, it is important to know, as much as possible, nutrient contents of manures being applied, to prevent nutrient imbalances and to minimize the potential for surface loss or leaching of nutrients into groundwater. Information on the nutrient content of manure from various animals is shown in **Appendix A.24.**

Livestock manure can be substituted for commercial fertilizer where it is feasible to use. However, manure is extremely variable, so it is difficult to determine whether crop nutrient needs are being met. It is also difficult to time the release of nutrients from manure to match the timing of crop demands. Prior to using manure as a fertilizer source, it should be analyzed to determine nutrient content, then applied according to recommendations. Proper calibration of application equipment is likewise important.

Soil pH

Soil acidity or alkalinity, which is expressed in terms of pH, is also extremely important to crop production. A pH of 7.0 is neutral, while a soil pH below or above this point is acid or alkaline, respectively. Most forage crops do best at pH values between 5.8 and 6.5, although there are exceptions. Generally, nutrients are most available and many herbicides are most effective in this pH range. **Figure 9.5** shows the effect of pH on availability of phosphorus and several micronutrients.

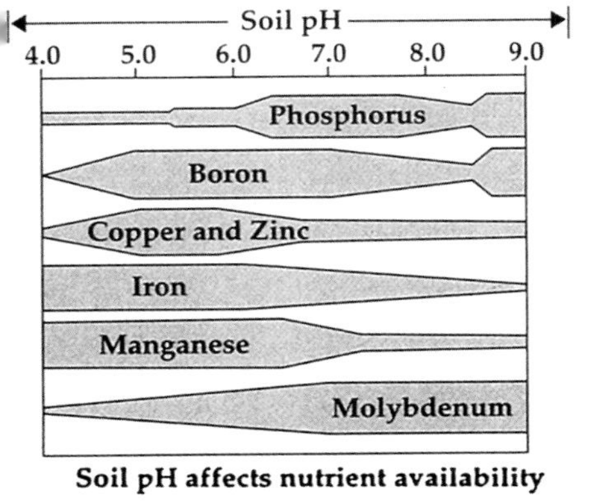

Figure 9.5. The optimum availability of phosphorus and the essential micronutrients occurs in the pH range of 6.0 to 7.0.

When soil pH becomes too low for good crop growth, as is the tendency for most soils in the South, it becomes necessary to apply sufficient lime to raise soil pH to the desired level. Dolomitic lime, which contains both calcium and magnesium, should be recommended if the magnesium level of the soil is low. The effectiveness of lime or other materials in reducing soil acidity is expressed in terms of calcium carbonate ($CaCO_3$) equivalent. Dolomitic lime contains $CaCO_3$ and magnesium carbonate ($MgCO_3$).

Lime moves very slowly through the soil profile. Therefore, it should be tilled into the plow layer in cultivated fields. In perennial sods, surface application is appropriate. Lime reacts slowly and should normally be applied well in advance of establishing a crop that requires an upward pH adjustment.

In areas where subsoil acidity is a severe problem, 1 to 3 tons of gypsum (calcium sulfate) per acre can be applied. This material will readily move downward through the soil, providing there is no physical drainage problem, alleviating manganese and aluminum toxicity and allowing deeper plant root development.

Keeping soil pH and fertility at satisfactory levels is important for several reasons. Thousands of agronomic experiments have shown that fertilization increases forage yields. Nitrogen fertilization also affects forage quality, mainly by increasing the protein content of grasses. Application of other nutrients may affect forage quality by changing the levels or balance of nutrients within plant tissue (for example, the calcium/phosphorus ratio). Further, nitrogen use efficiency depends on balanced nutrition, including phosphorus, potassium, and other essential nutrients. Finally, proper fertilization promotes the development of healthy, vigorous stands of desirable forage species, that offer strong competition to weedy species and extends stand longevity.

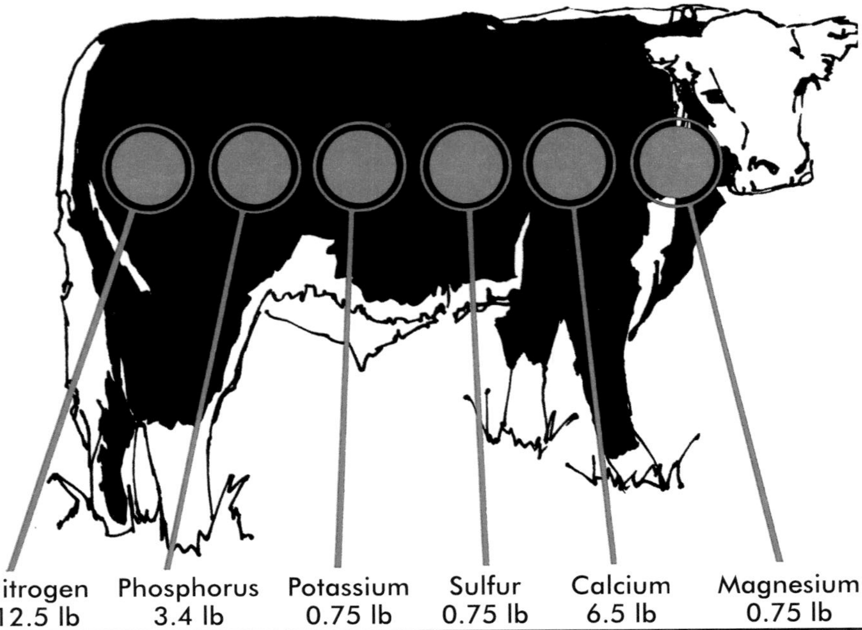

Figure 9.6. Approximate amounts of primary and secondary nutrients present in the body of a 500 lb steer. (Calculations based on percentage estimates from various sources.)

Table 9.4. Approximate pounds of nutrients removed by various forage crops at specified yield levels when harvested as hay.[1]					
	Species and assumed hay yield, tons/A				
	Alfalfa 5	Tall fescue 3.5	Sorghum-sudan 4	Orchard-grass 3	Bermuda-grass 6
Nitrogen	280	135	160	150	258
Phosphate (P_2O_5)[2]	75	65	61	50	60
Potash (K_2O)[3]	300	185	233	185	288
Magnesium	25	13	24	13	18
Sulfur	25	14	25	13	30

[1]Source: Potash & Phosphate Institute.
[2]$P_2O_5 = P \times 2.29$; $P = P_2O_5 \times 0.43$.
[3]$K_2O = K \times 1.2$; $K = K_2O \times 0.83$.

Nutrient Removal and Recycling

A livestock producer should be aware that when forage growth is removed as hay, virtually all the nutrients in the above-ground portions of the plants are being removed. However, in pasture situations, nutrients in the above-ground portions of plants are consumed by grazing animals, much of which will be recycled through dung and urine. The bodies of grazing animals contain relatively small quantities of nutrient elements (**Figure 9.6**).

The effectiveness of the nutrient recycling process in pastures is greatly affected by grazing management. Under non-intensive grazing methods, a high percentage of recycled nutrients is concentrated in areas where animals congregate, such as near water, shade, and mineral feeders. In more intensive grazing methods, such as high stocking rates and rotational stocking, distribution of recycled nutrients is more uniform. Regardless of the grazing method, losses from volatilization of nitrogen from urine range from 30 percent under cool, moist conditions to over 70 percent when weather is hot and dry. Nitrogen is the only nutrient lost in this manner.

Some producers spread dung in pastures with a chain-link harrow to improve the distribution of recycled nutrients, but economic justification of this practive is difficult. Exceptions might include dragging a feeding area that has excessive treading damage and accumulated dung pats or to improve seed-soil contact when broadcasting clover or other seed (photo on page 106).

Nutrient recycling can have an important influence on the fertility status and fertilizer needs of various fields or even of an entire farm. For example, fields in which livestock are wintered benefit from nutrient recycling much more than fields where livestock are present only for short periods of time. Decisions regarding the purchase of hay or other feed materials to be fed to livestock on the farm or the selling of hay produced on the farm can greatly affect fertilizer needs. The nutrient flow from, or into, a farm inevitably has an impact on economics. When the recycling process is poor or forage is removed as hay, certain nutrients may quickly become deficient. **Table 9.4** provides the approximate rate of removal of various nutrients for selected forage crops. SF

10 Seed

Except when planting a small area for evaluation purposes, a producer should plant only seed of species and varieties known to be adapted and productive in the area(s) in which they will be grown. Agricultural Extension agents can provide variety trial test results. Once species and variety decisions have been made, good quality seed must be located and handled properly.

Seed Quality

Several factors affect the potential of seed to produce a healthy, vigorous stand. Collectively, these factors determine the quality of a seed lot. Fortunately, certified seed marketed through normal seed channels are labeled with tags that provide the needed information. The following is normally provided (on a weight basis):

Germination (or Germ)—The percentage of seed that is capable of producing healthy plants when placed in a suitable environment.

Pure Seed—The percentage of seed that is of the variety and species on the label.

Other Crop Seed—The percentage of seed that are of some other crop species.

Weed Seed—The percentage of seed that are of weed species.

Inert Matter—The percentage of sticks, stems, broken seed, sand, or other such material mixed with the seed.

Noxious Weed Seed—Some harmful weeds such as dodder are classified as noxious weeds. This designation refers to the number of noxious weed seed present per pound of crop seed.

Hard Seed—The percentage of seed that is viable but that will not germinate immediately due to a hard or waxy seed coat. Seed of some forage species, especially certain legumes, should be scarified before being sold for planting. Scarification refers to a process seed cleaning facilities use to break down the hard seed coats. Bahiagrass is an example of a forage crop that has a waxy seed coat that requires either time or scarification to allow moisture penetration.

Use of certified seed helps ensure establishment success.

Total Germination and Hard Seed—The total percentage of viable seed, obtained by adding together the germination (the percentage of seed that will readily germinate when placed in a suitable environment) and the hard seed (seed that are viable but that will not germinate immediately).

Fungus or Endophyte Level—In some states it is required that the percentage of tall fescue seed infected with the fungal endophyte *(Neotyphodium coenophialum)* be listed on the seed tag (see Chapter 24).

It is not possible to accurately determine the quality of seed by visual examination. This is why the information on seed tags is of such importance. All of this information should be read and understood before seed is purchased.

Classes of Seed Involved in Certification

When a new variety is developed, the plant breeder typically has only a small quantity of seed of the new variety at the date of its release. The seed must then be increased until there is enough to meet the demand by the public. State crop improvement associations have developed a systematic and efficient means of ensuring that the genetic identity of seed is not lost. This is referred to as the Seed Certification Program, and it is used for forage crops as well as other types of crop plants.

Four classes of seed are recognized through state Seed Certification Programs. The first three are: 1) breeder seed; 2) foundation seed; and 3) registered seed. These classifications ensure the genetic identity of a variety while seed supplies are being increased.

The fourth class is certified seed. This term is applied to seed produced in a field that was planted with either foundation or registered seed (registered seed is an optional class). Certified seed is then made available to producers who want to grow the variety. Certified seed is labeled with a blue tag, which serves as a guarantee of genetic purity.

The seed increase process is closely monitored by crop improvement association personnel, and all requirements are strictly enforced. Seed increase fields are inspected to make certain that a designated variety has been planted and to ensure that there are no substantial populations of noxious weeds present. These fields are also isolated from other fields of the same crop species to avoid pollination by other varieties or types. The higher the classification (the closer to breeder seed classification), the more rigid the requirements.

Most producers do not need to be concerned with breeder, foundation, or registered seed unless they want to produce, harvest, and sell seed of certified or higher classification. However, forage producers should be familiar with the certified seed classification. In order for seed to be certified, it must meet standards in each of the seed quality areas discussed at the beginning of this chapter. Buying certified seed is the best way to ensure that seed purchased is of high quality, genetically pure, and capable of producing thick, productive forage stands.

General Information

Seed is bought and sold on a weight basis, rather than a volume basis. Therefore, although a bushel is a commonly used measure for seed, in reality the term bushel refers to the number of pounds of a particular crop seed normally required to occupy a bushel volume (32 quarts).

Identification of Legume and Grass Seed Parts

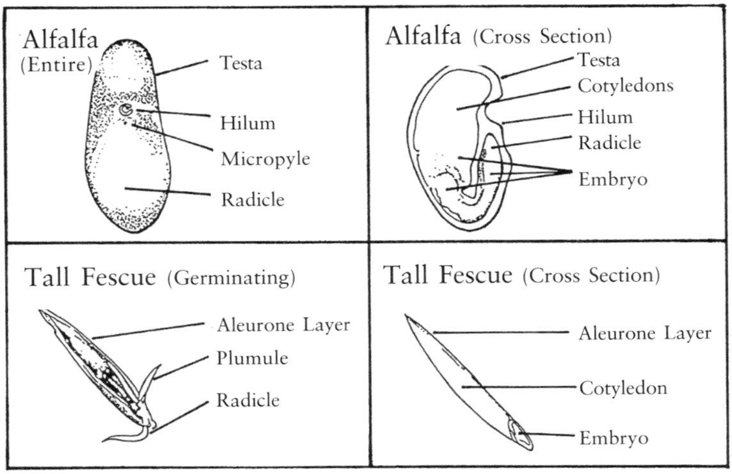

Definitions

Testa–Seed coat.
Aleurone layer–The outer layer of a grass seed.
Hilum–Scar at the point of seed stalk attachment.
Micropyle–A pore located near the hilum.
Epicotyl and Hypocotyl–The portions of the embryo above and below the point of cotyledon attachment, respectively.
Plumule–Shoot. End or growing portion of the epicotyl.
Radicle–Root. End or growing portion of the hypocotyl.
Cotyledon–Seed leaf. Grasses have one cotyledon, legumes two.
Endosperm–Stored food.
Embryo–The tiny dormant plant within a seed.

Figure 10.1. Identification of legume and grass seed parts.

Since the number of pounds per bushel may vary depending on seed production conditions, the term test weight is used to refer to actual weight of a bushel of seed. Test weight is not always specified, but it is commonly used for some types of seed, particularly the small grains. If the test weight is substantially lower than usual, that particular lot of seed is presumed to be of somewhat lower quality, which may impact on seedling population.

Seed of various forage crops differ in size, shape, and weight. Thus, the number of seed per pound varies tremendously as does the weight per bushel. Although these numbers are not exact, **Table 10.1** provides approximate weights per bushel and numbers of seed per pound for selected forage crops. Drawings that show the shape and other characteristics of seed of various forage crops commonly planted or found in the South are provided in Chapters 5, 6, 7, and 8. **Figure 10.1** illustrates parts of legume and grass seed.

Seed should normally not be carried over from year to year. When carryover is unavoidable, the producer should be aware that germination and seed vigor will generally decline. This varies with species, but is particularly true of grasses. If storage is unavoidable, a cool, dry location should be selected. The seed should be retested for germination before use.

Table 10.1. Weight per bushel and number of seed per pound of selected forage crops.

Forage crop	Approximate lb/bu	Approximate no. of seed/lb	Forage crop	Approximate lb/bu	Approximate no. of seed/lb
Alfalfa	60	227,000	Kudzu	54	37,000
Alyceclover	60	301,000	Lappa clover	60	680,000
Alsike clover	60	728,000	Oats	32	16,000
Annual lespedeza	25	238,000	Orchardgrass	14	416,000
Annual ryegrass	24	224,000	Pearl millet	48	82,000
Arrowleaf clover	60	400,000	Perennial ryegrass	24	330,000
Bahiagrass	46	273,000	Persian clover	60	642,000
Ball clover	60	1,000,000	Rape	50	156,000
Barley	48	14,000	Red clover	60	272,000
Bermudagrass (hulled)	40	2,071,000	Reed canarygrass	47	480,000
Berseem clover	60	207,000	Rescuegrass	8-12	52,000
Bigflower vetch	60	32,000	Rose clover	60	164,000
Birdsfoot trefoil	60	370,000	Rye	56	18,000
Black medic	60	266,000	Sericea lespedeza (hulled)	60	372,000
Browntop millet	50	142,000	Small hop clover	60	884,000
Button clover	60	153,000	Smooth bromegrass	14	135,000
Caleypea (Roughpea)	55	18,000	Sorghum	50	24,000
Carpetgrass	18-36	1,012,000	Sorghum-sudan	48	35,000
Corn	56	1,400	Soybean	60	4,500
Cowpea	60	3,600	Spotted burclover (hulled)	10	250,000
Crabgrass	25	825,000	Striate lespedeza (Kobe)	25	200,000
Crimson clover	60	150,000	Subterranean clover	60	54,000
Dallisgrass	14	281,000	Sudangrass	40	43,000
Foxtail millet	50	213,000	Switchgrass	55	280,000
Hairy vetch	60	16,000	Tall fescue	25	227,000
Indiangrass	10	200,000	Timothy	45	1,152,000
Japanese millet	35	143,000	Triticale	48	15,000
Johnsongrass	28	119,000	Wheat	60	11,000
Kentucky bluegrass	21	1,440,000	White clover	60	768,000
Korean lespedeza (hulled)	59	238,000	White sweetclover	60	259,000

Pure Live Seed—The percentage of pure live seed (PLS) is an indicator of seed quality. It is often used in connection with seeding rate recommendations for species that typically have relatively low germination rates and/or frequently contain a substantial quantity of inert material. As such, PLS is not normally provided on seed tags, but it can be easily calculated if purity and germination are known.

For example, assume that a bag of seed has a purity of 97.5 percent and that the germination is 70 percent. PLS is determined by multiplying the two and dividing by 100. In this case PLS = 97.5 x 70.0 ÷ 100. Therefore, PLS = 68.25 percent.

In order to calculate the amount of seed needed per acre, the PLS seeding rate recommendation should be divided by the PLS percentage and multiplied by 100. Thus, if it is recommended that 10 lb/A PLS be planted and the PLS is 68.25 percent as calculated in the previous paragraph, the actual amount of seed needed would be 10 ÷ 68.25 x 100 = 14.65 lb/A. In other words, 14.65 lb of the material taken from the bag or lot need to be planted in order to plant 10 lb of PLS. This calculation is only necessary when the seeding rate provided specifies pure live seed or PLS.

Coated Seed

An increasing amount of commercially available seed is coated prior to being marketed. Coating of forage legume seed ensures that high numbers of *Rhizobium* bacteria adhere to the seed and improves survival.

Current seed coating technology allows the incorporation of a fungicide, an insecticide, and/or fertilizer nutrients onto the seed coat. It may also facilitate broadcasting or seed flow through a drill. Any of the preceding may be important, depending on the species involved. Thus, some high-value small-seeded grasses such as bermudagrass are coated prior to being marketed. Planting the same weights of coated or uncoated seed typically results in equivalent stands.

Seed Storage

It is best to plant new crop seed, but circumstances sometimes arise that require seed to be stored from one year to the next. In such situations, knowledge of factors affecting seed viability is helpful. Some of these factors are as follows:

Type of seed—Legume seed generally maintain viability longer than grass seed. There are also differences among species.

Initial viability—The higher the initial viability of seed, the higher viability is likely to be after storage.

Seed moisture—Seed having a low moisture content stores best. A level of 13 percent moisture or less is usually considered acceptable, with 6 to 8 percent being considered optimum for long-term storage.

Temperature and humidity—The lower the temperature and humidity, the better seed will maintain viability. Carryover seed should be stored in a cool, dry place (ideally, no more than 60°F and 60 percent relative humidity).

Length of storage—Even with optimum storage conditions, viability will decline as length of storage increases. SF

Forage Crop Establishment

Forage crop establishment is critical. Errors that will seriously reduce the returns from forage production are more likely during establishment than at any other time. The requirements for establishment of the forage crops included in this book vary greatly, and space does not permit detailed discussion of each one. However, this chapter emphasizes basic points important in establishment into a prepared (tilled) seedbed, while Chapter 12 discusses sod-seeding. In addition, some points relevant to proper establishment of various species are mentioned in Chapters 5 through 8.

Fertility and Liming

After the decision has been made to establish a forage crop or forage mixture in a particular field, a soil sample should be obtained and submitted for testing to determine nutrient needs. Ideally, this should be done several months in advance of planting. Early testing is particularly important in fields that may require liming to raise the soil pH level.

If a field to be tilled is highly acid, it may be advisable to apply one-half of the recommended quantity of lime several months in advance of planting and then till the field before applying the remainder. This helps mix the lime into the tilled layer so that neutralization of the acidity is well underway prior to planting.

Tilling the land a few weeks or even months ahead of planting may be helpful even if lime is not incorporated. The initial tillage and any subsequent periodic additional tillage prior to planting is likely to stimulate germination of weed seed. Since these weed seedlings will be killed during final seedbed preparation, later weed populations may be reduced.

In addition, rains will settle the soil after tillage and often create a moist, firm seedbed that is more likely to result in a successful forage stand. However, the potential for erosion should always be considered before making decisions regarding tillage.

Fertilizer recommended by soil test should normally be applied just prior to the final seedbed preparation so that it will be incorporated into the seedbed at a shallow depth. It is important to get nutrients such as phosphorus and potassium mixed with the soil in advance of planting. Young, developing roots need access to nutrition for rapid growth to occur. A robust root system is essential to both yield potential and stand longevity.

A common problem associated with establishing perennial grasses is competition from weeds, especially annual grasses. Application of high levels of nitrogen fertilizer at or near planting enhances this problem due to stimulation of growth of weed seedlings. Thus, when establishing perennial grasses, no more than 20 to 30 pounds of nitrogen per acre should normally be applied at planting. Keeping newly sown weedy fields grazed or clipped closely can also help minimize damage from weed competition.

Seed Considerations

Seed of good quality should always be used (see Chapter 10). Seed cost is a minor portion of the total establishment expense, so the use of cheap, low quality seed is neither agronomically nor economically sound.

Variety tests typically show wide variation in performance among commercially available varieties. Careful review of research information before making variety decisions is time well spent. If the variety desired is not readily available, it may be profitable to go to extra effort to find a source. In some cases, seed of a particular variety can be ordered if the seed dealer has adequate advance notice. If legume seed were not pre-inoculated, the proper inoculant should be purchased along with the seed (see Chapter 13).

Using a suitable seeding rate is highly important in obtaining a good forage stand. Many universities and seed companies have developed seeding rate recommendations for various forage crops. **Table 11.1** provides rates often recommended for forages commonly grown in the South. However, these are subject to local variation. Producers should check with their

Table 11.1. Usual recommended time of planting, seeding rates, and seeding depths for tilled seedbed plantings of forage crops commonly grown in the South.

Forage crop	Time of planting	Seeding rate, lb/A[1]	Seeding depth, inches[1]
Alfalfa	Late summer and autumn, also spring in Zones C and D	15-20	¼-½
Alyceclover	Spring, early summer	15-20	¼-½
Bahiagrass	Spring, summer, also autumn in Zone A	15-20	¼-½
Barley[2]	Autumn	90-120	1-2
Bermudagrass, common	Spring, summer	5-10 (hulled)	0-¼
Bermudagrass, hybrid	Early spring	20 or more bu sprigs	1-3
Big bluestem[3]	Spring	6-10(PLS)[1]	¼-½
Birdsfoot trefoil	Late summer, autumn	4-6	0-¼
Bluegrass, Kentucky	Autumn	10-15	0-¼
Bromegrass, smooth	Spring or late summer	15-20	¼-½
Caleypea (singletary pea)	Autumn	50-55	½-1
Clover, arrowleaf	Autumn	5-10	0-½
Clover, ball	Autumn	2-3	0-¼
Clover, berseem	Autumn	20-25	¼-½
Clover, crimson	Autumn	20-30	¼-½
Clover, red	Autumn, and early spring Zones C and D	12-15	¼-½

(continued)

Table 11.1. continued.			
Forage crop	Time of planting	Seeding rate, lb/A[1]	Seeding depth, inches[1]
Clover, subterranean	Autumn	10-20	¼-½
Clover, white and ladino	Autumn, and early spring in Zones C and D	2-3	0-¼
Cowpea	Late spring, early summer	100-120	1-3
Dallisgrass[3]	Spring	10-15(PLS)[1]	¼-½
Fescue, tall	Fall, early spring in Zones C and D	15-20	¼-½
Indiangrass[3]	Spring	6-10(PLS)[1]	¼-½
Johnsongrass	Late spring, early summer	20-30	½-1
Lespedeza, annual	Early spring	25-35	¼-½
Lespedeza, sericea	Spring	20-30	¼-½
Millet, browntop	Mid spring, early summer	25-30	½-1
Millet, pearl	Mid spring, early summer	25-30	½-1½
Oats[2]	Autumn	90-120	1-2
Orchardgrass	Autumn	15-20	¼-½
Reed canarygrass	Autumn	5-8	¼-½
Rye[2]	Autumn	90-120	1-2
Ryegrass	Autumn	20-30	0-½
Sorghum, forage	Late spring, early summer	15-20	1-2
Sorghum-sudan hybrids	Late spring, early summer	30-35	1-2
Sudangrass	Late spring, early summer	30-40	½-1
Switchgrass[3]	Spring	5-6(PLS)[1]	¼-½
Timothy	Late summer, early autumn	6-8	¼-½
Triticale[2]	Autumn	90-120	1-2
Vetch, common	Autumn	30-40	1-2
Vetch, hairy	Autumn	20-25	1-2
Wheat[2]	Autumn	90-120	1-2

[1]These are general guidelines for broadcast plantings. Drill plantings may require less seed. Specific recommendations for a given area may vary, and some crops are adapted only in certain regions (see Chapters 5-8). Seeding rates may vary considerably from these when some crops are planted for seed. PLS = Pure live seed (see Chapter 10).
[2]The small grains usually have approximately the following lb/bu: barley, 48; oats, 32; rye, 56; wheat, 60; and triticale, 48. See **Table 10.1**, page 89.
[3]Germination rate is often low.

agricultural Extension agent to obtain recommendations for their area.

Despite the usefulness of general seeding rate recommendations, there can be circumstances that dictate changing the rate used. One such factor is seed quality. Most seeding rate recommendations are based on the assumption that germination rates are high. If the seed to be used is old or is known to have a low germination level and/or low seed vigor, it is advisable to increase the seeding rate accordingly. However, it is best to avoid planting poor quality seed.

Seedbed preparation has a major influence on the percentage of seed that will ultimately produce healthy plants. A well-pulverized, level seedbed is conducive to planting at the right depth and getting good germination and establishment. The seeding rate recommendations provided in **Table 11.1** are generally appropriate for optimum conditions, but it may be desirable to increase them under less favorable circumstances.

The method of planting is a major factor influencing optimum seeding rate. Generally, a seeding rate at least 20 percent lower can be used when drill-planting than when broadcast-seeding (this is due to the more precise depth placement possible when forage crops are drill-planted). Aerial seeding from a plane or helicopter may justify using higher amounts of seed. A higher-than-normal seeding rate may also be required when a soil-conserving cover is needed quickly to protect highly erodible areas.

Since seed cost is generally one of the lowest inputs in the establishment of a forage stand, producers should use at least as much seed as is recommended. No one wants to waste money on seed, but it is better to slightly exceed the recommended seeding rate than to use too little seed. This is particularly true if planting conditions are less than optimum. When planting mixtures of forage species, it is advisable to use one-half to two-thirds as much seed of each species as would be used when establishing only one species.

When domination by one species in a mixture is likely, use of the proper planting technique can often extend the length of time before this occurs. For example, tall fescue normally out-competes white clover, but planting tall fescue in rows and broadcast-planting white clover usually keeps this from happening as quickly as it otherwise would.

Time of Planting

Planting dates vary considerably depending on location. General recommendations are presented in **Table 11.1**. Weather plays a major role in determining the proper time to plant, and there is usually a fairly short period of time during which planting conditions are optimum or near optimum. To miss this period can mean the difference between success and failure.

Adverse weather conditions often delay plantings. Therefore, it is advisable to plant a crop as early as possible within the recommended period. Seeding an autumn-planted crop too late may result in winter-kill. Planting a spring-planted crop too late may result in excessive weed competition and possibly death of forage seedlings due to drought. Conversely, seeding an autumn-planted crop too early may cause plant death due to heat stress, while planting a spring-planted crop too early may result in cold damage.

Final Seedbed Preparation

Seedbed preparation should include applying and incorporating any needed lime and fertilizer, and the seedbed should be relatively firm prior to planting. This is especially important for small-seeded legumes such as alfalfa and clovers. Weeds and plant residue should be eliminated from the soil surface, and the seedbed should be reasonably smooth. Ridges and depressions need to be smoothed, as they may hinder the operation of equipment for years to come. When establishing hay meadows, care should be taken to assure obtaining as smooth a field as possible to reduce costly equipment repairs and to facilitate efficient harvesting.

Weed Control

Weed control needs vary tremendously among forage crops. It may be desirable to apply herbicides before planting, at planting time, or after emergence of a forage stand, depending on the crop being established and the weeds present or anticipated. Consult local advisors for recommendations on weed control in specific forage crops.

Insect Control

Problems with insect pests vary greatly with different crops and different situations. It is desirable to closely observe a new forage stand for insect damage. If such damage is detected, the insect should be identified, and a treatment threshold level should be determined. Agricultural Extension agents can assist in this regard. There are usually several insecticides that can be used for pest control. Insect control is especially important during establishment. Mature, well-established forage plants with a well-developed root system can withstand considerable insect damage, while seedlings cannot.

Seeding Technique

Forage crops can be seeded by many different techniques as shown in the photos on the next page. Spin-seeders that operate from the power takeoff of tractors or from batteries, band seeders, cultipacker-seeders, and drills can all be successfully used. In general, large-seeded species such as the small grains or vetch are best seeded with a drill.

Broadcasting followed by shallow disking may cover seed with too much soil. Small-seeded species may be drilled if care is taken to avoid planting too deeply. A cultipacker-seeder is the ideal tool to use for planting clovers, birdsfoot trefoil, and alfalfa.

Clovers, bermudagrass, and other small-seeded species may need to be planted at rates so low that the equipment available cannot be adjusted to

Forage crops can be seeded effectively by several different methods.

put out such small quantities of seed. In such cases, it may be necessary to thoroughly mix the seed with coarse-grained sand or some other inert material to increase the volume enough to allow planting at the proper rate.

Regardless of the type of seeder, a record should be kept of the setting used to plant a certain rate of seed. Such information can be of great value the next time the equipment is used to plant the same forage species.

Broadcast seeding is also acceptable for planting small-seeded forage crops, but on a prepared seedbed this should be followed by adequate firming with a cultipacker to obtain good seed-soil contact. This is an important point. Many stand failures of clovers and alfalfa have resulted from not having a properly firmed seedbed. If the seedbed is not firm, the seed may end up too deep due to settling of the soil. A rule of thumb for evaluating a seedbed for these crops is that when one walks over the field, the shoe prints should not be much deeper than the sole of the shoe.

When planting legumes, both the seed and the inoculant need to survive the planting process. Seedings should ideally be in moist soil to ensure survival of the inoculant and to enhance germination. Legume seed should generally not be mixed with fertilizer, as salts can kill the inoculant. It is desirable to have a shallow soil cover over legume seed to protect the inoculum from the elements and to reduce risk for the germinating seed. However, great care must be taken to prevent seed from being covered too deeply, or they will not emerge properly. Another rule of thumb is that seed should be planted no deeper than eight times the thickness of the seed. General guidelines regarding seeding depth are provided in **Table 11.1**.

Most farms contain a diversity of soil types, so it is important to match the crop to the soil on which it will be planted. When a producer does not know what forage species are adapted to a particular area, a soils map or a knowledgeable and experienced individual such as an Extension agent

Table 11.2. A checklist of potential problems in forage establishment.

Failure to germinate	Seed germinated but seedling did not emerge from soil	Seedlings emerged but did not survive
Dry seedbed	Planted too deep	Soil too acid or low fertility
Non-viable seed	Soil crusted at surface	Insects or diseases
Hard or dormant seed	Poor seedling vigor	Drought
Unfavorable temperature	Insects or diseases	Weed competition
Herbicide residue	Extreme temperature—too cold or too hot	No legume nodulation
Waterlogged soil		Winterkill
		Heaving from freezing and thawing of soil
		High winds caused sandblasting of seedlings
		Grazing too early—pulled up plant or trampling damage

should be consulted.

Despite all efforts, failures sometimes occur in forage stand establishment. When a failure does occur, it is important to diagnose the cause so the problem can be avoided in the future. A checklist of potential problems that can be responsible for stand failures is provided in **Table 11.2**.

Vegetative Establishment

Some forages, such as hybrid bermudagrasses and perennial peanuts, are routinely established from vegetative plant parts rather than seed. These crops produce little or no viable seed and must be vegetatively propagated.

One of the first and most important considerations in establishing hybrid bermudagrass fields is obtaining high quality certified planting material. Sprigs are usually sold by the bushel, but could also be offered by the cubic foot or by the thousand. A bushel normally contains about 1,000 sprigs, while a cubic foot will contain around 800. However, there can be great variation in the amount of planting material per unit of volume, depending on the extent to which it has been compressed.

Many sprig producers will furnish sprigs and plant them in a prepared seedbed. If a livestock producer wants to obtain and personally plant sprigs, great care needs to be taken to handle them correctly before planting. If possible, sprigs should be planted the same day they are dug. They should be kept moist and, if necessary, turned often to prevent heating. When transported, they should be kept tightly covered to prevent drying by sun and wind. Sprig survival is better when temperatures are cool, rather than warm.

Nursery Establishment

Many producers who plan to establish sizable acreages of bermudagrass establish a nursery in which they grow their own planting material. This greatly reduces the cost of establishment and also provides a convenient source of material.

A bermudagrass nursery should be established on well-drained, preferably sandy soil that is free of perennial grasses, especially common bermudagrass. A good seedbed should be prepared, and fertilizer should be applied according to soil test recommendations. To avoid excessive stimulation of annual grasses, only about 30 lb/A of nitrogen should be applied at planting.

To reduce weed competition in row plantings, the fertilizer can also be applied at appropriately reduced rates in rows 3 to 4 feet apart. Then, when the soil is moist, bermudagrass sprigs can be planted in the rows where the fertilizer was applied. Individual plants should usually be spaced at 18 to 24 inches within rows.

Whether bermudagrass is planted in rows or broadcast, application of a preemergence herbicide to inhibit crabgrass and other annual weeds is highly desirable. The bermudagrass sprigs should have roots covered with soil, but ideally the tips of the sprigs should be at or near the soil surface. In moist soil, a 2 to 3 inch planting depth is about right. Slightly deeper planting may be appropriate if moisture is marginal. If necessary, tillage or direct application of herbicides can be used to control weeds between the rows.

Additional nitrogen can be applied to the rows within three to four weeks after the grass has begun to root and grow. Once the rows begin to lap, or if bermudagrass is planted broadcast rather than in rows, 40 to 60 lb nitrogen/A should be broadcast every four to six weeks until September.

Field Planting Techniques

Weed control should be started well ahead of planting. Any existing perennial plants, especially common bermudagrass, should be killed. If practical, the land should be tilled in the autumn prior to planting.

Bermudagrass sprigs can be planted in several ways. It is possible to plant by hand, but the labor involved makes this approach prohibitive for most producers. However, if planted in rows by hand, as little as 10 bu/A can be used.

When bermudagrass is planted with a commercial sprigging machine, it is customary to use at least 20 bu of sprigs/A. Up to 40 bu/A might be appropriate for a slow-spreading variety. (Normally, 80 to 120 bu/A of perennial peanut rhizomes are planted.) Most states in the lower South have custom operators who will sell sprigs and/or plant fields. Since these people are experienced in planting hybrid bermudas and they generally have the proper equipment to do a good job, hiring them is usually money well spent.

A producer who has established a nursery must devise a way to dig and plant sprigs. If there is no access to a sprig digger, a spring toothed harrow can be used to loosen sprigs, followed by raking them together with a hay rake. Then they can simply be forked or scooped onto a truck or trailer and broadcast over a fresh, moist seedbed. Next they should be lightly disked into the soil followed by firming the field with a cultipacker. At least 20 to 30 bu/A should be used when this technique is employed.

Sprigging of bermudagrass (right) should be followed by rolling or cultipacking (left).

Bermudagrass should be planted into a moist, freshly prepared seedbed. A postemergence herbicide application may be needed to control broadleaf weeds. If annual grasses are a problem with a new planting, frequent clipping will help reduce competition. Keeping fertility high is essential in getting good spread of the bermudagrass.

The timing of planting is also of critical importance in getting a stand. The best time to plant is just before the bermudagrass rhizomes break dormancy. In most of the South this is in late February or March. The longer planting is delayed after this time, the lower the chances of success.

Failures of bermudagrass establishment with sprigs are usually due to:

- Planting when there is inadequate soil moisture;
- Using poor quality sprigs (usually dried out);
- Planting too few sprigs;
- Covering sprigs too deeply;
- Failing to firm soil around sprigs;
- Failing to control weeds.

Establishment from Clippings

Clippings (the above-ground growth) of hybrid bermudagrasses can also be used to establish a new stand, but the feasibility of this varies greatly with variety as some root much more easily than others. With appropriate varieties, clippings to be used for establishment can be cut when forage growth reaches about 18 inches and there are several nodes on each stem. The clippings should be generously spread over freshly-tilled moist soil and lightly disked in the same day they are cut, followed by rolling or cultipacking the field. The objective is to cover one or more nodes of the stems, on average. This technique is more labor intensive and risky than machine sprigging, but is inexpensive. SF

Sodseeding/No-Tillage Planting

Sodseeding is a general term used to describe the practice of establishing forage crops into perennial, usually grass-dominant, hay and/or pasture fields without destroying the existing sod. Many other terms are also used to describe this practice, including: renovation, overseeding, interseeding, frost seeding, honeycomb freeze seeding, no-till seeding, and minimum-till seeding, as well as tread-in, trampling, and walk-on seeding.

Applications of this practice have been used with success throughout the South for many years. However, two situations are by far the most common. In the upper South, establishment of legumes (alfalfa, red clover, annual lespedeza, and/or white clover) into tall fescue, Kentucky bluegrass, or orchardgrass sod is an important forage improvement practice.

In the lower South, cool season annual grasses and/or legumes are often planted into dormant perennial warm season grass sods, especially bahiagrass or bermudagrass. These and other sodseeding techniques can be used to great advantage by many Southern livestock producers.

Benefits of Multiple-Species Pastures and Hayfields

There are several important potential benefits associated with establishing other forage crops into existing grass sods. Research and farmer experience have shown that the addition of legumes to grasses can result in improvements such as:

1. **Higher yields.** The total yield of forage per acre is likely to be increased unless high levels of nitrogen fertilizer are used on grasses. A study conducted in Kentucky compared renovation of a tall fescue pasture interseeded with red clover to fertilizing the

Red clover established into tall fescue pasture. Red clover, white clover, or both (inset photo) are commonly sodseeded into tall fescue, orchardgrass, or dallisgrass.

grass with nitrogen (**Table 12.1**). In this test, red clover growing with tall fescue produced higher yields than tall fescue fertilized with up to 180 lb nitrogen/A.

2. **Improved quality.** Adding legumes to grass fields improves forage quality over grass alone. This results in increased palatability, intake, digestibility, nutrient content, and animal performance.

   Research has shown that legumes improve animal growth rates, reproductive efficiency, and milk production. For example, growth rates of beef steers in Alabama were increased when white clover was planted in endophyte-infected tall fescue pastures (**Table 12.2**). Higher gains per acre were also recorded, mainly as a result of improved forage quality. In another Alabama study, overseeding bermudagrass with arrowleaf and crimson clovers increased both

Table 12.1. Dry matter yields of tall fescue-red clover vs. tall fescue with nitrogen (N) fertilizer. (Lexington, Kentucky, two-year average.)

Treatment	Yield, lb/A
Tall fescue-red clover 6 lb seed/A	11,100
Tall fescue + N	
0 lb N/A	3,900
90 lb N/A	6,700
180 lb N/A	9,900

Source: T.H. Taylor. Kentucky Agric. Ext. Ser. Pub. AGR-26.

Table 12.2. Performance of steers grazing endophyte-infected tall fescue with and without ladino clover in north Alabama, two-year average.

Pastures	Average daily gain, lb	Gain/ steer, lb	Gain, lb/A
Tall fescue + white clover	1.53	307	582
Tall fescue + 150 lb N/A	1.06	203	374

Source: C.S. Hoveland, R.R. Harris, E.E. Thomas, E.M. Clark, J.A. McGuire, J.T. Eason, and M.R. Ruf. Alabama Agric. Exp. Stn. Bull. 530.

Table 12.3. Performance of beef cows and calves on Coastal bermudagrass pasture overseeded with winter annuals in southeastern Alabama, three-year average.

			Cows	Calves	
Species overseeded on bermuda sod	N rate, lb/A/yr	Dates on pasture	Average daily gain, lb	Average daily gain, lb	Gain, lb/A
Rye and arrowleaf and crimson clovers	100	Jan. 8-Oct. 5	0.90	1.91	511
Arrowleaf and crimson clovers	0	Mar. 11-Oct. 5	1.37	1.94	410
Ryegrass	150	Feb. 14-Oct.5	0.81	1.76	422
None	100	Apr. 6-Oct. 5	0.49	1.57	293

Source: C.S. Hoveland, W.B. Anthony, J.A. McGuire, and J.C. Starling. Auburn Univ. Agric. Exp. Stn. Bull. 496.

Table 12.4. Value and amount of nitrogen fixed by various legumes.				
	N fixed,	N value, $, @		
Crop	lb/A/year	25¢/lb	35¢/lb	45¢/lb
Alfalfa	150-250	38-63	53-88	68-113
Red clover	75-200	19-50	26-70	34-90
White clover	75-150	19-38	26-53	34-68
Vetch, lespedeza, and other annual forage legumes	50-150	13-38	18-53	23-68

cow and calf average daily gains with no nitrogen fertilizer (**Table 12.3**).

3. **Nitrogen fixation.** Legumes fix nitrogen that can be used for growth by the legumes and also by associated grasses (see Chapter 13). The value of the fixed nitrogen depends on the cost of nitrogen fertilizer (**Table 12.4**).
4. **Longer growing season.** Most cool-season grass growth occurs during spring and autumn. In the upper South, legumes such as red clover, alfalfa, or lespedeza make more summer growth than cool-season grasses. Thus, growing grasses and legumes together can improve the seasonal distribution of growth of a pasture and provide more summer growth.

Addition of cool season annuals to bermudagrass, bahiagrass, or dallisgrass permits production of quality feed during winter and early spring when pastures would otherwise be unproductive. Many cool season annual forages can be sodseeded, either alone or in mixtures, but annual ryegrass is the single most widely used species. In addition, annual legumes such as arrowleaf or crimson clovers are often used, as are rye and wheat. Seeding cool season species into warm season perennial grass sods can substantially lengthen the grazing season.

Other systems used in the South involve the seeding of various forage species into crop stubble with no-till techniques. Examples include seeding alfalfa or other species into warm season annual grass stubble (sorghum-sudan hybrids and millets), corn silage stubble, and small grain stubble. Large-seeded species such as small grains must be drilled into warm season grass sods. Small seeded species such as ryegrass and clover may be drilled or broadcast.

Sodseeding Principles

In many forage establishment situations, sodseeding offers advantages over tillage. Since much forage land throughout the South is rolling and prone to erosion when tilled, sodseeding can conserve soil (see Chapter 32). Likewise, sodseeding can conserve time, labor, fuel, and soil moisture.

Soil Conservation. Following heavy rain on a well-tilled seedbed, severe soil erosion may be readily apparent. Only after the plants are established is the amount of run-off water and soil loss greatly reduced under tillage establishment. Sodseeding can minimize soil loss during establishment.

Time. Conventional seeding normally requires several trips over the field to get the seedbed properly prepared and seed precisely planted. Sodseeding techniques may require only one pass over the field. Even if additional trips are required for fertilizing and spraying, total trips are still fewer than required by conventional seeding techniques.

Scientists in Kentucky studied the time required to establish clover into tall fescue pastures using a sodseeder as compared to disking and seeding conventionally. Their results showed the land area which could be covered per unit of time was 3.90 acres per hour using a sodseeder, compared to 0.62 acres per hour using conventional techniques.

Fuel. If fewer trips are required over a field to accomplish the same results, fuel will also be saved. In the studies mentioned above, conventional seedings required 4.95 gallons of fuel per acre, while the sodseeding method required only 1.04 gallons.

Moisture. Moisture conditions in either spring or late summer can potentially result in an advantage for sodseeding. In late winter or spring, moisture is often surplus, delaying seedbed preparation and seeding if conventional (plow-disk) techniques are to be used. With sodseeding techniques, seeding can be made earlier since a no-till drill can be used in a field several days or even weeks earlier than it can be tilled.

During late summer and early autumn, moisture shortage is common in the South. Much of the limited soil moisture is often lost during seedbed preparation with conventional seeding. With sodseeding, very little moisture is lost since only a small amount of soil is disturbed.

Specific recommendations will not be given to cover all possible sodseeding situations existing throughout the South. However, some general principles include the following.

Proper techniques of overseeding a warm season grass sod resulted in this ryegrass/arrowleaf clover pasture near Montgomery, Alabama.

Experimental study showing competition from existing grass controlled by tillage, herbicides, and mowing.

1. **Fertility.** A soil test should be taken and the resulting recommendations used as the guide for amounts and kinds of soil amendments to be applied. Application of any needed lime, phosphorus, and potassium is especially important for successful establishment of legumes into grass sods. Nitrogen should be applied whenever pure stands of winter annual grasses are planted. Rates can be reduced when legumes are seeded with annual grasses, depending on seeding date and species or species combination used.
2. **Reduce existing vegetation.** Failure to control existing grass vegetation is the most common reason for stand failures from sodseeding. Reducing the vegetative cover on the field is necessary for successful sodseeding. Reducing vegetative cover will reduce competition for the newly seeded forage species as well as make it easier to get good seed-soil contact during seeding. Existing grass vegetation can be reduced by heavy grazing, herbicides, tillage, or combinations of these approaches. Methods used for reducing vegetation will depend on several factors, including amount and kind of grass, legume(s) to be seeded, livestock numbers, and experience.

   Many producers use their livestock as a tool for improvement of tall fescue pastures. Heavy stocking will reduce the existing vegetation, and hoof action will provide some seedbed preparation. In late winter, red or white clover seed can be broadcast and trampled in with excellent results.

   Clover seed placed in contact with bare ground usually gets covered at or near ideal depth after a few freeze-thaws. Late freezes that give the soil a honeycomb appearance provide an excellent surface for legume seed. As the honeycomb thaws, the small seed usually settle just below the soil surface in an excellent

Establishing alfalfa via no-tillage techniques can result in excellent stands when proven principles are followed and weather conditions are favorable.

environment for later germination.

Herbicides can be used to suppress or kill the entire stand of existing grass (i.e., no-till alfalfa seeding) or to suppress a sufficient amount of grass to get the newly seeded legumes established. The zebra technique, sometimes used when establishing clover in cool season grass sods, requires adjusting the nozzles on the spray boom such that only about 50 percent of the grass is sprayed. After the herbicide has suppressed the grass, the field develops a striped or zebra appearance with half of the grass brown and the remainder green. Clover seed can be planted in the sprayed strips, either simultaneously with or following spraying.

3. Use high quality seed. Regardless of the species or combination of species to be seeded into existing grass sod, the use of high quality seed of a productive, adapted variety is essential. Poor quality seed is never a bargain, regardless of price.
4. Inoculate legumes. If not pre-inoculated, all legume seed should be inoculated properly with the correct strain of bacteria before seeding (**Appendix A.21**).
5. Plant on time with the correct amount of seed. Seeding dates and rates vary across the South. Local Extension offices can provide recommendations for specific areas.
6. Seed-soil contact. Many methods exist for sodseeding, ranging from cyclone seeders to no-till drills (see photos). Regardless of the method used, the objective is to plant high quality seed uniformly throughout the field.
7. Control competition. Competition from existing vegetation must be suppressed prior to, and at, seeding. Grazing or mowing can be used to keep the existing grass short during the first few weeks after planting while the newly-seeded plants are becoming established.

Closely grazed tall fescue pasture being seeded with a no-till drill, near Cadiz, Kentucky.

Ladino clover being overseeded on closely grazed tall fescue pasture, near Princeton, Kentucky.

8. Control pests. Insect populations are often high on grass sods in autumn and should be monitored and controlled as needed. Safe, effective insecticides are available and should be used if sufficient insect damage is apparent.

Table 12.5 summarizes no-tillage forage systems. Sodseeding offers much potential for producers desiring to improve productivity and quality of their pastures. SF

Arrowleaf clover established in sod in plots in Georgia. At left, insecticide was used to control striped field crickets. At right, no insecticide was used.

Table 12.5. Summary of no-tillage forage systems.

Sod or crop stubble to be planted into	Species planted	Zone	Usual planting time
Cool season perennial grasses			
Tall fescue, orchardgrass	Alfalfa	A,B	Autumn
		C,D	Late win.-early spr., Late sum,-early aut.
Kentucky bluegrass, timothy	Red clover	A,B	Late win.-early spr., Late sum.-early aut.
		C,D	Late win.-early spr.
	Birdsfoot trefoil	CD	Late win.-early spr., Late sum.-early aut.
	Ladino/white clover	B	Late aut.-mid winter
		CD	Late win.-early spr., Late sum.-early aut.
Warm season perennial grasses			
Bermudagrass and bahiagrass	Small grains; annual ryegrass; arrowleaf, berseem, crimson, and subterranean clovers; vetch	A,B	After killing frost
Dallisgrass	White and red clovers; caleypea	A,B	After killing frost
Small grain stubble Rye, wheat, oats	Pearl millet; sorghum-sudangrass	C,D	Late spring
	Alfalfa	C,D	Late sum.-early aut.
	Red clover	C,D	Late win.-early spr.

Legume Inoculation

Nitrogen is required in large quantities for high levels of forage production, and nitrogen deficiency is a common limitation to forage/livestock production. The atmosphere consists of about 80 percent nitrogen, and each acre of land has an estimated 37,000 tons of nitrogen above it. However, the nitrogen in the atmosphere is in the form of an inert gas that is unavailable to plants.

There are several sources of nitrogen for plant growth. Minute quantities are supplied by free-living soil bacteria and blue-green algae. Rainfall typically adds a few pounds per acre, mainly converted from atmospheric nitrogen by lightning. Most commercial nitrogen fertilizer is produced by the Haber-Bosch process which, under conditions of high temperature and pressure, utilizes natural gas for the production of ammonia. Legume plants also produce substantial quantities of low-cost nitrogen.

The unique ability to obtain nitrogen from the air helps make legumes especially valuable in forage programs. The nitrogen they produce can be used for their own growth, by associated grasses, or by other crops grown in rotation. In addition, pasture legumes can ultimately provide nitrogen for plants a considerable distance from where they are growing because much of the nitrogen taken into the bodies of livestock is recycled in dung and urine (see Chapter 9).

Most legumes have a symbiotic (mutually beneficial) relationship with bacteria in the genus *Rhizobium*. The bacteria infect the roots of legume plants from which they obtain food, and the bacteria obtain nitrogen from soil air and fix it in a form usable by the plants. The nitrogen is accumulated in small appendages called nodules that form on legume roots.

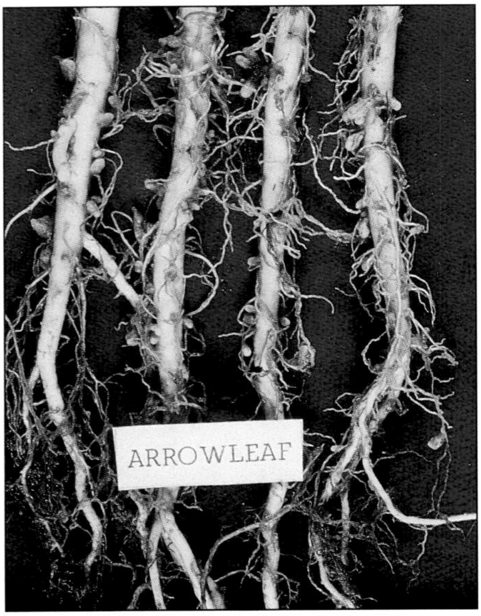

When legume seed have been properly inoculated, nitrogen is fixed in nodules on the plant roots.

The enzyme nitrogenase is produced by the bacteria. It is this compound which, in the presence of molybdenum, is responsible for reducing gaseous nitrogen to ammonia. The nitrogenase enzyme is the only natural substance known to react with inert atmospheric nitrogen at normal temperature and pressure.

Nitrogen fixation is influenced by many factors including *Rhizobium* population in the soil, temperature (approximately 77° to 84°F is optimum), soil moisture (which can be either inadequate or excessive), soil pH, soil fertility, amount of shading, and legume species. Nitrogen fixation is adversely affected by factors that reduce photosynthesis. Thus, nitrogen fixation is higher during the day than at night, during sunny rather than cloudy weather, and when leaf area is high as compared to when plants have been heavily defoliated.

Several nutrients deserve special mention in connection with nitrogen fixation. Calcium and/or potassium deficiency decreases nitrogen fixation, while application of more than around 25 lb nitrogen/A will generally reduce legume nitrogen fixation and stimulate the growth of competing plants. Competition from weeds or grasses reduces nitrogen fixation by competing with legumes for potassium and by shading. *Rhizobium* bacteria also require minute quantities of molybdenum, and nitrogen fixation will be hindered where supplies are inadequate.

On-Farm Inoculation

Good nitrogen fixation requires that large numbers of live *Rhizobium* bacteria are present on legume roots. Assurance that this will occur can be obtained by inoculating the seed (putting bacteria on the seed), a standard practice since the early 1900s.

It is important to distinguish legume seed inoculants from other products marketed as soil inoculants or activators of microbial processes. Inoculation of legume seed with *Rhizobium* bacteria is of proven practical value, and all references made here to inoculation refer only to this process.

Specific species of *Rhizobium* bacteria are required for specific species of legumes (see **Appendix A.21**). Since some *Rhizobium* strains are more effective than others, inoculant companies select within species. Thus, use of high quality inoculum of the proper type is critically important. Peat-based legume inoculants are commercially available where legume seed is sold; usually one package can be used to inoculate 50 lb of seed.

When inoculant is purchased, a producer should check the label to be certain that: 1) the legume to be inoculated is specifically listed on the package, and 2) that the expiration date has not already occurred. Prior to use, the inoculant should be stored in a reasonably cool place (40° to 70°F or refrigerated) and out of direct sunlight. Countless inoculation failures have resulted from inoculant being carelessly left in the heat of a pickup truck cab or similar locations.

The native population of *Rhizobium* may vary from none to several million per gram of soil. It is of critical importance to use inoculated legume seed when planting in areas where the legume species to be planted has not been grown before. Some legume bacteria will remain in the soil for several years, but since inoculant is inexpensive, inoculation is cheap insurance, even where legumes have previously been grown. Inoculation should always be done with fresh inoculant, not with inoculant saved from a previous year. Inoculated seed should not be mixed with fertilizer, because salts in the fertilizer can kill *Rhizobium* bacteria under conditions of high humidity or if the seed is not planted immediately. Legume seed should be inoculated just prior to planting following the directions on the inoculant package.

Low soil pH (less than about 5.8), or extreme heat or drought can quickly reduce *Rhizobium* bacteria numbers. Under extremely adverse conditions, less than 0.01 percent of the original *Rhizobium* population present on the seed will survive for two days. Bacteria survival will be much better if the seed is planted in slightly moist soil or if planted just prior to a rain. Although great care should be taken to avoid covering small-seeded legumes with more than ¼-inch to ½-inch of soil, a light or partial soil covering, such as can be accomplished with use of a cultipacker-seeder, will help protect the bacteria.

Coated Seed

Much of the commercially-marketed seed of alfalfa, white clover, red clover, and some other legumes is preinoculated and thus does not require inoculation by the producer. This seed is coated using a commercial process that involves putting an adhesive on the seed, then applying the proper legume inoculant (and usually a fungicide to prevent seedling diseases), plus a lime- or clay-based coating.

Coated seed offers the advantage of higher populations of *Rhizobium* bacteria attached to the seed than would normally be the case with on-farm inoculation. In addition, the coating helps protect the inoculant and ensures longer bacteria survival in the soil. However, in order to ensure survival of the sensitive bacteria, coated seed must be protected from heat during transportation, by the seed dealer, and by the producer. Also, seeder calibration is essential, as coated seed flows up to 35 percent faster than uncoated seed.

The coating has volume and weight, so when producers purchase coated seed, some of the cost of the seed product purchased is actually the coating. Also, since coated seed is slightly larger, planting the same number of pounds of coated seed per acre as uncoated seed results in fewer pounds of actual seed being planted. However, studies have shown that in terms of stands obtained, there are normally no differences when planting the same weight per acre of either coated or uncoated seed.

The Nitrogen Fixation Process

Rhizobium bacteria infect root hairs of legume plants near the point of root elongation. Only a small percentage of the root hairs of a given plant become infected. The larger the number of the appropriate type of bacteria that are present in the soil, the more root hairs will become infected.

After legume plants are three to four weeks old and the seedling has developed its first true leaf, tiny nodules become visible along the taproot. As plants get older, the number, size, and color of the nodules present will indicate the extent of nitrogen fixation. In older plants that have been properly inoculated, some nodules form on secondary roots, nodule size increases, and the interior of effective nitrogen-fixing nodules will be pink to dark red in color. A white or green color indicates the nodules are ineffective and not fixing nitrogen.

With time, legume nodules slough off, decompose, and the nitrogen

Proper inoculation of seed can result in more early-season forage, as shown by this test with arrowleaf clover in central Alabama.

becomes available to the host legumes or other plants growing in association with them. Many *Rhizobium* bacteria continue to live in the soil, assuming soil conditions are suitable. Amounts of nitrogen (lb/A/yr) fixed by various legumes vary greatly depending on conditions, but good legume stands range from about 50 to 150 for annual clovers and vetches; 75 to 200 for birdsfoot trefoil, white clover, and red clover; and 150 to over 200 for alfalfa.

Where very little or no nitrogen fixation is occurring, the plants will indicate nitrogen deficiency by stunted growth and yellowing, especially of the lower leaves. When inoculation has failed, it is sometimes possible to improve nodulation by broadcasting or drill-planting inoculated sand or by spraying an inoculum/water mix in the field, either of which should be done just prior to a rain or irrigation. Such an approach may or may not be effective, but is more likely to work if done soon after planting when seedlings are small.

Although legume seed inoculation is a simple process, it is highly important and deserves careful attention. The hot, dry conditions often encountered at planting time in the South can greatly reduce numbers of *Rhizobium* bacteria very quickly. Poor inoculation and the resulting poor nodulation and nitrogen fixation are major reasons why production of legumes is often difficult in the South. SF

Forage Physiology

Physiology refers to the processes and activities associated with the functioning of a living organism. The growth patterns of forage grasses and legumes are influenced by physiological characteristics of the plant species and the ever-changing environmental conditions to which they are exposed. Physiological responses differ for annuals as compared to perennials and for cool season as compared to warm season species. Thus, an understanding of the physiology of forage plants can help in making better management decisions.

Light

Photosynthesis. Green plants have the capacity to capture energy in sunlight and use it to collect carbon dioxide from the air and water from the soil, converting them into products that can be consumed as food by animals. This process, photosynthesis, has a relatively low rate of efficiency, with light energy conversion of less than 3 percent for cool season grasses and about 5 to 6 percent for warm season grasses. These differences in efficiency are a result of different chemical pathways for the photosynthetic process. Cool season grasses such as tall fescue or ryegrass, as well as all legumes, fix energy into 3-carbon units and are called C_3 plants. Warm season grasses such as bermudagrass, pearl millet, and corn fix energy into 4-carbon units and are called C_4 plants.

The C_4 pathway in photosynthesis is more efficient for several reasons. Individual leaves of C_4 plants can utilize nearly full sunlight while C_3 plants become light-saturated at only 25 to 50 percent of full sunlight (**Figure 14.1**). The C_3 plants, unlike C_4 grasses, have photorespiration that may waste up to 40 percent of the energy captured in photosynthesis. Thus, C_4 grasses have the potential for much higher forage yields than C_3 plants.

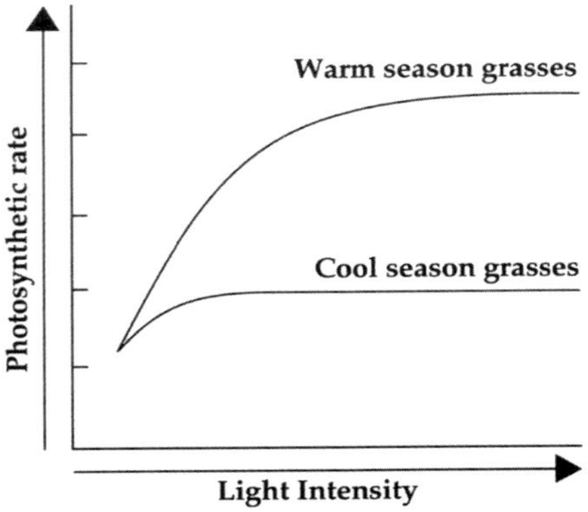

Figure 14.1. Photosynthetic potential of warm season (C_4) grass leaves is much higher than cool season (C_3) grasses.

Photosynthesis occurs in structures within plant leaves, called chloroplasts, in the presence of the pigment chlorophyll. Once carbohydrates have been formed, they can be rapidly translocated to various parts of the plant where they are used for metabolism, growth, or storage. Temperature, water availability, and other factors affect this translocation process.

The movement of materials within plants is made possible by specialized connective tissues that collectively are called the vascular system. The xylem transports water and minerals from the sites of absorption in the roots upward

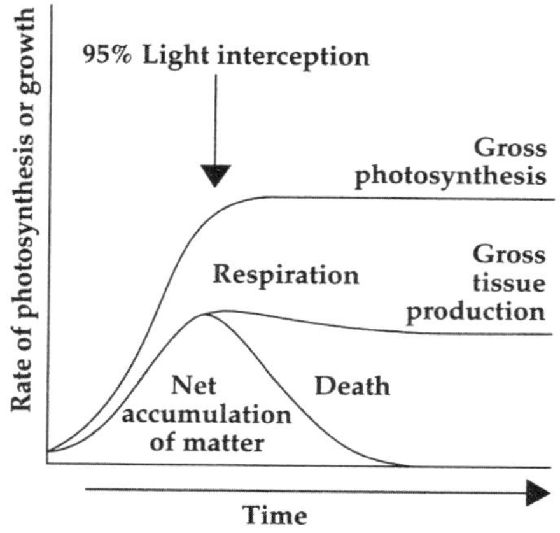

Figure 14.2. Forage growth following cutting, showing the balance between the rate of gross photosynthesis, loss in respiration, and death, and the rate of net accumulation of forage. Adapted from: A.J. Parsons, E.L. Leafe, C. Collett, P.D. Penning, and J. Lewis. J. Appl. Ecol. 20:127-139.

through the stem to the leaves. The phloem carries sugars and other compounds from the leaves where they are produced to other parts of the plants where they are used or stored.

Individual leaf photosynthesis. Nitrogen deficiency and water stress greatly reduce the photosynthetic rate of leaves. Conversely, adequate fertilization and/or irrigation can enhance photosynthesis. Leaves that emerge in partial shade have a lower photosynthetic potential than leaves that emerge in full sunlight. The photosynthetic rate of individual leaves decreases with age. Young leaves actively capture sunlight, peaking at about three weeks of age, then slowly decline until about four to eight weeks when they become inactive. Grazing old, non-productive leaves in a pasture allows more new young leaf growth, which can increase yield and quality. The leaf aging process occurs more rapidly under warm than cool conditions.

Light relations in a pasture. The growth rate of a pasture or hayfield is related more to the total photosynthesis of the stand than to the photosynthesis rate of individual leaves. The reason for this is that leaves of forage grasses and legumes do not photosynthesize at their full potential in shade. This can be illustrated by the growth of forage after cutting (**Figure 14.2**), when the proportion of sunlight that is intercepted by individual leaves increases. Initially, all the leaves contribute to growth of the sward. However, as leaf numbers increase and shading of lower leaves increases, the average photosynthetic contribution declines. This is a result of both shading and leaf aging. As leaf mortality increases, net accumulation of green matter decreases, while gross tissue production remains about the same.

Effects of shading. Shading affects pasture and hay plants in many ways. The immediate effect is reduced photosynthesis. Shading also increases leaf length, but reduces leaf width and thickness. Bud development and development of grass tillers and branching of legumes are decreased by shading. Internode length and plant height increase with shading. Shading of legumes reduces nodulation and N fixation.

The arrangement of leaves within the canopy affects the amount of light intercepted and the photosynthetic potential of the sward. Horizontally displayed leaves, as with white or crimson clovers, absorb a greater amount of light than more vertical leaves such as those of tall fescue, allowing light to penetrate deeper into the crop canopy. Plants with horizontal leaves need to be grazed or cut more frequently to avoid self-shading and rapid leaf death. Tall-growing legumes such as alfalfa allow more light deeper in the canopy, resulting in greater photosynthetic potential and higher yield. Warm season grasses such as corn, pearl millet, or sorghum-sudangrass, with leaves set at an acute angle on tall stems or stalks, have a high photosynthetic potential and can produce large forage yields over a short growing season.

An understanding of light relationships in a pasture can be helpful in devising management approaches to maximize productivity (Chapter 25). Forage removal should be frequent enough to prevent the high leaf death losses occurring from shading and aging (**Figure 14.2**). However, after forage removal, there should be sufficient green leaves left for photosynthesis to permit rapid regrowth. These objectives are often achieved under continuous stocking when adjustments are made at intervals to maintain short and desirable pasture height.

Regardless of the grazing method used, there is often a need to periodically mow or graze closely to stimulate new shoot production and regain the photosynthetic efficiency of a pasture. Light is needed to maintain a high population of active tillers (the leaf-producing unit) from buds at the basal portion of grass plants. Heavy shading in undergrazed tall fescue pastures reduces tiller numbers for active autumn growth. Late-cutting of overmature tall fescue hay will result in low tiller populations and delay recovery growth for grazing.

Basal bud development in annual legumes such as arrowleaf or crimson clovers is greatly affected by shading. Frequent defoliation will maintain a high population of new shoots and furnish grazing through late spring. When a hay cutting is made during initiation of flower buds, little or no regrowth can be expected, as there are few or no live buds remaining at the bases of the plants. Light is essential for a high bud population in both grasses and annual legumes. Perennial legumes such as alfalfa and red clover maintain a relatively high number of buds on basal crowns and regenerate new shoots soon after each cutting. Birdsfoot trefoil has active branching at nodes above the ground, so regrowth occurs there when light is adequate. With this legume, it is important to maintain several inches of leaves for rapid regrowth.

Competition for light. Competition for light is especially important where plant species are grown together. Successful competition for light depends on tolerance to low light levels and/or the potential to raise leaves above other plants. Although all pasture plants are sun-loving species, there are differences in tolerance to shading. Among the winter annual clovers, crimson and subterranean are more productive in shade than arrowleaf. Tolerance to shading can be valuable for persistence of a species in an undergrazed pasture. But where frequent grazing is done, this attribute will be of little value.

The proportion of different species in a mixture may shift substantially, depending on changes in light relations caused by cutting or grazing management. A closely grazed tall fescue-ladino clover pasture is likely to have a

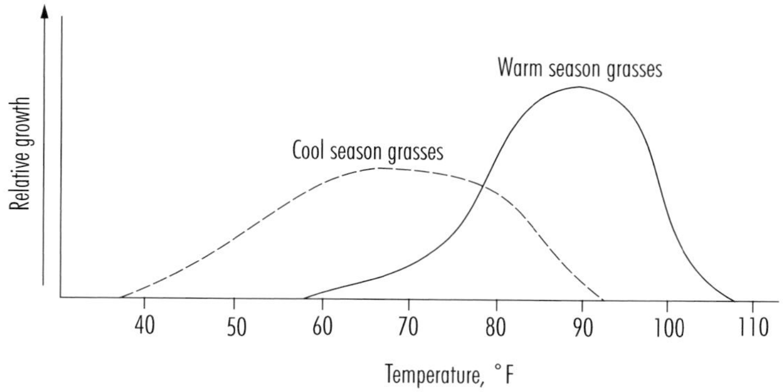

Figure 14.3. Relative growth rate of warm season grasses is greater than cool season grasses at high temperatures, but cool season grasses are productive over a wider temperature range.

high proportion of clover, but when undergrazed, the clover will be shaded out, and the pasture will become grass dominant. When a hybrid bermudagrass-alfalfa mixture is adequately fertilized with nutrients needed by alfalfa and is cut for hay, alfalfa will dominate because it will shade out the bermudagrass.

Temperature

Species response to temperature. At optimum temperatures, the maximum growth rates of warm season grasses such as bermudagrass, pearl millet, and switchgrass are much greater than those of cool season grasses such as tall fescue and orchardgrass. The optimum temperature for growth of warm season grasses is about 85 to 95°F, but only 60 to 80°F for cool season grasses (**Figure 14.3**). Individual legume species differ some, with optimum temperatures being 65 to 75°F for clovers, about 78°F for alfalfa, and 80 to 85°F for tropical legumes.

The temperature range over which forage is produced at near peak levels is much greater in cool season than in warm season grasses. Growth of warm season grasses falls off rapidly at temperatures below 75°F, with virtually no production at 50°F.

The rather narrow temperature range of warm season grasses means that the productive season gets progressively shorter as they are grown farther north where cool nights during spring and autumn limit growth. Based on temperature adaptation, warm season perennial grasses can be placed into three groups:

1. Intolerant to cold and easily winterkilled, such as Tifton 85 bermudagrass, which has a long productive season of seven to eight months in the Gulf Coast area.
2. Relatively cold-hardy, such as Coastal, Tifton 44, and Midland bermudagrass hybrids, which have a shorter productive season the farther north they are grown.
3. Cold-hardy, such as big bluestem, indiangrass, and switchgrass, which can be grown as far north as Minnesota.

Winter dormancy and winter productivity. In colder areas of the upper South, winter dormancy in perennial forage varieties is important. Otherwise, they will begin growth during short warm periods in winter and consume carbohydrates needed for winter survival and early spring production. For this reason, alfalfa, red clover, orchardgrass, and tall fescue varieties grown in the upper South are winter-dormant types. Non-dormant types should not be grown in this region as they can be winterkilled or severely weakened by depletion of stored food reserves as a result of green-up during winter.

When winter-dormant varieties are grown in the lower South, they do not grow during the milder winter temperatures. Cool season forage plants of Mediterranean origin generally make more winter growth in the lower South than plants originating in colder climates. With less winter dormancy, they develop new leaves rapidly, with rapid leaf expansion during short periods of favorable temperature. This feature was exploited in the development of AU Triumph and other winter-productive tall fescue varieties. In the lower part of Zone B, these varieties will yield 30 percent more forage than Kentucky 31 tall fescue during February-March and 25 percent more during November-December. However, when they are grown farther north, there is little yield advantage, and they may be injured by cold. When grown along the Gulf Coast, highly non-dormant alfalfa varieties may remain green all winter and be harvested from March through November. However, when planted in the upper South, such varieties may winterkill.

Impact of temperature on plant functions. Within the desirable temperature ranges for the C_3 and C_4 forage species, higher temperatures increase rate of leaf appearance and expansion. Lower temperatures delay leaf aging and reduce respiration rate, increasing availability of carbohydrates for both roots and shoot development. In cool season grasses and legumes, lower temperatures result in wider, thicker leaves with higher levels of available carbohydrates. The optimum temperature for root growth of grasses and legumes is about 10°F lower than for shoot growth. Thus, in early spring, root growth is more active and competes more effectively for available carbohydrates that may be needed for leaf initiation. In pastures that have been badly overgrazed and have low available carbohydrates, regrowth will be delayed, as roots only have access to limited amounts of stored food.

Warm season-cool season grass competition. Common bermudagrass and tall fescue can be found growing in mixtures from the lower to the upper South. When grown together, the competitive aspects of these grasses, one a C_4 and the other a C_3 species, are greatly affected by climate and other environmental variables. In the upper South, bermudagrass has a short growing season. Temperatures are favorable for tall fescue growth during much of the growing season; therefore, tall fescue dominates a pasture or hayfield for most of the year.

Farther south, both grasses have restricted periods for favorable growth, and dominance by one or the other depends on weather conditions and management. During a wet year, tall fescue will be more likely to dominate, while in a dry year bermudagrass will be most abundant. Nitrogen fertilization in autumn and late winter will favor tall fescue, while fertilization in late spring and summer will favor bermudagrass. Close grazing in summer will further favor bermudagrass, especially at more southern locations. In the Coastal Plain, bermudagrass clearly has the competitive edge because of favorable temperatures over much of the year, sandy soils with high populations of nematodes that attack tall fescue roots, and often a long autumn drought that inhibits tall fescue growth.

In the mid South where both warm and cool season grasses are widely adapted, it is often possible to favor one or the other by adjusting management. Therefore, proper management can result in a mixed warm and cool season grass pasture that provides grazing over much of the year. In addition to bermudagrass-tall fescue, other combinations of C_3 and C_4 plant species can be used in some areas, such as dallisgrass-white clover, dallisgrass-tall fescue, annual ryegrass-arrowleaf clover overseeded on bermudagrass, and rye or ryegrass overseeded on bahiagrass or bermudagrass.

Water

Water use. Water shortage is often the major factor limiting plant growth, even when soil fertility and temperature are favorable. Although water is a major raw material in photosynthesis, less than 1 percent of the water taken up by the roots is used to produce food. The vast majority of plant water is transpired or lost by diffusion through the leaf stomata (tiny pores in leaves). Water escaping from leaves cools the plant and in its movement through the plant carries minerals, sugars, and amino acids. About 300 to over 1,000 lb of water are used to produce a pound of dry matter.

Water use efficiency differs among forage species. The C_4 species (warm season grasses) are generally about twice as efficient as C_3 plants in dry matter production per unit of water. This is impressive, considering that the major production of C_4 species occurs during summer under high temperatures with high evapotranspiration rates, whereas the C_3 species (except a few species such as the lespedezas) make most of their growth during cooler periods of the year.

Warm season perennial grasses differ in water use efficiency. In one study, well-fertilized Coastal bermudagrass and Pensacola bahiagrass with high rainfall utilized less water per pound of forage than common bermudagrass because of their higher yield potential (**Table 14.1**). However, in a drought year, Coastal bermudagrass was far more efficient, probably because of the deeper root system measured in the study. In terms of drought tolerance, the grasses ranked: Coastal bermudagrass > Pensacola bahiagrass > common bermudagrass.

Water stress. Drought or moisture stress is a common problem in the South even though average annual rainfall is high (Chapter 3). High summer temperatures cause high losses of water from plants and soil. High intensity, short-duration rainfall causes substantial runoff so that much of the rain does not enter the soil, particularly on clay soils such as in the Piedmont.

Table 14.1. **Water use efficiency of several warm season perennial grasses in south Georgia in a wet year and a drought year.**

Grass	lb water used/lb of dry forage Wet year	Drought year
Coastal bermudagrass	800	640
Pensacola bahiagrass	870	1,240
Common bermudagrass	1,550	4,340
Rainfall April 1-Oct 31, in.	40	14
Rainfall as % of normal	135	47

Adapted from: G.W. Burton, E.H. DeVane, and R.L. Carter. Agron. J. 46:229-233.

Subsoil acidity adds to the problem by limiting deep soil penetration by roots of many species, especially legumes. Thus, with shallow root development, much of the subsoil water is unavailable for plant growth. Forage species tolerant of subsoil acidity can utilize deeper soil water during periods of drought, furnishing higher yields. Thus, it is important to have deep-rooted forage species that maintain growth during periods of limited rainfall.

When soil moisture becomes limiting, many plant biological processes are affected. Cell division and enlargement are first reduced, which stops tiller production and growth. When leaf growth and tiller development cease, photosynthesis continues at a reduced rate. This results in an increase in soluble carbohydrates, which can improve digestibility of drought-stressed forage. Minerals, especially potassium, accumulate in drought-stressed plants. Less nitrogen is metabolized to amino acids and proteins, resulting in accumulation in some plants of products such as nitrates and alkaloids, which can be toxic to livestock consuming the forage (Chapter 22).

As water stress develops, root growth may continue at a greater rate than foliage growth, thus allowing exploration of a greater volume of soil. This may result in the plants maintaining a reduced rate of photosynthesis over a considerable time, as roots are extracting some water from the soil. As water stress increases, photosynthesis will decrease even more, and eventually carbohydrate production will stop. Leaf rolling in many grass species and folding of leaves in legume species are common responses to water stress. This reduces the heat load on the plant in the form of intercepted sunlight and lowers transpiration water losses. If water stress is prolonged, premature leaf aging and death by desiccation occur.

Forage plants with roots that grow deep and have a high root volume with which to explore the soil should be most drought tolerant and productive during periods of low rainfall. Warm season perennial grasses are generally deeper rooted, but do not necessarily have more total roots than cool season grasses (**Table 14.2**). For example, bermudagrass roots grow deeper in the soil, but have a lower total weight of roots than bahiagrass, reed canarygrass, or tall fescue. Among the cool season species, reed canarygrass has a greater weight of roots, but rooting depth is similar to tall fescue. However, root pruning by soil nematodes can drastically reduce the rooting depth of susceptible forage species. Tall fescue and especially orchardgrass are generally short-lived on sandy Coastal Plain soils because of

Table 14.2. Rooting depth and total roots in the soil profile for various warm and cool season perennial forage plants in central Alabama, two-year average.

Species	Total roots, lb/A	Maximum depth of roots, in.
Warm season forages (C_4)		
Coastal bermudagrass	4,762	78
Common bermudagrass	3,950	79
Pensacola bahiagrass	6,276	61
Sericea lespedeza	3,085	50
Cool season forages (C_3)		
Reed canarygrass	12,768	48
Tall fescue	9,011	48
Orchardgrass	2,934	38
White clover	2,701	38
Red clover	2,323	45

Adapted from: O.L. Bennett and B.D. Doss. Agron. J. 52:204-207; B.D. Doss, D.A. Ashley, and O.L. Bennett. Agron. J. 52:569-572.

root pruning by nematodes, which increases drought susceptibility.

Flooding and poor drainage. Flooding and poor soil drainage reduce growth mainly by restricting oxygen supply to the roots. Consequently, forage species in a dormant state are much more tolerant of flooding than when actively growing. Oxygen requirements increase with temperature. Thus, growing plants often die under flooding or poor drainage. Also, some forage disease problems such as *Phytophthora* root rot in alfalfa increase.

Forage species differ greatly in their tolerance to poor drainage (see **Appendix A.16** and **A.17**). Annual ryegrass, reed canarygrass, johnsongrass, and dallisgrass are extremely tolerant of poor drainage, followed by bahiagrass and tall fescue. This contrasts with hybrid bermudagrass, wheat, and orchardgrass, which require good drainage for survival and production. Alfalfa is intolerant of poor drainage, while clovers vary greatly. Persian, white, berseem, and ball clovers are quite tolerant of, and productive on, wet soils. Arrowleaf and crimson clovers are intolerant of flooding and require good drainage for satisfactory production.

Carbohydrate Reserves

Photosynthesis supplies the energy needs of perennial forage plants for respiration and growth. Excess energy from photosynthesis is stored as carbohydrates in various plant parts. The main storage organs are roots in alfalfa, red clover, kudzu, birdsfoot trefoil, and sericea lespedeza; rhizomes in bermudagrass, bahiagrass, reed canarygrass, johnsongrass, and switchgrass; stolons in ladino clover; and stem bases in dallisgrass, tall fescue, orchardgrass, and big bluestem. These storage carbohydrates support respiration needs during winter or summer dormancy, allow regrowth after dormancy, promote flowering and seed formation, and contribute to cold and heat resistance of the plant. The levels of carbohydrates in storage organs are quite dynamic since many factors affect both their accumulation and use.

Cool season grasses such as tall fescue and orchardgrass depend on reserve carbohydrates for initiation of new leaf growth following a stress period such as after a hay cutting, a period of very close grazing, a severe drought, or after winter in the upper South. In these species, continuous close grazing during summer reduces leaf area for photosynthesis and depletes carbohydrates so regrowth will be slow and stands weakened. This problem is more severe in the lower South than in the upper South. Good management of these grasses should leave adequate leaf area for photosynthesis so carbohydrate levels are not depleted. Carbohydrates accumulate under conditions of low nitrogen, cool temperatures, and moisture stress. Carbohydrate depletion occurs when active growth is stimulated by nitrogen fertilization, adequate moisture, and higher temperatures. In contrast, low-growing, rhizomatous species such as Kentucky bluegrass can be grazed closely without damage.

Warm season grasses with erect growth habit such as johnsongrass, switchgrass, or big bluestem are vulnerable to damage by continuous close grazing and should be rotationally stocked to recharge carbohydrate storage organs. In contrast, bermudagrass and bahiagrass maintain large quantities of leaf area close to the ground and can be grazed closely without adverse effects.

Alfalfa, sericea lespedeza, and birdsfoot trefoil are especially sensitive to frequent close defoliation that depletes carbohydrates. Root carbohydrates in alfalfa have to be carefully managed in the northern U.S. and in the upper South where plants are dormant for several months in winter. Respiration of roots during this dormant period utilizes energy in northern areas, so it is important to not harvest alfalfa for four weeks before a killing frost to allow adequate carbohydrate accumulation. Otherwise, plants will be weakened, the likelihood of winter injury will be increased, and forage yields the following spring will be decreased. Where alfalfa is grazed and rotationally stocked in the upper South, at least 8 inches of growth should remain when animals are moved during mid-September to early November. This will allow sufficient carbohydrate accumulation for winter.

In the lower South, alfalfa root carbohydrates are depleted after each cutting, but they are recharged more readily than farther north (**Figure 14.4**). Since alfalfa remains green and maintains a low rate of photosynthesis during autumn, it is not necessary to leave it uncut prior to frost. Thus, alfalfa can be cut for hay or silage every 30 to 40 days throughout the growing season in the lower South.

When alfalfa, sericea lespedeza, or birdsfoot trefoil are closely and continuously grazed, carbohydrates are rapidly depleted and both yields and stands will decline. Rotational stocking is imperative to maintain productivity of these species (Chapter 25). Grazing-tolerant alfalfa varieties maintain more leaves near the soil surface, higher root carbohydrate levels, and persist better under grazing. White clover, a prostrate species with stolons, can be grazed closely with no stand loss. Winter annual clovers do not accumulate carbohydrates for regrowth, but depend on residual leaf area and rapid leaf regeneration from active buds.

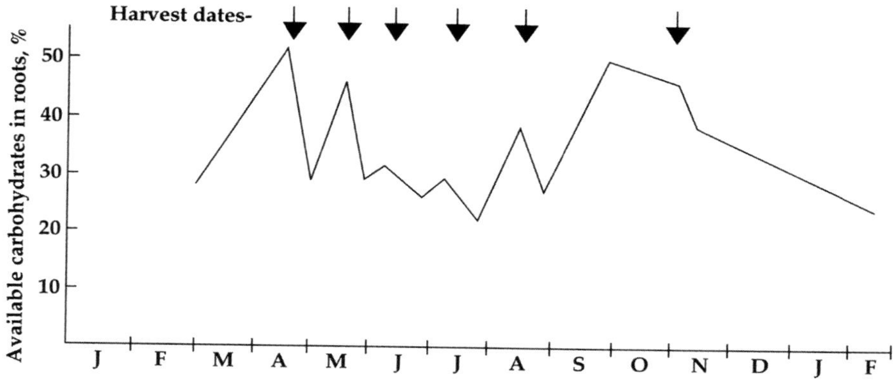

Figure 14.4. **Seasonal trend in percent available carbohydrates in alfalfa harvested for hay at Athens, Georgia.** Source: L.G. Brown, C.S. Hoveland, and K.J. Karnok. Agron. J. 82:267-273.

Vernalization and Photoperiod

An initial period of spring vegetative growth is normally followed by a reproductive period when flowering and seed production occur. Most cool season perennial grasses must be exposed to winter conditions (low temperatures and long nights) to initiate flower buds. Temperatures between 32 and 50°F (vernalization) and about a 16 hour night initiate flower buds. Later in spring, short nights and mild temperatures cause inducted buds to grow to flowering stems. Warm season grasses such as dallisgrass and bahiagrass flower in early summer in response to short nights and warm temperatures. Some warm season grasses are extremely sensitive to short variations in night length that affect flowering.

Plants can be grouped into three categories based on their flowering response to daylength: 1) Plants that flower during spring when the daylength is increasing are referred to as long-day (short night) plants. Cool season grasses and legumes fit this category. 2) Plants that flower only in summer or early autumn when daylength is decreasing are short-day (long night) plants. Examples include annual lespedeza, sericea lespedeza, and kudzu. 3) Other plants such as alfalfa may flower throughout much of the growing season and are referred to as day-neutral. Though of little practical importance, it is the length of the uninterrupted dark period, rather than light, that causes the flowering response in long-day and short-day plants.

Plant Hormones

There are numerous types of plant hormones, including auxins, gibberellins, cytokinins, and ethylene. Each of these compounds has important influences on specific aspects of plant growth. Among other processes, plant hormones are responsible for the downward growth of roots and the upward growth of stems in response to gravity (geotropism), the leaning of plants toward a light source (phototropism), stem elongation of plants deprived of adequate light (etiolation), and rapid cell division and elongation at growing points.

Seeds

Seeds are the key organs of propagation, preserving the genetic characteristics of the plant and dispersing the genetic diversity generated during reproduction. A seed has three essential components: an embryo that will give rise to a new plant, an energy store of food, and a protective seed coat (**Figure 10.1**). It is the only part of a forage plant that can withstand drying to moisture contents below 10 percent. The dormant dehydrated seed has an extremely low metabolic rate, requires no outside nutrition, and is resistant to drought, microbial decay, and temperature extremes if humidity is low.

A seed is a young plant in a resting stage, but if stored too long, especially under poor storage conditions, seed will eventually die. Seed ages, but the rate of aging depends on the harvest and drying conditions prior to storage and how it is stored. The slower the aging process, the greater the length of time the seed retains its viability or longevity. Forage species vary greatly in their normal storage life span. Species with a short storage life span of one to three years include bermudagrass, dallisgrass, orchardgrass, pearl millet, and annual lespedeza. Species with a storage life span of three to five years include bahiagrass, tall fescue, annual and perennial ryegrass, timothy, sericea lespedeza, and berseem, crimson, red, and subterranean clovers. Some hard-seeded legume species such as alfalfa, and arrowleaf, ball, and white clovers have storage life spans of five to 10 or more years.

Two environmental factors, temperature and relative humidity, affect the rate of seed deterioration in storage and eventual viability. When both temperature and relative humidity are low and diurnal fluctuations are also low, seed deterioration is reduced. There are two general rules for seed longevity in storage:

1. Each 1 percent reduction in seed moisture doubles seed longevity.
2. Each 9°F reduction in seed temperature doubles seed longevity.

Ideally, seed should be stored under cool, dry conditions to maintain seed viability. In most areas this requires refrigerated, dehumidified conditions, which are not practical for large-scale forage seed storage. Most forage seed is produced in the western U.S., and storage in the cool, dry conditions there is favorable. When seed is moved to the southern U.S., warehouses are hot and humid during many months of the year, accelerating the aging process. Moisture-proof bags of aluminum foil laminated with mylar or polyethylene plastic are used to maintain viability of non-toxic endophyte-infected tall fescue and are also useful for extending seed life.

Satisfactory seed germination requires seed capable of germinating, favorable temperature (which varies with forage species), adequate moisture (97 percent relative humidity at 66°F), and sufficient oxygen (no prolonged flooding). Rapid uptake of water during the first few hours of germination initiates enzyme mobilization of stored food reserves for seedling development. The rate of seedling development is then determined by the temperature and oxygen supply. Thus, for successful seed germination, it is important to plant high-quality seed at the proper time of year at the correct depth and in close contact with the soil. SF

Forage ecology pertains to interrelationships of grasses, legumes, weeds, and grazing animals with their environment. Compared to production of a crop such as corn or soybeans, forage ecology is more complex because it involves more components. Though it may be difficult for a livestock producer to look beyond the specific problems and opportunities that arise on a daily basis, an awareness and understanding of the influences that affect pastures or hayfields are necessary to be a good manager.

A forage production area is an ecosystem consisting of plants, other organisms, and their physical and chemical environment. Pasture ecosystems consist of four categories: 1) non-living components such as water, soil, air, and sunlight; 2) plants that capture solar energy; 3) herbivore consumers such as cattle, wildlife, and insects that consume pasture plants, as well as carnivores or meat eaters such as coyotes and snakes; and 4) decomposers such as fungi, bacteria, and earthworms that consume organic matter (**Figure 15.1**). Since grazing is the major method of utilizing forages in the southern U.S., the main emphasis in this chapter will be on pasture.

An ecosystem consists of a food chain with trophic (food) levels where solar energy captured by the plant is then transferred as food energy to succeeding levels. At each transfer, about 80 to 90 percent of the energy is lost as heat. Thus, the amount of energy stored at each successive trophic level becomes smaller with each step. Nutrients such as carbon, nitrogen, phosphorus, potassium, oxygen, and water are also recycled in a pasture

Figure 15.1. Components of a pasture ecosystem.

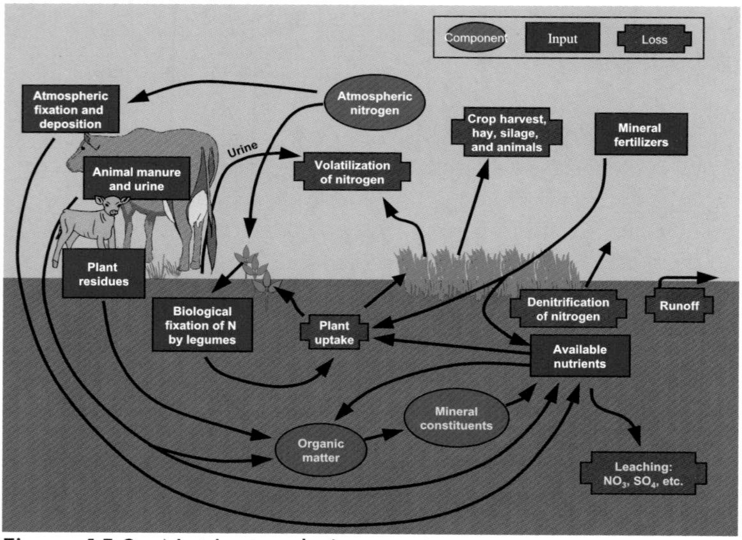

Source: Potash & Phosphate Institute (www.ppi-ppic.org)

Figure 15.2. Nutrient cycle in a pasture ecosystem.

ecosystem, with only small amounts removed by animal product (**Figures 15.2** and **9.6**). A pasture in a humid environment is an open ecosystem in which lost nutrients must be replenished by fertilization and/or biological nitrogen fixation in order to maintain a high level of productivity. Substantial losses of nitrogen result from volatilization and by leaching of urine and feces from grazing animals. Phosphorus losses are low, so this nutrient is reasonably well recycled. Some potassium is lost by leaching, particularly on sandy soils, so it is not recycled as well as phosphorus.

Management Inputs to Enhance Pasture Ecosystems

Natural ecosystems, such as range grasslands, depend mainly on inputs of sunlight and rain for their relatively low productivity. In humid climates, much higher productivity can be obtained by planting and properly managing pastures of improved forages. In these higher rainfall areas, pasture management inputs are used to capture more solar energy, harvest more of this energy, and convert more of the energy into animal product.

Some of the approaches taken to improve efficiency of solar energy capture are use of improved grass and legume varieties, liming, fertilization, and irrigation. Harvesting more solar energy can be achieved by better grazing management to reduce forage waste, and by controlling losses from pests. Improving the efficiency of solar energy utilization can be accomplished by improving cattle diets with mineral or nutrient supplements and maintaining good health by vaccinations or other treatments.

Physical Factors of the Pasture Environment

Atmosphere. The adaptation of a forage species or variety is primarily determined by temperature and rainfall. Since both of these factors can vary greatly from year to year, adaptation depends on extremes rather than average conditions. Winterkill may occur in northern zones with species or varieties best adapted to areas farther south. Conversely, environmental stress on cool season perennials increases as they are grown farther south due to higher summer temperatures, erratic rainfall, soils of low water-holding capacity, competition from vigorous warm season perennial grasses, and greater insect and disease loads. In areas with long, hot summers, cool season perennial grasses such as tall fescue and especially orchardgrass are at a competitive disadvantage and may not persist unless rested or grazed lightly in summer. Summer rainfall in the southeastern U.S. is mainly from intense, short-duration thundershowers. As a result, there can be high runoff, especially on clay soils with low infiltration rates. Thus, droughts are common even though total annual rainfall may range from 40 to over 50 inches.

Radiation intensity is high in summer, but daylengths are shorter than in the northern U.S. The generally mild temperatures and adequate rainfall during the winter months favor cool season annual pastures in the lower South, although short daylength and cloudiness may reduce growth. During winters with heavy cloud cover, pasture growth can be appreciably reduced even though temperature and moisture are favorable.

Site. Elevation is an important factor in forage plant adaptation. Higher elevations are colder in winter, but cooler and wetter during the main growing season. This reduces the competitiveness of warm season grasses such as bermudagrass, but favors growth of clovers as well as grasses such as perennial ryegrass and timothy that do not normally persist in much of the southern U.S.

Soil type greatly affects forage plant adaptation and potential pasture performance. Clay soils may form hard crusts and reduce emergence of legumes. During winter, ice layers may form in clay soils and cause heaving of small legume seedlings. Although clay soils have higher water and nutrient holding capacities than sands, infiltration rates are lower, so runoff is higher. Many soils in this region are highly leached and thus have very acid subsoils that release toxic aluminum into the soil solution and inhibit root development of some forage species. Forage plants tolerant of acid subsoils include bahiagrass, pearl millet, and tall fescue, as well as annual and sericea lespedeza.

Poorly drained soils limit the adaptation of many forage species. Forage plants tolerant of these conditions include bahiagrass, dallisgrass, johnsongrass, tall fescue, caleypea, white clover, and ball clover. Competition from certain undesirable plants such as sedges and rushes is often a problem in extremely wet areas. Drainage ditches and tiling can improve such areas to permit production of desirable pasture species.

Slope and exposure are important in determining success of forage species in a pasture. North-facing slopes are cooler and have better soil moisture than west- and south-facing slopes and may favor species such as clovers. South- and west-facing slopes are warmer and will result in earlier spring growth. However, they are hotter and drier in summer, often favoring species such as sericea lespedeza, bermudagrass, bahiagrass, or tall fescue that are more tolerant of adverse conditions.

Forage crops cannot escape the locations at which they are growing, and location influences affect pasture composition and growth. Various combinations of soil and climatic factors often create microclimates within a field that mitigate or intensify general conditions, thus favoring botanical diversity and varying productivity within a given pasture.

Plants in the Pasture Environment

Plants are the producer organisms in a pasture ecosystem. Even though only one forage species may be intentionally planted in a pasture, it typically is invaded by other annual and perennial species, so a pasture normally consists of a community of plants. Many plant species may be represented, each having its own characteristics. Even plants of the same species may exhibit genetic differences that affect competition unless they were propagated vegetatively such as with hybrid bermudagrass or perennial peanut. Small plants are more likely to die than larger neighboring plants, even if they are the same species. Over time, size of individual plants in a pasture tends to increase, with a corresponding decrease in plant number.

What causes these pasture dynamics that affect productivity and survival? First, environmental stresses such as drought, cold, or excess rainfall directly limit plant growth and survival. Sometimes individual plants of one species may provide shade or temperature moderation that favors another species. In addition, tillage or grazing will modify interactions among plants and affect competition.

Various characteristics can make plants competitive in different situations. Grasses such as tall fescue, wheat, or rye are tall, allowing them to more effectively compete for light with lower-growing plants. Some such as bermudagrass have rhizomes and stolons, giving them an advantage both above and below ground. Plants such as sericea lespedeza may deposit a great deal of leaf litter and smother seedlings of other species. Generally, competitive plants have higher potential growth rates than less competitive plants. Annual weeds such as crabgrass, little barley, and chickweed are commonly found in closely grazed pastures or where there has been recent tillage. These species have high growth rates and produce large amounts of seed that lie in the soil until favorable growing conditions occur.

Plants in a pasture are constantly involved in a struggle for survival. The success of a single plant depends on how well its characteristics match the demands of the environment and allow it to cope with stresses as compared to neighboring plants with which it is competing. From the perspective of a pasture manager, it would be good if all desirable species in a pasture competed at similar moderate levels and if undesirable plants were less competitive. In practice, this does not occur, so it is the task of the manager to exercise management that will increase the competitiveness of the desired species and/or decrease the competitiveness of undesirable plants.

Light. The most important input for forage production is light energy from the sun. Leaves may be likened to solar panels with photoelectric cells that collect solar energy for use in photosynthesis. Thus, a pasture or hayfield may be thought of as a massive biological solar collector, operating day after day with minimal maintenance. Light collection and utilization are influenced by forage species, leaf angle, canopy density, leaf aging, and availability of water and nutrients in the soil. Shading, as occurs in undergrazed pastures or in overmature hay fields, reduces tiller development and production of new leaves. Shading by tall plants affects competition and may reduce persistence of shorter plants such as clovers. Thus, decisions made by the livestock producer have a major impact on light collection needed for photosynthesis (see Chapter 25). Good grassland farming basically involves managing a pasture or hayfield to collect as much of the incoming sunlight as possible and convert it into forage.

Soil moisture and nutrients. When soil moisture and nutrients are adequate, clovers may shade out pasture grasses in spring. During a wet year, clover content of cool season perennial pastures often increases so it may be referred to as a clover year. Moisture stress gives grasses a competitive advantage over clovers because they have deeper roots and longer root hairs. On soils having acid subsoils, plants such as sericea lespedeza and bahiagrass with roots tolerant of aluminum are able to secure water at greater depths and can survive drought much better than many other species.

Many weed species are quite tolerant of low soil pH, while many of the most desirable forage species are less tolerant. This can lead to pastures that are dominated by weeds and can make weed control difficult. On a few soils in the southern U.S., alkalinity has a major effect on pasture botanical composition.

Various soil nutrient levels favor different plant species. For instance, potassium is critical for competition of clovers with grasses. When soil potassium levels decline, grasses can survive, but clovers rapidly become less competitive and are often lost from the pasture (see photo at right). Sericea and annual lespedeza are effective at extracting phosphorus from the soil, even at low levels, giving them a competitive advantage in low phosphorus soils.

Potassium-deficient clover does not compete well with grasses in pastures and may be lost from the stand.

Knowing the general fertility requirements of various pasture plants has important practical applications. For example, bahiagrass pastures can tolerate relatively low levels of fertility and still maintain good stands. However, success in overseeding bahiagrass with winter annual forages in such low fertility situations requires application of fertilizer. Well-fertilized tall fescue or mixed tall fescue-bermudagrass pastures are usually too competitive for annual lespedeza. However, this high-quality legume is much more competitive at low fertility, and thus it is an excellent reseeding summer legume for low-input pastures in the mid and upper South. In contrast, overseeding of tall fescue pastures with red clover or white clover will not succeed when soil fertility is low.

Space. Space within a pasture is finite, and any bare ground is quickly populated with plants such as little barley, chickweed, dock, cudweed, goosegrass, primrose, or crabgrass. Bare ground in a perennial pasture is most often caused by a stress of some kind that has reduced the stand and/or vigor of the forage plants by overgrazing, low nutrient status, or drought. Competition for space also occurs underground among roots of various species. As space becomes more limited, so do moisture, light, and nutrients needed for growth.

Competition between warm and cool season species. During hot weather or on droughty soils, warm season perennial grasses such as bermudagrass or bahiagrass are generally more competitive than cool season perennial grasses because of their deeper root development, drought tolerance, and high growth rates. In addition, bahiagrass has rhizomes, and bermudagrass has both rhizomes and stolons, making these grasses very aggressive. The competitive advantages of warm season grasses are even more pronounced as compared to perennial cool season legumes, especially with regard to their tolerance to lower levels of soil pH, phosphorus, and potassium. The lack of forage growth during the long winter dormancy period of warm season grasses is often mitigated by planting cool season annual grasses or clovers into the sod. The competitive advantage of warm season perennial grasses decreases in the upper South because of the shorter active growing season. In the mid and upper South, temperatures are favorable for tall fescue over a longer season of the year, so it typically dominates mixed swards in this area.

Maintaining a balance of both warm and cool season perennial grasses in a mixed sward requires favoring the weaker species (which may vary depending on location) with strategic timing of nitrogen fertilization and grazing management. In the mid and upper South, heavy grazing pressure during spring and nitrogen application in early summer will help maintain bermudagrass in association with tall fescue. Farther south, bermudagrass is the more aggressive species, so nitrogen application should be done only in mid to late winter and again in autumn to favor tall fescue in the mixture.

Allelopathy. Some plants excrete substances injurious to other plants. This chemical interference is called allelopathy. For example, some weed species such as bitter sneezeweed and dogfennel can inhibit seedling growth of annual ryegrass and alfalfa, but there are few other documented examples of allelopathy among other forage species. Autotoxicity, resulting in poor stands of alfalfa due to chemicals produced by older alfalfa plants, can occur when it is planted into an old stand of this legume or soon after its destruction.

Consumer Organisms in the Pasture Environment

There are a number of consumer organisms in a pasture ecosystem. Obviously, the most important ones are livestock such as cattle or horses. At many locations, native deer may also consume substantial amounts of forage in pastures. In addition, disease pathogens, insects, and soil nematodes can consume or destroy substantial amounts of plant material. These losses can be reduced by planting pest-resistant varieties or strategically applying a pesticide. At the next trophic level, carnivore consumers such as coyotes and feral (wild) dogs can kill and consume young animals in a pasture.

Grazing animals have profound effects on pastures with regard to stand density, botanical composition, plant vigor, and stand persistence. These effects result from three activities: 1) timing and intensity of defoliation; 2) treading; and 3) excretion of dung and urine. A basic understanding of these influences is essential for effective grazing management.

Defoliation. The timing and extent of plant defoliation normally have more influence on the vigor and botanical composition of pastures than any other factor. Removal of leaf tissue reduces the photosynthetic area and thus the ability of the plant to manufacture food. If overgrazing occurs, regrowth depletes food reserves and weakens plants, with some plants being much more sensitive than others.

Various characteristics help different plant species cope with being grazed. Some plants have spines, thick hairs, waxes, or tough leaves that make them unpalatable to grazing animals. Such plants often become weed pests in pastures. Other plants contain chemicals that deter grazing, such as tannins in sericea lespedeza or alkaloids in reed canarygrass. Several important pasture species, including bermudagrass, bahiagrass, Kentucky bluegrass, and white clover, have rhizomes or stolons, or both, that maintain substantial food reserves and improve grazing tolerance. Buds or green leaves at the ground surface can also help some species renew growth after close grazing. Other plants such as tall fescue and dallisgrass maintain food reserves in stem bases and also have many buds to regenerate growth after being defoliated. White clover stolons, even under close grazing, continue to photosynthesize and store carbohydrates to support new leaf growth as they extend into vacant spots between grass plants. Intermediate-leaf white clover varieties with more abundant stolons and basal leaves than large-leaf or ladino types have a competitive advantage and persist better in grass pastures.

In contrast, bunchgrasses such as switchgrass, eastern gamagrass, and big bluestem have few leaves near the plant base and elevate their growing points early in development. When growing points are removed by grazing, regrowth from dormant basal buds is slow. If close grazing is continued, there will be insufficient food reserves for regrowth the following year, resulting in weakened plants and eventual death. Perennial legumes such as alfalfa, red clover, sericea lespedeza, and kudzu have few leaves near the ground and require a rest period after each grazing to recharge food storage in the large taproot. Thus, when grazed continuously and closely, they are weakened and may die.

Plants in pastures that are continuously stocked at a high density will be frequently defoliated, so there is little shading of leaves in the lower part of the canopy due to constant leaf removal. In such a full light environment, plants develop short leaves and high tiller density. With rotational stocking there is less frequent defoliation, so shading of lower leaves increases during the regrowth period. With each defoliation event there is a rapid change in available light and plant architecture of the canopy. As length of time between grazing periods is increased in rotationally stocked pastures, leaves will be longer and tiller numbers less than in more frequently grazed pastures.

The intensity and frequency of grazing or cutting can have a tremendous effect on the competitive ability of many pasture plants. Continuous close grazing of a hybrid bermudagrass, such as Coastal, over several years may result in invasion by grasses such as bahiagrass or common bermudagrass that form dense sods originating from seed transported by cattle. In contrast, well-fertilized Coastal bermudagrass harvested for hay typically has fewer seed introduced and will better resist invasion by these species because rapid regrowth after cutting shades out new seedlings. A well-fertilized, thick alfalfa stand cut for hay at intervals of five to six weeks will resist invasion by bermudagrass, crabgrass, and goosegrass seedlings. Likewise, rotationally stocked alfalfa that has a rest period of four to five weeks between grazing periods will resist grass invasion, but continuous stocking will usually result in more grass competition and hasten decline, even of grazing-tolerant varieties.

Pasture species vary greatly in their tolerance to grazing. Johnsongrass often increases in hybrid bermudagrass cut for hay, but when grazed closely it disappears from pastures as it is highly palatable and cannot tolerate frequent close defoliation. Bahiagrass is one of the most tolerant of all grasses to close continuous grazing, generally resisting weed invasion because of its dense sod with many leaves at the ground surface. Endophyte-infected tall fescue is fairly tolerant of close grazing and is often quite competitive with bermudagrass even in stressful environments of the lower South. These grasses have a large number of growing points close to or below the soil surface. However, endophyte-free tall fescue is soon dominated by bermudagrass in these environments unless pastures are rotationally stocked. Orchardgrass and smooth bromegrass are also weakened by close continuous grazing, so stands decline and are often invaded by tall fescue or Kentucky bluegrass in the mid and upper South. In contrast, close continuous grazing favors white clover in mixtures with tall fescue or orchardgrass, while red clover soon disappears unless grazed less severely.

Perennial plants are more tolerant of defoliation after they are well established. Thus, overgrazing is especially damaging to a young forage stand and may result in stand loss, especially in the case of defoliation-sensitive plants and/or in conjunction with other stresses such as drought. It should be kept in mind that stresses are additive, even across seasons.

Weeds may or may not be less palatable than planted pasture species, and many are readily grazed when small, making them less competitive. Generally, broomsedge dominance of pastures is blamed on low fertility and soil acidity, but grazing management is often an important factor. Livestock will consume broomsedge in spring when tender new growth emerges, but the plant becomes extremely unpalatable with age, causing livestock to avoid it. The unpalatability trait of broomsedge allows it to become established in situations where pastures are undergrazed during surplus spring growth and overgrazed in mid to late summer. With undergrazing in spring, young broomsedge plants are allowed to become mature. During summer and early autumn when pasture forage availability may decline, livestock refuse to eat broomsedge but heavily graze improved pasture grasses, thus reducing their competitiveness. Heavy stocking during spring will weaken broomsedge and thus tend to favor desirable pasture grasses (see photo below).

Treading. Treading effects of animals walking on forage crops include physical damage (which is especially detrimental to young plants), soil compaction, and wasted forage. The extent of treading damage depends on many factors, including soil type, amount of soil moisture, stocking rate, and sod density. The greatest treading damage occurs when plants are small and the soil is loose, so new pastures planted into a prepared seedbed are particularly vulnerable. New pastures should not be grazed until the ground is settled and the plants have an adequate root system so they will not be pulled up by livestock.

Control of broomsedge in tall fescue by heavy cattle stocking in spring (right) as compared to light stocking (left) in northern Alabama.

Treading and livestock resting sites can cause forage to lie in a horizontal position where it may be trampled and wasted. Treading can reduce plant growth, the reduction being greater on wet than dry soils and being worse with some forage species than others. For instance, bermudagrass, bahiagrass, tall fescue, and Kentucky bluegrass are more tolerant of treading than orchardgrass. White clover varieties with abundant stolon production are more tolerant of treading than red clover. Heavy hoof pressures cause soil compaction, especially on wet clay soils, creating difficulties for some pasture species.

Excretion. Grazing animals collect nutrients from a pasture and concentrate them on small areas as dung and urine. Dung contains all of the phosphorus excreted by animals and a small amount of nitrogen and potassium. Forage around dung pads is avoided, initially because of smell and later because the ungrazed forage is mature and less palatable. Although a substantial amount (30 to 70 percent) of the nitrogen in urine is volatilized, some is also leached along with potassium from urine patches. Forage around urine patches has no long term rejection problems.

Spread of seed. The ability of animals to spread seed of both forage plants and weeds is often underestimated. Some seeds cling to the bodies of grazing animals and are transported. However, more important is the fact that grazing animals consume seed, some of which can germinate after passing through the alimentary tract. Bahiagrass, sericea lespedeza, and many weeds have this ability. Even with tall fescue, which has soft seed, over 10 percent of the seed can pass through an animal without being digested. Some clovers produce hard seed that can pass through an animal unharmed, but any clover seed that does not have a hard seed coat will be destroyed. Feeding forage seed to livestock to increase stands of desired species is seldom feasible because of additional seed cost and the uneven distribution of fecal material.

Decomposer Organisms in the Pasture Environment

Pasture soils contain large numbers of microorganisms and earthworms that play an important role in decomposition of dead plant material and animal wastes. Organic matter is a valuable component of pasture soils, improving nutrient availability, soil structure, and water holding capacity. Fungi are the most important microorganisms in attacking organic residues containing starch, gums, cellulose, and lignin. A specialized group are vesicular arbuscular mycorrhizae (VAM) that form a symbiotic association with forage plant roots to improve availability of phosphorus and other nutrients in infertile soils. Actinomycetes (thread bacteria), found mainly in well drained soils with a pH above 6, help break down more resistant organic compounds. Bacteria are also abundant in pasture soils and responsible for some decomposition, but their most important roles are nitrification, sulfur oxidation, and nitrogen fixation.

Earthworms are common in fertile, healthy soils. Good pastures can have over 3 million per acre. Earthworms burrow and turn over large quantities of soil, up to 25 percent of the top soil annually in favorable pasture situations. They remove large amounts of surface litter and incorporate it into the soil. Pasture soils with few earthworms develop a mat of undecomposed surface plant material. Soils with high earthworm populations have improved soil structure, greater porosity, better nutrient availability, and higher water infiltration rate. Lime, mineral fertilizers, and animal wastes improve earthworm activity.

A Key Factor in Successful Forage Ecosystems

Many of the factors affecting plant growth and survival vary in intensity over time, resulting in pasture ecology being dynamic and complex. Thus, only a slight change in a particular environmental factor may determine death or survival of an individual plant. This is why pasture management is so important.

In a well-managed pasture, the practices imposed by the livestock producer can favor desirable species and reduce negative influences. Stocking rate, grazing method, and amount and timing of proper fertilizer nutrient applications and pesticide use are examples of management decisions that have major impacts on pasture productivity, persistence, and livestock performance. In many cases, factors interact with each other, thus compounding the effects. For example, poor root growth of a seedling stand due to inadequate fertilization accentuates later drought stress. Plants weakened by drought may be more susceptible to disease. Increased winterkill may be associated with low soil fertility and/or stress-weakened plants. Overgrazing may weaken plants, or undergrazing may reduce tiller production so that in both cases growth is reduced several months later.

Some producers fail to obtain the full benefits of a superior pasture species or variety because they fail to use proper management required by most improved forage plants. Many factors that influence pastures can in some way be affected by management. Thus, the livestock producer plays a critical role and is the key to a successful pasture ecosystem.

Sustainability of Forage Ecosystems

A sustainable agricultural ecosystem is one that can maintain production at some level indefinitely at the same site without mineral and fossil fuel inputs. To achieve this would require a pasture ecosystem producing animal output indefinitely without such inputs. Natural grasslands in less developed parts of the world with animals herded by people come closest to being sustainable without other inputs as long as they are not overstocked. However, with natural grasslands in low rainfall areas of the western U.S., inputs of fencing, fossil fuel for transport, and labor exceed the value of output of animal product so they are not sustainable.

In humid areas such as the southern U.S., planted pastures are subsidized with substantial amounts of mineral and fossil fuel energy to obtain higher animal product. Without these inputs, animal product would be extremely low. For example, it is estimated that beef production on native grassland in the Coastal Plain of Georgia was less than 30 lb/A annually. Obviously, modern highly productive pasture ecosystems with improved forages in humid areas are not sustainable without substantial inputs of minerals and fossil fuel energy. Realistically, the questions are: What factors contribute to the low level of forage ecosystem sustainability and what can be done to reduce the high inputs for profitable animal production?

Some Modern Forage Ecosystem Problems and Possible Solutions

Most perennial pasture legume varieties are not persistent, and most annual legume species do not reseed dependably. This results in substantial investment to replant and maintain adequate stands in the pasture ecosystem. Dependable persistent legumes are needed to provide forage of high nutritional quality and reduce inputs of nitrogen fertilizer. Endophyte-infected tall fescue, bermudagrass, bahiagrass, and dallisgrass make up most of the perennial grass pastures of the humid southern U.S. One annual species, crabgrass, is also important. These grasses are dominant because of their dependability and adaptability to a wide range of soils, stressful environments, low fertility, and poor grazing management. Most legumes lack tolerance to these conditions and require higher inputs of lime, phosphorus, and potassium to remain productive.

Progress has been made by plant breeders in improving grazing tolerance and stand life of species such as alfalfa, white clover, and novel (non-toxic) endophyte tall fescue. Sericea lespedeza, a long-lived perennial legume, has the potential to provide low cost hay and pasture with very low inputs of phosphorus, potassium, and lime. Another less conventional possibility is interplanting small legume trees such as mimosa in pastures to supply nitrogen to the grass as well as provide palatable high-quality leafy forage to grazing animals.

Too much pasture and hay are wasted, utilizing inputs of energy and nutrients that do not benefit animal production. Improved grazing methods such as rotational stocking and limit grazing can reduce pasture waste. Stockpiling forage and utilizing it by strip grazing can extend the pasture season and reduce winter hay needs. Better hay storage and hay feeding can greatly reduce inputs into the forage ecosystem.

Nutrient recycling is often poor in many ecosystems. Mineral fertilizers and lime require high inputs of fossil fuel energy to extract, prepare, transport, and apply them to pastures and hay fields. Greater use of rotational stocking allows more uniform recycling of nutrients in animal urine and dung. Animal manures and other waste products should be applied wisely at suitable rates to prevent excess application of unneeded nutrients.

Feedlots in which silage and other feeds are transported and fed to animals utilize huge inputs of energy as compared to animals harvesting forage from pastures. Livestock production with feedlot systems is likely to encounter more problems as energy costs rise and if grain subsidies diminish. Smaller production units based on pasture with lower inputs would likely result in lower production per animal, but might offer the potential for greater sustainability.

Livestock and crop production have become separated by specialization. This has resulted in less rotation of grain and other crops with forages, increasing dependence on pesticides, reduced soil organic matter, recycling of nutrients, and increased soil erosion. Mixed livestock and crop farming offers the potential of greater long-term sustainability, but is often not economically attractive.

Our Challenge

Most forage research has been focused on what is economically acceptable on a short-term basis, not on what is ecologically sustainable. This focus has been based on cheap nitrogen fertilizer and fossil fuel. If costs of these inputs rise it will likely encourage lower-cost management systems for humid climate forage ecosystems in the future.

A major problem with animal production from pasture ecosystems is the low level of trophic efficiency by human beings consuming meat and milk rather than directly consuming plant products. In the U.S., the high use of grain in feeding these animals makes the trophic energy efficiency even lower. However, as long as economic conditions permit human consumption of animal products produced with high nutrient and energy subsidies, livestock production is likely to remain a major enterprise. There will probably be greater use of legumes and greater emphasis on developing forage species that are tolerant of drought, soil acidity, and lower soil nutrient levels. In addition, different management systems could emphasize better efficiency in recycling of nutrients, less waste in production, and better utilization. This would not be a totally sustainable ecosystem, but one that would be more friendly environmentally and economically. SF

Forage Quality

Many attempts have been made to define forage quality in terms of leafiness, stem thickness, color, smell, or by content of protein, fiber, or lignin. Chemical composition of forages is a useful, but imperfect, measure of quality. However, it is the animal rather than the human that ultimately determines quality. Thus, forage quality is best defined in terms of animal performance such as daily gain, reproduction, milk, or fiber production.

Palatability

Selectivity normally results from livestock showing preference for the most palatable plants or plant parts, though behavioral factors may have an influence. Generally, high quality forages are highly palatable and vice-versa, but not always. Animal selection of one forage species over another depends on smell, touch, and taste. Palatability may be affected by texture, aroma, succulence, hairiness, leafiness, fertilization, dung pads, urine patches, sugar content, or some other factor.

When animals are restricted to a less palatable species, their performance may be quite satisfactory if forage nutritive quality is high and intake is not reduced. For example, grazing animals will select oats in preference to rye even though they will perform well when restricted to rye pasture.

In cafeteria-style plots, horses consistently selected and grazed oats (being grazed) or annual ryegrass as compared to rye (right), wheat, or triticale. Athens, Georgia.

Annual ryegrass is even more palatable than oats to horses. Thus, palatability alone can be a misleading indicator of forage quality. In addition, palatability of a forage species may change during the growing season.

Forage Digestion by Animals

Ruminant animals (i.e., cattle, sheep, goats, deer, camels, buffalo, llamas, and alpaca) have an enlarged three- or four-compartmented stomach that permits them to digest large amounts of forage with a high fiber content. This unique and valuable characteristic enables these animals to utilize materials that cannot be efficiently utilized by non-ruminants. Forage consumed by ruminants moves from the esophagus into the rumen and reticulum, then is regurgitated and chewed before being digested by rumen microflora (**Figure 16.1**).

Volatile fatty acids from the digestion process are absorbed through the rumen wall and utilized by the animal. Microbes and undigested material pass into the omasum where water is absorbed. Then the microbes are degraded in the abomasum (true stomach) and the products are absorbed in the small intestine for use by the animal. Starch and sugars are absorbed in the small intestine. Digestibility (the proportion of the forage consumed in passage through the alimentary tract) varies, depending on the type of material consumed by the animal. Immature leafy grasses or white clover may be 80 to 90 percent digestible, but mature stemmy material is often below 50 percent.

Certain non-ruminant animals such as horses and mules have a functional cecum and colon where microbes digest fiber (**Figure 16.2**). However, the cecum (the fermentation vat) and colon follow the small intestine, and the total stomach capacity is much smaller than for ruminants. Hence, microbial activity is low in the horse. Horses break down only about 30 percent of the fiber in forage, whereas ruminants utilize 60 to 70 percent. Horses cannot digest as much low-quality material as ruminants, thus higher quality forage must be fed for good performance.

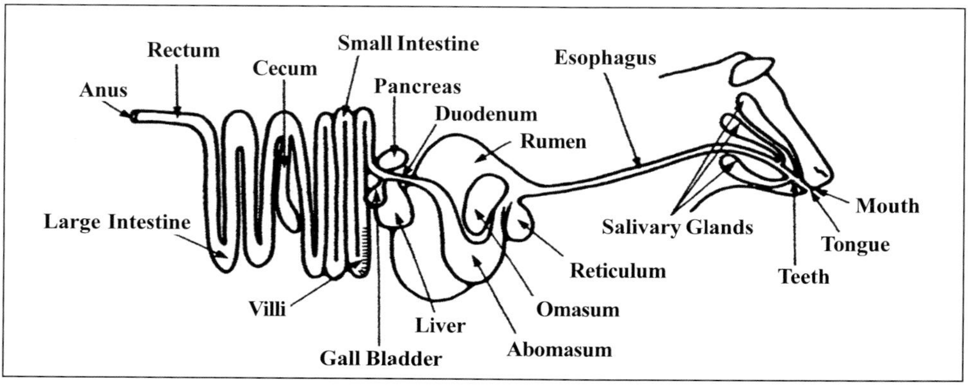

Figure 16.1. Digestive system of a cow.

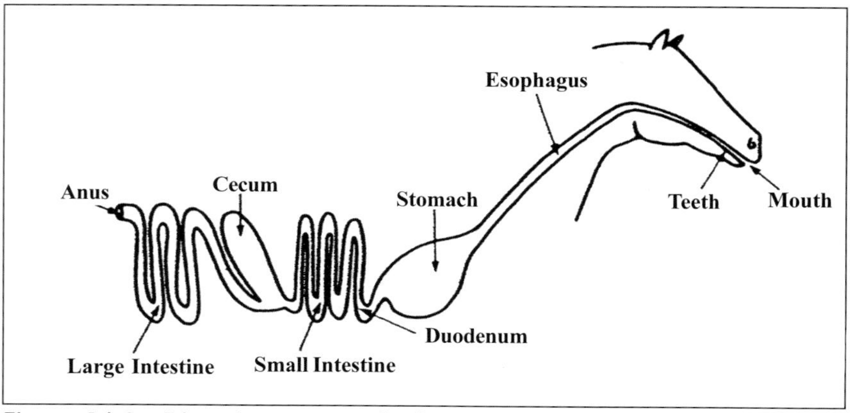

Figure 16.2. Digestive system of a horse.

Forage Composition

Leafy, growing forage plants usually contain 70 to 90 percent water, but it is preferable to express forage yields and chemical analyses on a dry matter basis. Forage constituents (see **Appendix A.26**) can be divided into two main categories: 1) those present as cell contents or the non-structural part of the plant tissue (mainly protein, sugar, and starch) and 2) those that make up the structural components of cell walls (primarily cellulose, hemicellulose, and lignin).

Cell contents are almost completely digested, while cell walls vary in digestibility due to many factors, including forage species, age, and temperature. In addition, minerals, vitamins, and anti-quality factors such as tannins, nitrates, alkaloids, cyanoglycosides, estrogens, and mycotoxins influence animal performance, depending on the plant species and environmental conditions.

Protein

Digestible proteins are located in the cell cytoplasm (cell contents), and relatively indigestible proteins are found in the chloroplasts (structures located within the cytoplasm), where they make up about 40 percent of the total protein. Cell walls tend to retain large protein molecules, often making them unavailable to the animal during digestion. Chemical analyses for proteins are most commonly expressed as crude protein (CP), indicating some of the proteins may be unavailable for animal utilization.

The portion of CP that is unavailable varies with crop species, stage of maturity at harvest, and other factors. In plants such as bermudagrass and bahiagrass, which have highly lignified cell walls, much of the CP may be unavailable to the animal. However, protein quality is not of great importance for beef cows on pasture since all amino acids can be synthesized by rumen microorganisms.

Young, leafy grasses and legumes are normally high in protein and usually meet the protein needs of grazing animals. Perennial cool season grasses generally contain less protein than legumes, but have adequate amounts for most types and classes of animals. Winter annual pastures such as small grains and annual ryegrass contain high levels of crude protein, yet growing stocker cattle gain faster when supplemented with rumen bypass protein feeds such as fish meal or certain grain components. The reason is that a large portion of the digestible nitrogen in the forage is soluble and is quickly converted to ammonia in the rumen and lost.

Well-fertilized warm season pasture grasses or hay cut at early stages of maturity generally contain adequate protein for beef cows. However, insufficient protein can be a problem in warm season grasses that received inadequate nitrogen fertilizer, and especially on frosted pasture during winter or in hay cut at advanced stages of maturity.

Digestible Energy

Carbohydrates are chemical compounds composed of carbon, hydrogen, and oxygen. They are extremely important nutritionally because they are the main source of energy in food. Non-structural carbohydrates in forages are readily digested by animals of all types. However, ruminant animals have the unique ability to digest some of the structural carbohydrates located in the cell walls of plants.

Cellulose and hemicellulose are structural carbohydrates that may be digested by bacterial action in the rumen, but digestion is sharply reduced as lignin content increases. Lignin, indigestible in ruminant and non-ruminant animals, is low in legumes such as white clover and birdsfoot trefoil or immature small grains and ryegrass. Alfalfa, a high-quality legume at immature growth stages, declines rapidly in digestibility as stem lignin content increases with maturity. Warm season perennial grasses such as bermudagrass and switchgrass develop lignin rapidly as they mature, which reduces their digestibility. Highly lignified forages remain in the rumen for long periods of time because of their slow rate of digestion, thus decreasing dry matter intake and therefore markedly reducing animal performance.

Digestible energy is generally the most limiting nutritive factor affecting forage intake and animal performance. Animal production falls off rapidly, and weight loss may result when highly lignified, overly-mature warm season perennial grasses are consumed. Forage utilization and animal performance are dependent on digestibility and voluntary intake of the forage. Generally, there is a high correlation between digestibility and forage intake and between intake and animal performance.

Factors Affecting Forage Quality

1. Plant species

Cool season grasses are generally more digestible than warm season grasses. For instance, tall fescue forage is usually more digestible than Coastal bermudagrass. Furthermore, cool season annual species (annual ryegrass, oats, wheat, and rye) are more digestible than cool season perennial grasses (orchardgrass, tall fescue, or Kentucky bluegrass) at the same stage of maturity. There are also differences among species having similar seasonal distribution of growth, as evidenced by warm season grasses such as dallisgrass and johnsongrass, which are more digestible than bahiagrass, bermudagrass, or carpetgrass at the same stage of maturity.

Breeding work with bermudagrass has resulted in significant improvement in digestibility. For example, Tifton 85 bermudagrass is approximately 11 percent more digestible than Coastal bermudagrass. Since it is also 26 percent higher yielding than Coastal bermudagrass, it can greatly improve animal productivity (see **Table 27.1**).

Legumes such as alfalfa, clovers, and birdsfoot trefoil generally produce higher quality forage than grasses, and digestibility falls less rapidly with maturity than is the case with warm season perennial grasses. Legumes also generally contain higher levels of protein than grasses.

Plants can also contain unique compounds that have an adverse effect on forage quality. For example, tannins in some sericea lespedeza varieties reduce digestibility, intake, and animal performance. Fortunately, plant breeders have developed low-tannin varieties that result in improved animal performance. Likewise, the development of low-alkaloid varieties has improved animal performance on reed canarygrass.

2. Plant part

Forage quality varies within the canopy of a given forage species or forage mixture. Leaves are higher quality than stems, and young leaves are higher quality than older leaves. Similarly, stems in the upper canopy are higher quality than lower stems. Young green leaves are higher quality than dead leaves. Thus, an aim of pasture management should be to keep available forage in a leafy, highly nutritious state throughout the grazing season for higher animal performance.

Table 16.1. Seasonal change in in-vitro dry matter digestibility (IVDMD) and crude protein (CP) content of Apollo alfalfa pasture in central Georgia, two-year average. Pastures were sampled at the beginning of each two-week grazing period followed by four weeks of rest in a rotational system.

Month	IVDMD, %	CP, %
April	69	25
May	65	22
June	61	18
July	57	16

Adapted from: C.S. Hoveland, N.S. Hill, R.S. Lowrey, Jr., S.L. Fales, M.E. McCormick, and A.E. Smith. J. Prod. Agric. 1:343-346.

Some varieties have better quality forage as a result of selection for a higher leaf-to-stem ratio. Reducing leaf loss is important in hay harvest, especially with legumes. If hay is handled poorly and many of the leaves shatter, quality will suffer. Diseases or insects that reduce leaf percentage also lower hay quality.

3. Climate

Digestibility of warm season and cool season perennial species is highest in spring, falling to a low level in mid to late summer, and increasing in autumn. Even alfalfa under rotational stocking declines in digestibility and crude protein during hot summer weather (**Table 16.1**).

Though drought stress can present danger from nitrates or prussic acid in some situations (see Chapter 22), it otherwise has little effect on forage quality as long as the plants remain alive. Moderate stress may actually increase digestibility. Animal gains on drought-stressed forage are often above average as long as adequate quantities are available.

Table 16.2. Seasonal changes in forage tannin concentration of high- and low-tannin sericea varieties at Athens, Georgia, three-year average.

	Tannin content, %		
Variety	June	August	October
Appalow (high-tannin)	7.9	12.8	10.5
Serala (high-tannin)	8.0	11.6	9.5
AU Donnelly (low-tannin)	4.3	5.3	5.3
AU Lotan (low-tannin)	3.1	4.9	4.6

Adapted from: C.S. Hoveland, W.R. Windham, D.L. Boggs, R.G. Durham, G.V. Calvert, J.F. Newsome, J.W. Dobson, Jr., and M. Owsley. Georgia Agric. Exp. Stn. Res. Bull. 393.

Excess rainfall may increase the moisture content of forage, having no effect on digestibility. However, with species such as sorghum-sudan hybrids and pearl millet, it may result in reduced dry matter intake and animal performance. Excess rainfall may also reduce protein in grasses as a result of leaching nitrogen from the soil.

High temperature lowers digestibility by increasing lignification. Tannin content of sericea lespedeza also increases with high temperature, reducing intake and digestibility when grazed (**Table 16.2**). Tannin levels decline in sericea lespedeza harvested for hay.

4. Stage of maturity

Maturity usually has a greater effect on nutritive value than does any other factor. As plants mature, cell walls become more lignified and they constitute a larger proportion of the cell, resulting in an overall decrease in digestibility and CP content. This decline in quality with maturity is greater and more rapid in warm season than cool season grasses.

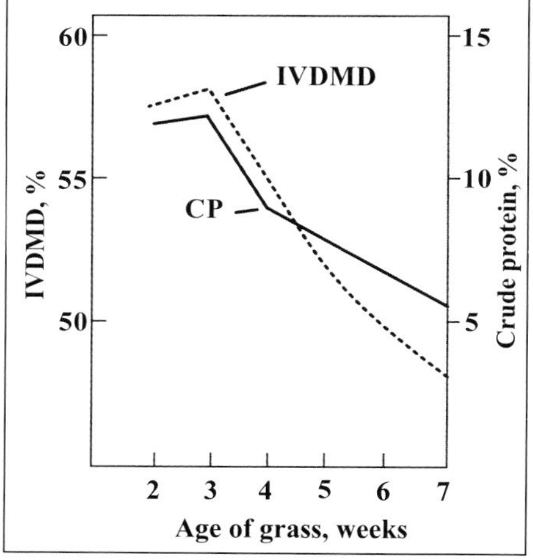

Figure 16.3. IVDMD and CP of Coastal bermudagrass as affected by plant maturity in south Georgia.
Source: W.G. Monson, USDA, Coastal Plain Exp. Stn., Tifton, Georgia.

As bermudagrass becomes more mature, yield increases, but digestibility and CP decline substantially (**Figure 16.3**). At seven weeks of age, forage quality can be very low, with digestibility below 50

Table 16.3. Changes in Kentucky 31 tall fescue forage CP and IVDMD as affected by stage of maturity at first spring harvest. Athens, Georgia. Three-year average.		
Maturity stage	CP, %	IVDMD, %
Pre-boot	19	72
Late boot	16	71
Early bloom	14	66
Seed dough	8	53

Source: C.S. Hoveland and N.S. Hill, University of Georgia.

percent and CP below 8 percent.

Cool season perennial grasses such as tall fescue also decline in nutritive quality with advancing maturity in spring (**Table 16.3**). While CP remains high until early bloom, it is low at dough stage (see **Appendices A.27** and **A.29**). Tall fescue hay cut at dough stage is just adequate in quality to supply the needs of a dry pregnant beef cow. Well-fertilized aftermath tall fescue harvested in summer can have CP and IVDMD values of 14 and 53 percent, respectively. Autumn-harvested tall fescue is of high quality with CP and IVDMD levels as much as 16 and 65 percent, respectively.

Immature grass may contain 65 percent soluble cell contents and 35 percent cell walls. However, at a mature stage, the same grass species may contain only 40 percent cell contents and 60 percent cell walls, of which 7 percent may be insoluble lignin. Crude protein content may decline from more than 20 percent at an immature stage to only 5 or 6 percent when mature.

Legume species likewise differ in digestibility as they mature. White clover, lacking true stems, maintains its high quality over time. Birdsfoot trefoil stems remain highly digestible as the plants mature. Alfalfa stems become lignified, and digestibility drops sharply after early bloom (**Table 16.4**). Among the annual clovers, arrowleaf stems remain more digestible than crimson as they mature.

5. Fertilization.

Up to a point, application of nitrogen fertilizer to grasses increases crude protein content, assuming other nutrients are not deficient. However, nitrogen generally has little effect on digestibility of young leaf material. Application of sulfur and calcium to deficient soils may enhance forage digestibility. This can occur because sulfur improves rumen fermentation, and calcium affects plant cell wall composition. Nutrients such as phosphorus, potassium, and magnesium are essential for animals and may need to be added by fertilization or supplementation (see **Appendix A.22**).

Table 16.4. Relationship of the stage of alfalfa maturity at harvest to total digestible nutrients (TDN), CP, and acid-detergent fiber (ADF).			
Maturity	TDN, %	CP, %	ADF, %
Pre-bud	65	21.7	28
Bud	62	19.9	31
1/10 bloom	58	17.2	34
1/2 bloom	56	16.0	38
Full bloom	54	15.0	40
Mature	52	13.6	42

Adapted from: Nutrient requirements of dairy cattle. Nat. Acad. Sci. Publ. 1349.

6. Diurnal fluctuations.

Soluble carbohydrate levels in forage vary, depending on the time of day. These highly digestible carbohydrates accumulate during daylight hours, but much of the accumulated material is used by the plant during the night. Therefore, levels are lowest in the morning and highest after a day of bright sunshine.

Hay cut in the afternoon is somewhat higher in quality than morning-cut hay. This may have practical use for improving quality of irrigated hay harvested in dry climates or for haylage and balage in humid areas. However, afternoon harvests may not be advisable in high rainfall areas where every hour of good drying time is needed to cure hay.

7. Other

In humid regions such as the southeastern U.S., rain is a major concern when making hay. Rain during field drying damages legume hay more than grass hay. Also, the drier the hay when rain occurs, the greater the damage. However, delayed harvest due to concern about rain often results in more forage quality loss than does rain damage.

Major losses in forage quality often occur due to poor storage and feeding techniques (see Chapter 19). Producing stored forage with good nutritive value is not enough; good animal performance results when animals consume forage that is suitably high in nutrients and low in fiber.

Methods of Measuring Forage Quality

Laboratory evaluation of forages is an attempt to predict the extent and rate of biological degradation that will occur in the consuming animal. The objective is to be able to formulate diets from compositional information that will result in predictable animal response.

Neutral-detergent fiber (NDF) and acid-detergent fiber (ADF). These methods chemically distinguish the readily available, soluble cell contents from the less digestible cell walls. Neutral-detergent fiber represents all cell wall material, while ADF is a measure of only the lignified or otherwise undigestible portions. Neutral-detergent fiber values are negatively correlated with forage voluntary intake by the animal, while ADF (NDF less the hemicellulose component) is negatively correlated with digestibility (see **Appendix A.27**). Fiber values are often used in equations to calculate energy as total digestible nutrients (TDN).

In-vitro fermentation. In this procedure, forage is digested in rumen fluid, followed by treatment with acid pepsin to simulate the digestive process in the ruminant animal. Results from this procedure give a good approximation of digestibility expressed as in-vitro digestible dry matter (IVDMD).

Near infrared reflectance spectroscopy (NIRS). This rapid, reliable instrument technique is based on the amount of light reflected from, or transmitted through, a finely ground forage sample. The desired quality constituents (CP, NDF, ADF, IVDMD) are not measured directly by instru-

Table 16.5. TDN, IVDMD, CP, NDF, and ADF of four perennial grasses.[1]						
	Age at harvest,	%				
Grass	weeks	TDN	IVDMD	CP	NDF	ADF
Coastal bermudagrass	4	55	62	13	58	29
Coastal bermudagrass	8	49	47	8	65	40
Tall fescue	4	66	63	14	58	31
Orchardgrass	4	66	62	15	58	33
Timothy	4	67	67	13	56	35

[1]Bermudagrass was grown in Georgia, the other grasses in Kentucky. All were harvested as regrowth in summer after an initial spring cutting.
Source: W.R. Windham, USDA Russell Research Center, Athens, Georgia.

mentation, but rather from prediction equations developed from calibration samples analyzed by traditional chemical methods. This approach is commonly used by laboratories that serve livestock producers. A comparison of the different forage quality measurements of several important perennial grasses is shown in **Table 16.5**. When comparing grass species, it is important that they be harvested at the same stage of maturity or age.

Relative feed value (RFV). In recent years, ADF and NDF values have been useful in developing a relatively simple index to evaluate and compare forages. This index, called the RFV, is a prediction of the rate of intake and energy value of a particular forage. Relative feed value compares or ranks forages according to their digestible dry matter (DDM) and potential dry matter intake (DMI). It is calculated by DDM x DMI divided by a constant. Relative feed value is expressed as percent compared to full bloom alfalfa that has an RFV of 100. The RFV increases as forage quality increases

Table 16.6. Quality standards for legume, grass, or grass-legume hay.						
Quality standard	CP	ADF	NDF	DDM	DMI	RFV
	- - - - - - - - - -	- - - - - - - - - -	- - - - - - %	- - - - - - - - - -	- - - - - - - - - -	- - - - - - - -
Prime	>19	<31	<40	>65	>3.0	>151
1	17-19	31-35	40-46	62-65	3.0-2.6	151-125
2	14-16	36-40	47-53	58-61	2.5-2.3	124-103
3	11-13	41-42	54-60	56-57	2.2-2.0	102-87
4	8-10	43-45	61-65	53-55	1.9-1.8	86-75
5	<8	>45	>65	<53	<1.8	<75

% DDM = 88.9-0.779 ADF (% DM).
DMI = 120/forage NDF (% DM).
RFV calculated from (DDM x DMI)/1.29.
Reference hay of 100 RFV contains 41% ADF and 53% NDF.
Source: Hay Market Task Force, American Forage and Grassland Council.

(**Table 16.6**).

Digestible dry matter values used to calculate RFV are a percentage estimate of the portion of a feed or forage that is digestible. This is usually estimated from ADF values, but may be based on animal feeding trials. Different equations are used with ADF values obtained for grasses and legumes, and sometimes for different regions of the U.S.

Dry matter intake values used to calculate RFV are estimates of the relative amount of forage an animal will eat. The DMI may be based on animal feeding trials, but usually is a calculation based on NDF values. As with DDM, different equations are used with different categories of forage.

In states where hay auctions are held, RFV has influenced hay prices more than any other factor in recent years. More and more producers are becoming oriented toward this term, which allows a comparison of the feed value of various lots and/or types of hay.

Relative feed value is a good predictor of the ability of a forage to supply nutrients to livestock. The ADF and NDF values are important in determining the RFV of a forage. Acid-detergent fiber values are used to calculate DDM; the lower the ADF, the higher the DDM. Dry matter intake is calculated using NDF values, and a low NDF results in high DMI.

While this system using RFV may seem confusing, it is just another way to numerically express a comparison of different forages. The same principles known for many years still apply: Forage quality is best when fiber levels are low and digestibility is high. Furthermore, high intake by animals is indicative of high forage quality. High protein levels are desirable, but protein is not used in calculating RFV.

Relative feed value is a one-number estimate of the energy value of a forage, haylage, or silage. The RFV of mature (three-fourths to full bloom) alfalfa is equal to 100. A forage with an RFV of 125 has 25 percent more energy than mature alfalfa. Likewise, an RFV of 75 means a forage has 75 percent of the energy of mature alfalfa.

Relative feed value is not intended to be used to balance diets. Calculated energy (obtained from fiber values) and protein values will continue to be used for that purpose. However, RFV is of value in pricing hay because it provides a relative estimate of the feed value (with regard to energy). The RFV is normally used to compare lots of hay of the same species, or at least of a similar type (for example, two legume hays).

Using Forage Quality Information

It is not necessary to understand how forage quality is measured in a laboratory, but some understanding of how forage quality affects animals is a fundamental requirement for obtaining good animal performance (see Chapter 17). A diagram that illustrates feed and forage components is provided in **Appendix A.26.** A livestock producer needs to be aware of the major influences on forage quality, such as stage of maturity, plant species, and variety influences. It is the total quantity of available nutrients in a given amount of forage, not the total quantity of forage, that is of primary importance in obtaining good animal performance. SF

Nutrient Requirements of Livestock

Ruminants have the unique ability to consume large quantities of forage and convert the fiber components (cellulose and hemicellulose) into useable forms of energy. Energy constitutes the largest nutrient requirement for ruminant livestock and is supplied by pastures, hay, silage, and sometimes grain. The most limiting factor in forage quality is digestible energy. Digestible energy is generally lower in perennial warm season grasses than in cool season grasses and declines as plants become more mature (see Chapter 16).

All animals need a certain amount of protein in their daily diet. Energy requirements, which are more likely to be the primary concern on most livestock farms in the South, are higher for lactating and growing animals than for mature ones. Most essential minerals are adequately supplied in forages. Calcium and phosphorus supplements may be needed when animals are consuming low-quality hay or grazing frosted warm season perennial grasses in winter.

Nutrient requirements of ruminant animals differ greatly, depending on class of livestock, weight, and desired daily production. The TDN and CP requirements of several livestock classes are illustrated in **Table 17.1.** Forage species differ considerably in their digestibility and suitability as energy sources for different classes of cattle (**Figure 17.1**). For each category of forage species there is a range in digestibility that reflects variations caused by stage of maturity and season of the year. Good pasture management is necessary to keep nutritive quality at the upper end of this range for best animal performance.

Table 17.1. Total digestible nutrients (TDN) and crude protein (CP) requirements of selected animal classes.

Animal class	TDN, %	CP, %
Growing beef steer		
450 lb (1.5 lb/day gain)	65	11-13
650 lb (1.7 lb/day gain)	68	10-11
Beef cow		
Lactating	60	10-12
Dry, pregnant	50	7-8
Sheep		
Lamb (finishing)	70	12
Ewe (lactating)	65	13
Ewe (maintenance)	55	9
Fallow deer		
Doe (lactating)	66	14-16
Growing buck	60-64	12-14
Meat-type goat		
Doe (lactating)	62	14
Growing buck	65	14
Horse (maintenance)	70	10-11

Source: M.A. McCann, Virginia Tech University.

Growing Animals

Growing animals such as steers or lambs have high requirements that can be met by small grains, annual ryegrass, or cool season perennial grasses such as orchardgrass, Kentucky bluegrass, and novel endophyte or endophyte-free tall fescue (see Chapter 27). Clovers, alfalfa, or birdsfoot trefoil companion crops can sometimes be used to enhance animal gain on perennial grasses. Warm season perennial grasses such as bahiagrass

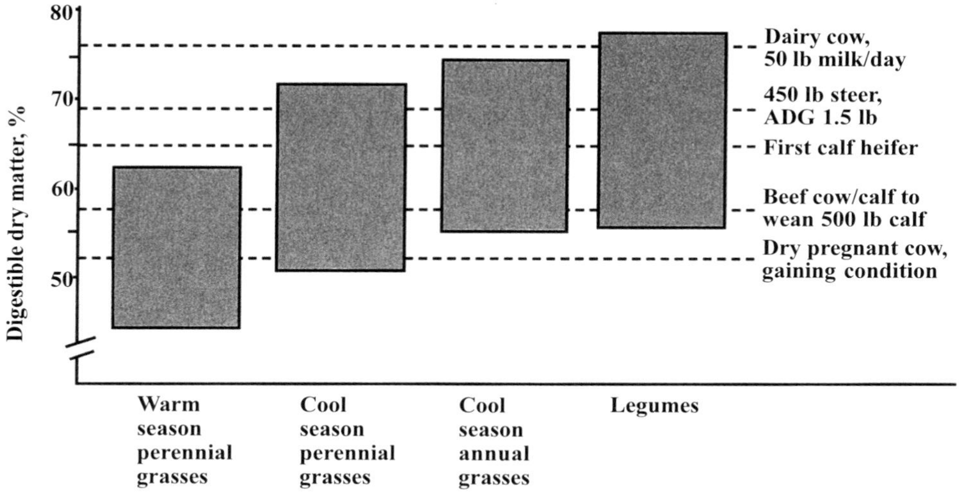

Figure 17.1. Forage digestibility ranges and their suitability for different classes of livestock (ADG = average daily gain).
Adapted from: H. Lippke and M.E. Riewe. Texas Agric. Exp. Stan. Res. Monograph RM6C: 169-206.

or bermudagrass lack the quality for high gains and are usually unsatisfactory for profitable grazing of beef steers, lambs, and deer. Warm season perennial grass pastures can provide satisfactory gains for short periods of time in late spring and early summer if closely grazed to maintain a high leaf percentage, but animal performance declines sharply as the season progresses.

Beef Cows and Calves

Most growing pastures of warm season or cool season perennial grasses in the South will adequately supply the needs of a dry beef cow (see Chapter 26). However, after killing frosts, the quality of bermudagrass and bahiagrass declines rapidly, especially with heavy rainfall. Protein needs of dry pregnant beef cows are low, but protein supplements must be fed on frosted warm season grass pastures for adequate nutrition. Protein supplementation may also cause cattle to consume more of this type grass and utilize it more efficiently.

After calving, nutrient requirements of beef cows increase markedly for rebreeding and providing milk for calves. Until a calf is about three months old, it is mostly dependent on its mother for food. If calving occurs during January and February when perennial grass pasture growth is very limited, it is important to provide good quality hay (**Figure 17.2**). Mineral supplements are also necessary at this time. Lactating ewes have higher energy and protein requirements than beef cows, so it becomes even more important to have high quality pasture and/or stored feed for good lamb growth.

Winter-born calves begin to consume significant amounts of forage in spring when pasture quantity and quality are high. Pasture quality normally

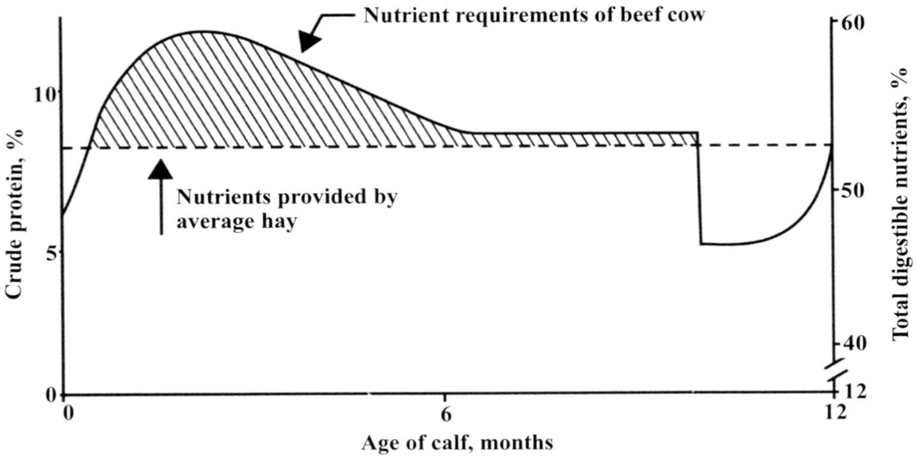

Figure 17.2. Average quality grass hay cannot supply nutrient requirements of a beef cow for rebreeding and providing milk for the calf.
Source: M.A. McCann, Animal Science Dept., Virginia Tech.

is lower in summer when cow milk production declines and the intake demands of calves are increasing. Overseeding pastures with legumes can improve forage quality and increase calf weaning weights. Creep feeding of grain to calves on pasture may increase weaning weights, but is only profitable in times of low grain prices and/or high calf prices.

At high stocking rates, creep grazing of beef calves can efficiently increase weaning weights. For autumn-born calves in the lower South, planting cool season annuals on prepared seedbeds and stocking at up to 10 calves per acre has been efficient. For spring-born calves, simply allowing calves creep access to the next pasture ahead of their mothers in a rotational stocking method can efficiently increase weaning weights (see Chapter 25).

Replacement Heifers

Replacement heifers require special nutritional consideration. If heifers are bred to calve first as 2-year olds, they should be fed good forage or grain during the first and second winters, similar to that of growing steers. Nutrients must be adequate for continued body growth, development of the fetus as well as the mammary system for feeding the new calf, and rebreeding. Ideally, high-quality winter annual or cool season perennial grass pastures can be used to meet the nutrient needs of this class of animal. If grass hay is fed, it will generally need to be supplemented with protein and minerals. It is important that replacement heifers grow adequately but not fatten. Allowing heifers to become fat prior to calving is expensive and may cause calving problems.

Controlled Breeding Season

A controlled breeding season is essential in matching animal nutrient requirements to available pasture forage and reducing supplemental feeding.

Generally, this is most easily accomplished with autumn or winter calving in the lower South, winter calving in the mid South, and early spring calving in the upper South. A controlled breeding season generally results in lower calf death losses, heavier weaning weights, and more efficient utilization of labor and resources.

Finishing

Although high quality forage will give good animal performance, grain feeding is needed to achieve maximum liveweight gain. However, since forage is a lower cost source of nutrients, it is usually more profitable to utilize high quality pasture rather than grain to put on as much muscle and frame as possible. When steers begin to fatten rather than grow (for British breed steers, between 800 and 1,000 lb), their requirements for digestible energy increase and cannot be met by warm season grasses. At this point, grain feeding is needed to achieve adequate finish in a reasonable time.

Grain feeding on high quality annual ryegrass, rye, or wheat pasture is usually not profitable. Higher stocking rates are possible with grain feeding, but there is little or no increase in individual gains as animals generally substitute grain for high quality pasture. While steers and heifers can be finished on cool season grass and clover pastures, they are usually only marginally fat and carcass fat is yellow. As a result, they will be discriminated against in price at slaughter. Therefore, it is typical in the U.S. for cattle to be fed on concentrated diets for at least 60 days and usually 120 to 140 days prior to slaughter.

Dairy Cows

Lactating dairy cows require large quantities of high-quality feed, including some grain, to achieve optimum production per cow. High-quality forages, such as alfalfa and corn for silage, are important for high milk production. During certain periods of the year, some forages produce enough high quality forage to meet most of the demand for high levels of milk production by dairy cows. Dairy producers must also utilize stored feed of known quality to provide a diet to maintain lactation at a high level. High quality alfalfa hay or haylage and corn silage with grain supplements have been commonly used for dairy production (see Chapter 28).

Deer Farming

The fixed breeding season of most deer species means that fawns are born during June, and lactation continues until weaning in September. The nutrient requirements to sustain lactation and provide rapid growth of fawns during this period are high, about double those needed in winter. High-quality alfalfa, clover, or chicory pasture can reduce supplemental grain feeding costs (see Chapter 30).

Summary

For efficient and economical production, forage quality must be matched to the nutrient requirements of the class of animal being fed. Grazing beef cows with calves on expensive cool season annual pasture is inefficient unless they are limit-grazed (for example, two or three hours per day for three to seven days per week). Grazing beef steers on low quality pasture is unprofitable as it will result in low daily gains even though available forage and stocking rates are high.

Forage quality and quantity of pasture vary greatly during the year. The length of the growing season on adapted forage species differs considerably from the lower to the upper South. The nutritive requirements of animals in each area can be met by utilizing a controlled breeding season to match quality and quantity of forage, supplemental feeding, and utilizing pasture legumes whenever feasible. SF

When pasture growth is scarce, it is necessary to provide some type of stored feed for grazing animals. Hay offers a number of advantages: It can largely be mechanized; it stores well when adequately protected; and it can meet the nutritional requirements of most classes of livestock.

Hay fits well with a grazing program because accumulated forage can be cut for hay during periods of excess growth, thus minimizing waste. Harvesting excess growth also results in the subsequent production of young, tender forage regrowth for later grazing.

Hay Crop Selection

The first step in hay production is deciding what forage species to plant. This decision is obviously limited to those species adapted to the location. Other considerations should include nutritional needs of the animals consuming the hay, the relative quality of hay that can be produced from various adapted species, probable hay yield, and cost of establishment and maintenance of each of the crops that could be grown. The information presented in **Table 18.1** provides a basis for comparison of some species that can be grown for hay.

It is generally more economical to produce hay from perennials than from annuals due to avoidance of annual establishment costs. This is especially true when producing hay for animals that have relatively low nutritional requirements. Growing a legume/grass mixture for hay production will generally improve hay quality as compared to using grass alone.

When considering the economics of hay production, it is important to realize that a large proportion (usually 30 to 40 percent) of the expenses involved are fixed costs. These are costs that will be essentially the same regardless of other factors. This provides incentive for striving for both high yield and high quality. If a livestock producer is going to expend time, energy, and money in producing hay, it is worthwhile to make it an efficient operation in which high production and excellent quality hay are obtained.

Producing the Forage

Perennial hayfields are normally in use for many years, and a poor start may have a negative impact for years to come. The goal should be a thick, vigorous stand of an adapted, productive forage variety. To achieve this, it is necessary to plant an adequate quantity of high quality, weed-free seed or vegetative material of an adapted variety. Recommended establishment practices as discussed in Chapters 11 and 12 should be followed.

Yield is important in obtaining economical hay production, so it is essential to lime and fertilize hayfields according to soil test recommendations. Weeds and insects should be controlled with management and/or pesticides as appropriate.

Some livestock producers do not fully understand what they should be

Table 18.1. Approximate hay yield, crude protein (CP), and total digestible nutrients (TDN) content of various hay crops.

Type of hay crop	Annual or perennial	Usual hay yield, tons/A[1]	Approximate usual nutrient level[2] CP, %	TDN, %
Cool season				
Alfalfa (early bloom)	P	3-6	17-22	57-62
Arrowleaf clover	A	2-3	14-17	56-61
Birdsfoot trefoil	P	1-3	16-20	57-62
Oats	A	1-4	8-10	55-60
Orchardgrass	P	2-5	12-15	55-60
Red clover	P	2-4	14-16	57-62
Rye	A	1-4	8-10	50-55
Annual ryegrass	A	1-4	10-16	56-62
Smooth bromegrass	P	2-4	12-15	55-60
Soybean	A	2-3[3]	15-18	54-58
Tall fescue	P	2-5	10-15	55-60
Warm season				
Annual lespedeza	A	1-2	14-17	52-58
Bahiagrass	P	3-5	9-11	50-56
Browntop millet	A	1-2	9-12	55-60
Coastal bermudagrass (four wks)	P	5-8	10-14	55-60
Common bermudagrass	P	2-6	9-11	50-56
Dallisgrass	P	2-4	9-12	55-60
Foxtail millet	A	2-3	9-12	55-60
Johnsongrass	P	2-5	10-14	55-60
Pearl millet	A	2-6	8-12	50-58
Sericea lespedeza	P	1-3	14-17	50-55
Sudangrass	A	2-6	9-12	55-60

[1]Assuming the crop is grown in an area to which it is adapted, using recommended production and harvesting practices.
[2]Dry matter basis, assuming recommended production and harvesting practices and no excessive weather damage. See Chapter 16 for more about forage quality.
[3]Higher yields are possible with new forage varieties.

striving for when producing hay. On many farms, the emphasis is generally on the quantity of hay produced per acre. The most important consideration, however, is not the quantity of hay produced, but rather the quantity of available and digestible nutrients stored and the level of animal performance that will result from feeding the hay.

The two most important criteria used in evaluating hay quality are the CP content and the energy value (see Chapters 16 and 17). Though both are important, low digestible energy is usually the main limiting factor in Southern livestock rations. Therefore, the emphasis with regard to forage quality of hay should generally be on improving the digestible or available energy value.

Factors that can influence hay quality include: plant species, plant variety, weeds, insect damage, diseases, weather at harvest, and harvesting techniques. However, once a hayfield has been established, hay quality is most likely to be affected by two other factors, both of which are under the control of the producer: 1) fertilization and 2) stage of maturity at harvest.

Nitrogen fertilization will, up to a point, increase the protein content of grass hay. Fertilization with other nutrients such as phosphorus, potassium, magnesium, and sulfur, may also influence the amounts of these elements that are present in forage as well as other quality factors.

Periodic soil testing followed by applying the recommended nutrients will allow the levels of specific nutrients in forage tissue to be adequate for animals. Fertilization may also improve hay palatability to animals and thus influence animal performance by increasing intake. Although important in obtaining good hay yields, fertilization normally has little or no influence on the energy level of hay.

The single most important producer-controlled factor influencing hay quality is stage of maturity at harvest. This is where many livestock producers can most easily and dramatically improve hay quality.

The stage of maturity at harvest influences the palatability, CP content, and especially the digestible energy level. In general, the best time to harvest for a good yield as well as high energy and CP levels is in the bud to early bloom stage for legumes and in the boot stage (just before seedhead emergence) for grasses. Exceptions to this rule are: sericea lespedeza–15 to 18 inches; summer annual grasses–30 to 40 inches; and hybrid bermudagrass–four to five week intervals or 15 to 18 inches. Forage quality deteriorates rapidly with advancing maturity, even though yield will continue to increase. Advice regarding specific times to cut various forages is provided in **Table 18.2.**

If a producer waits until past the recommended stage to cut hay, the fiber content increases, and palatability and digestibility decline. Waiting until later will increase the number of bales or tons of hay produced, but nutritive value decreases.

In addition to requiring more fuel, time and labor to store the hay, the further past the optimum stage that hay is harvested, the poorer animal performance will be because of low digestible energy and high fiber. Poor quality hay passes more slowly through the animal digestive system, causing lower intake of low quality hay, which further reduces animal performance.

Thousands of tons of hay have been harvested too late or rain damaged because of equipment problems. Before beginning the harvesting process, all hay equipment should be checked and serviced. This should include sharpening blades, checking belts, and lubrication.

Some hay crops require that a particular stubble height be left. For example, sudangrass, sorghum-sudan hybrids, and pearl millet should not be cut lower than 6 to 8 inches. Sericea lespedeza should not be cut lower than about 4 inches.

Hay should normally be cut when the dew has dried off the forage. It is important that the mower be set to cut forage at the proper height. The travel speed of the tractor should be slow enough that all the forage is cut

Plant species	Time of harvest
Alfalfa	Bud stage for first cutting, one-tenth bloom for second and later cuttings. For spring seedings, allow the first cutting to reach mid-bloom.
Orchardgrass, timothy, or tall fescue	Boot to early head stage for first cut, aftermath cuts at four to six week intervals.
Red, arrowleaf, or crimson clovers	Early bloom.
Sericea lespedeza	Height of 15 to 18 inches.
Oats, barley or wheat	Boot to early head stage.
Soybean	When pods are about half-filled and before bottom leaves begin to fall.
Annual lespedeza	Early bloom and before bottom leaves begin to fall.
White (or ladino) clover	Cut at correct stage for companion grass.
Hybrid bermudagrass	15 to 18-inch height for first cutting, then every four to five weeks or when 15 inches high.
Birdsfoot trefoil	Bud to early bloom or at correct stage for companion grass.
Sudangrass, sorghum-sudan hybrids, pearl millet	Height of 30 to 40 inches.

Table 18.2. Recommended stages to harvest various hay crops.[1]

[1]Adapted from: J.D. Burns, J.K. Evans, and G.D. Lacefield, Quality Hay Production, Southern Regional Beef Cow Calf Handbook, SR 5004. (See Appendix A.29).

cleanly and evenly. Periodic adjustments in speed may be necessary due to variability in stand thickness.

Many producers use mower/conditioners or have hay conditioners (or crimpers) that are used separately from mowers. Conditioners can reduce drying time by as much as 50 percent. They are essential for legumes and thick-stemmed grasses such as pearl millet and sorghum-sudan hybrids.

Respiration refers to the breakdown of food materials within plants. This process, which occurs in all living plants, continues at a substantial rate after forage plants are cut and does not decline greatly until the moisture content drops to below about 40 percent. Respiration can result in dry matter losses of 2 to 16 percent, depending on the situation. When drying conditions are good, respiration losses are minimized; when drying conditions are poor, respiration losses may be high.

Rain can damage hay in several ways. It leaches soluble nutrients and keeps the moisture level high, thus prolonging the period of high respiration loss and increasing the likelihood of mold.

Rain during field drying damages legume hay more than grass hay. Also, the drier the hay when rain occurs, the greater the damage. However, delayed harvest due to concern about rain usually results in more forage quality loss than does rain damage.

By crushing plant stems, a conditioner causes moisture levels to drop much more quickly to the 40 percent level at which respiration losses are greatly reduced. An additional benefit is that when hay dries more quickly, the likelihood of rain damage is reduced because the hay can be baled sooner.

Leaf losses are often high with legumes such as alfalfa, sericea lespedeza, and red clover. When legume hays are raked or tedded at low moisture levels, leaf losses of 5, 10, and 20 percent may occur at moisture levels of 50, 35, and 20 percent, respectively. Therefore, it is advisable to complete raking before legume hays fall below 40 percent moisture.

The usual moisture range for raking should be around 45 to 55 percent. To reduce leaf loss, hay should be raked in the same direction as it was mowed. It may be desirable to rake legume hay early in the morning before the dew has dried in order to minimize leaf shatter.

Raking should be done with great care because this is the greatest source of leaf loss during harvest. Windrows should not be too thick because this reduces the amount of hay exposed to the air. Narrow, thick windrows will not dry as rapidly as wide, thin ones. Also, hay dries more quickly in a swath than in a windrow.

Hay drying may also be speeded with commercial hay drying agents (dessicants), the active ingredient of which is usually potassium carbonate. Such products are normally applied with a spray boom mounted just ahead of the mower with a deflection bar in front of the boom. The bar bends the plants over and allows good spray coverage. Dessicants break down the waxy coating on the stems of certain legume hay crops, principally alfalfa, and can be of benefit on some farms.

Baling Hay

Baling should be done in the same direction as mowing and raking. Baling should progress at a slow enough speed that the hay will be cleanly and evenly fed into the baler. It is important to keep the density, size, and shape of bales relatively constant as this aids in storage and handling.

Leaf losses can also be high during baling operations, ranging from 1 to 15 percent. One way to reduce leaf loss at baling is to spray an organic acid (propionic acid is most commonly used) on the hay to inhibit microorganism growth, thus allowing baling at moisture levels up to 30 percent rather than the 15 to 20 percent range normally required for safe storage without mold damage.

Baling losses with conventional balers (producing small rectangular bales) are typically 3 to 8 percent, while baling losses with large round balers can vary from 5 to over 15 percent. Thus, the potential baling loss is greater with large round balers, but a skillful operator may keep such losses as low or lower than would be obtained with a conventional baler.

It should be emphasized that these figures do not account for storage or

A skillful operator can keep baling losses low with large package hay equipment.

feeding losses (see Chapter 19). Round bales stored outside may have a high spoilage loss, while hay stored inside should have virtually no storage loss. Feeding losses also tend to be much higher with round bales than with square or rectangular bales.

Forage Testing

The best way to determine the nutrient content of hay is to have a sample analyzed at a testing facility (see Chapter 16). To obtain accurate results from such tests, a good representative sample must be obtained. The best means of getting a good sample for testing is with a core sampler. At least 20 cores should be taken for each sample submitted for analysis. Once the results of a test are obtained and the quality of a lot of hay is known, that information can be used in effectively formulating diets for livestock.

Hay Storage and Feeding

Many of the factors important in storing and feeding hay are common sense. Nonetheless, much hay is wasted. Losses are often much more than a producer might think. Those resulting from improper storage and poor feeding practices are particularly objectionable because the expense of producing the hay has already been incurred.

Storage

Small rectangular bales of hay should be protected from the elements. Otherwise, weathering losses will be high because of the relatively high level of exposed surface area. Though it is best to store rectangular bales inside, stacks can be stored outside and covered with plastic or a tarpaulin. However, with time, wind may partially or totally uncover the hay. Also, moisture often condenses under the cover at the top of the hay stack, particularly with plastic, resulting in spoilage.

Large round bales and stack systems are popular storage options. One of the selling points for large package balers is that the bales can be stored outside. However, in many cases, this may be unwise.

Some round balers produce bales that sustain less weathering damage during outside storage than do other balers. Some balers compress hay more, resulting in a denser bale that sheds water better. In addition, the larger the bale diameter (other things being equal), the less total hay loss from weathering (see **Appendix A.36**).

While increased bale density reduces spoilage by reducing moisture penetration, it also reduces the rate at which moisture and heat can escape from a bale. Thus, as density increases, it becomes increasingly important to make certain that hay is in a safe moisture range for baling. Unfortunately, leaf shatter from legume hays also increases with decreasing hay moisture levels.

Great differences can occur in the amount of hay wasted during feeding, depending on management.

Large-stemmed grasses, such as pearl millet or sorghum-sudangrass hybrids, and crop residues do not form a tight bale and are easily penetrated by water. In addition, high quality hays such as alfalfa are so valuable that even a relatively small percentage of spoilage is costly and should not be tolerated.

Furthermore, legume hays stored outside sustain more damage than most grass hays. With such hay, it is usually best to minimize losses by storing it inside. If this cannot be done, such high risk or high quality hay should be fed early in the season to minimize losses.

Inside storage is best, regardless of the type of hay package. Research has shown that in humid climates such as the Southern U.S., it is common for 30 percent or more of the dry matter of hay to be lost during several months of outside storage. Lower forage quality and higher feeding losses associated with weathered hay further increase the cost of this practice.

The amount of loss incurred with outside storage varies greatly, depending on factors such as the type of hay, bale density, rainfall, humidity, length of the storage period, and storage conditions. However, as a study in Louisiana showed, losses related to storage can be extremely high (**Table 19.1**). Many producers could easily and quickly pay for building a hay barn through savings realized by reducing outside storage losses (see **Appendix A.35**).

Once hay is protected from the elements, it loses little nutritional value even if it is stored for several years. However, it will change color and become visually less attractive. Sometimes it is not feasible to store large packages of hay inside. In such cases, round balers should normally be used only for putting up types of hay that form a tight bale that readily sheds water (grass or grass/ legume).

When large round bales or hay stacks are to be stored outside, selection of a storage site is an important consideration. A hay stackyard should be located in an open, well-drained, sunny location convenient to feeding areas. It is particularly important to select a well-drained spot.

Much of the spoilage in large hay packages stored outside typically results from moisture being absorbed from the ground rather than penetrating from the top. Thus, it is desirable to reduce or eliminate hay/soil contact if possible. This can be done by storing bales on railroad ties, crushed rock, or a concrete pad.

Table 19.1. Effect of various storage methods on hay losses.

Storage method	Losses: Handling and storage	Losses: Animal refusal
On the ground	43	66
On gravel	32	49
On tires	37	43
On a wooden rack	31	38
On a wooden rack with plastic cover	12	14
In a pole barn	2	3

Source: B.D. Nelson, L.R. Verma, and C.R. Montgomery. Effect of storage method on losses and quality changes in round bales of ryegrass and alfalfa hay. Louisiana. Ag. Expt. Sta. Bull. 750.

Large bales or stacks should be promptly moved to a storage site to prevent killing spots of grass in the hayfield. It is best to leave a space of about 3 feet between bales to allow good drying after rains. Storing hay bales end-to-end (flat sides together) is acceptable, but storing them with the rounded sides touching is not advisable due to the creation of a site where moisture can accumulate.

If placed on a hill, rows of bales should run up and down the slope so they do not act as a dam for surface water. Stacking round bales on top of each other is an undesirable practice unless the stack is to be covered. There may be some benefit to storing bales with the flat sides facing north and south. Theoretically, this allows sunshine to help keep the bales dry a higher percentage of the time.

Large round bales should not be stored near wire fences or other objects that may attract lightning. Storing hay in more than one location will further minimize fire loss risk. Also, a road next to a stackyard may serve as a firebreak. Grouping hays of similar quality together in individual stack-yards can facilitate efficient feeding.

It is advisable to have more hay on hand than one expects to feed. Winters that are longer than expected or summer droughts can increase the amount of hay needed and often cause severe problems for producers who are not prepared. The minimum length of the winter feeding period varies depending on location, pasture species available, and weather. For a live-stock producer in Zone A who plants winter annuals in early autumn, the winter feeding period could be less than 30 days; on the other hand, it may be more than 120 days in Zone D.

A dry beef cow will consume at least 15 lb of hay per day while a lactating cow may consume 25 to 30 lb or more per day. A rule of thumb is that ruminants will usually consume 2.5 to 3 percent of their body weight in dry matter per day, horses 1 to 2 percent. By using these figures, one can calculate the approximate quantity of hay that should be needed to overwin-ter a group of animals and still have enough left over for emergency needs (see Chapter 26 and **Appendix A.44**).

Heating and Fire Hazard

Hay baled at too high a moisture level will heat. In addition to causing reduced digestibility of protein and hemicellulose, the hay may catch on fire. Because of the possibility of fire, fresh green hay should never be stored tightly against older, dry hay.

Hay temperature can be monitored by making a probe out of a 10-foot piece of 2-inch diameter pipe on which one end has been sealed with a sharpened plug. The pipe can then be driven into a stack or large bale of hay followed by lowering a thermometer into the pipe. Readings should be taken at several locations and depths, leaving the thermometer at each location for 10 to 15 minutes. When hay temperatures remain below 120°F, it is consid-ered safe; between 120 to 140°F is considered a caution zone, and the hay should be closely watched. If the temperature goes above 160°F, a fire is likely (see **Appendix A.33**).

Hay that is heating to an unacceptable, dangerous level should be moved to a spot where fire will not destroy anything except the hay. The danger of fire will generally subside within two to three weeks.

Feeding

Feeding losses occur mainly from trampling, refusal, and leaf shatter. Some feeding loss is inevitable, but it can vary from as little as 2 or 3 percent to well over 50 percent. Since hay production is a major expense in most livestock operations, a goal should be to develop a grazing program that minimizes the need for hay, and a feeding system that minimizes hay losses (see Chapter 21).

Prior to the introduction of equipment that packages hay in large bales, the traditional method of feeding, although labor intensive, was to feed rectangular bales in a manger or bunk or to transport them to a sod area for feeding. When only a one-day supply of hay is offered at a time, feeding losses are minimal.

Some balers produce small, round bales that may be left in the field and fed in place. This system works fairly well, but only if feeding losses are minimized by allowing the animals access to only a few days' supply at a time. Otherwise, feeding losses will likely be high.

The first rule of feeding hay is to prevent unlimited access, thus reducing losses. This can be accomplished by moving one or a few bales at a time from the stackyard to an area where they will be fed. Use of feeding racks or panels can also greatly reduce losses (**Table 19.2**).

The losses from feeding hay as round bales and as loose stacks were compared in east Texas[1]. In this work, 20 cow-calf units and a bull were group-fed baled hay or stacked hay. Cattle in the stack hay group were allowed access to one stack at a time. Baled hay was fed on the ground, and

[1] F.M. Rouquette, Jr., and N.K. Person. Texas Research Monograph RM6C, Texas Agric. Exp. Stn.

Table 19.2. Effect of feeding systems on losses of johnsongrass hay and on steer performance.

Item	Conventional bales on sod	Round bales on sod	Round bales with panels
Hay fed, lb/day	9.1	19.1	12.3
Days on test	79	79	79
Initial wt. (lb)	535	538	538
Final wt. (lb)	615	635	646
Gain/animal (lb)	80	97	108
Average daily gain (lb)	1.0	1.2	1.4
Lb hay required/lb of gain	9.0	15.6	9.0

Adapted from: W.B. Anthony, E.S. Renoll, and J.L. Stallings. Alabama Agric. Exp. Stn. Cir. 216.

Storing round bales of large-stemmed or high value hay under shelter can save money.

the number of bales fed was adjusted so that consumption was completed in a two-day period. Waste from the baled hay groups was approximately 3 percent. Hay waste from the stack hay group ranged from 18 to 25 percent. When stacks were enclosed by stack guard panels, hay losses were less than 5 percent. However, it is important to note that labor and fixed costs associated with protecting hay may partially offset the losses to waste.

Other methods of limiting animal access such as an electric wire or a gate may also be helpful. In order to minimize losses, access of the animals to the hay must be limited. In situations in which there is no feeding rack, panel, or other restrictive device, it is important to feed only as much hay as the animals can eat in one or two days. A rule of thumb is to provide one foot of access per cow to large hay packages being fed without feeding racks or panels.

If hay is fed on sod, the feeding areas should be rotated. This minimizes soil compaction and sod kill and results in dung and urine being more evenly distributed. Therefore, it is desirable to select less fertile fields or areas when feeding on sod.

There is less refusal and waste when high quality hay is fed, thus further emphasizing the importance of striving for high hay quality. An approach used by some producers is to force animals having low nutritional requirements to clean up a feeding area before more hay is fed.

Other Possibilities

Net wrap, plastic wraps of various types, sleeves, and tarps can all be used to reduce hay spoilage losses. These treatments may or may not be cost effective, depending on the vulnerability and value of hay to be stored, length of the storage period, and amount and seasonal distribution of rainfall

Feeding round hay bales from a bale wagon that can be moved to different pasture areas will result in better distribution of dung and urine.

in the area.

Barn drying is appealing from the standpoints of preserving hay quality and minimizing the risk of rain damage. The problems with barn drying are building an appropriate facility and economically providing the energy for drying. While barn drying is an intriguing concept, it does not appear likely to become popular unless a low-cost system of providing energy for drying is discovered.

The cost of building a shed for storing round bales varies considerably, as does the length of time for which storage may be needed. In addition, the amount of space needed is greatly affected by bale density. For example, it requires about half the space to store high density hay that weighs 10 pounds per cubic foot as for hay baled at a low density of 5 pounds per cubic foot.

Because the feasibility of using various techniques for protecting hay varies greatly, it is difficult to make general recommendations. Producers should rely on local experts and their own calculations when making decisions regarding hay storage techniques. SF

Silage is defined as plant material that has undergone fermentation in a silo. A silo is any storage structure in which green, moist forage is preserved.

Harvesting, preserving, and feeding forage crops as silage is a practice used throughout the U.S. Silage represents a convenient and economical source of feed for the dairy industry and is increasingly used in beef backgrounding and finishing programs.

Silage offers many advantages over other storage methods: 1) less field and harvest losses than occur with hay (**Figure 20.1**); 2) choice of many crops that can be used for silage; 3) mechanization of harvesting, storage, and feeding; 4) less likelihood of weather damage during harvesting; 5) when properly ensiled, it can be stored for long periods with only small losses of nutrients; and 6) it can be used in many livestock feeding programs. Obviously, these advantages should not be ignored. It is likely that many livestock producers could benefit by incorporating silage capability into their operations.

Some disadvantages of using silage include: 1) bulky to handle and store; 2) requires additional equipment and structures for harvesting, storing, and feeding; 3) excessive losses if not stored properly; 4) not readily marketable if not used on the farm; and 5) must be fed soon after removal from the silo to minimize spoilage.

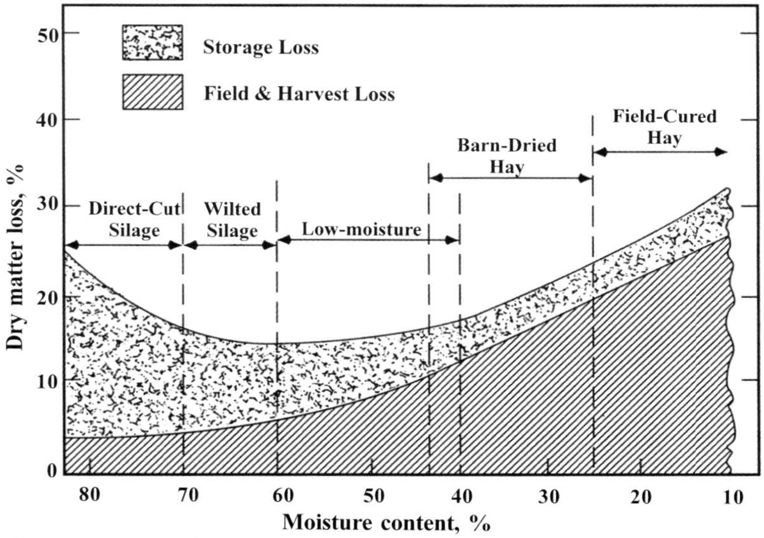

Figure 20.1. Estimated total field and harvest loss and storage loss when legume-grass forages are harvested at varying moisture levels and by alternative harvesting methods.
Source: C.R. Hoglund. Michigan Agric. Exp. Stn. Agric. Econ. Publ. 947.

Table 20.1. Annual yield and composition of silage crops.

Crop	Stage	Yield, tons/A[1] Dry matter	35% dry matter	Dry matter basis Crude protein, %	Crude fiber, %
Corn	Hard dough	6.0	17	8	24
Grain sorghum	Dough	4.0	11	9	28
Forage sorghum	Dough	5.0	14	8	33
Forage sorghum	Early head	4.0	11	11	29
Sorghum-sudan	Dough	4.5	13	10	34
Sorghum-sudan	Early head	2.5	7	12	26
Barley	Dough	2.5	7	9	27
Wheat	Dough	2.5	7	9	28
Oats	Dough	2.0	6	10	32
Rye	Boot	2.0	6	13	33
Alfalfa	Early bloom	4.0	11	18	31
Red clover-orchardgrass	Early bloom	2.5	7	12	33

[1]Yields vary with location, climatic conditions, fertilization, and other factors.
Source: S.J. Donohue, R.L. Harrison and H.E. White (Ed.). Handbook of Agronomy. Virginia Agric. Ext. Ser. Pub. 424-100.

Silage Crops

Many crops can be successfully preserved as silage. The type of livestock to be fed, expected yields, machinery available, soil types, and planting sites can enter into the decision as to what crops to plant.

Since most of the above-ground parts of the crop are removed from the field during silage making, removal of plant nutrients is much greater than when the same crop is harvested for grain. Necessary adjustments should be made in the fertility program to ensure adequate plant nutrients for the following crop.

High-energy crops (corn, grain sorghum, small grains) have been used extensively for silage (**Table 20.1**). Other forage crops (alfalfa, forage sorghum, legume-grass mixtures, and various grasses) are also used, but usually require wilting to reduce moisture content for proper ensiling. Corn ranks as the best silage crop. Corn silage is high in energy and results in good animal performance.

Silage made from grain-type sorghum is slightly lower in quality than corn silage. Forage sorghum is widely grown for silage. As with grain-type sorghums, it results in somewhat lower animal performance than does corn silage, but yield per acre can be high. Varieties have widely varying characteristics. For example, time from planting to harvest varies from 80 to 130 days or more.

The ratio of sorghum grain to forage varies from 6 percent (forage types) to 35 percent or more (intermediate types), and yields vary from 10 to 30 tons/A (wet basis) from a single harvest. In the extreme lower South (Zone A), it is possible to obtain two silage harvests from a single early planting of grain or forage sorghum. Considerable variation in yield and quality exists among sorghum varieties.

Summer annual grasses (pearl millet and sorghum-sudangrass hybrids), small grains, alfalfa, johnsongrass, and surplus pasture growth of many other forages can also be harvested for silage. When cut at the right stage and properly ensiled, grass silage quality can be good.

High moisture grass silage, cut and directly stored, makes poor quality silage unless an energy source is added. Warm season grasses such as Coastal bermudagrass are difficult to preserve as they have low available energy. Ground corn added at the rate of 100 to 150 lb/ton of green weight will facilitate bacterial fermentation and thus improve the quality of such silage.

The Ensiling Process

Many changes occur once green moist forage is placed in a silo. The speed with which these changes occur and the length of time required for ensiling vary with type of crop, moisture content, length of chop, and type of silo. If conditions are favorable, the entire process will be complete within 20 to 21 days, resulting in a stable, high quality, pleasant-smelling silage.

When ensiling forage, the overall goal is to use the oxygen and lower the pH so the forage material will be pickled or preserved. To accomplish this, two groups of bacteria are essential. The first group are oxygen-using (aerobic) bacteria that give off carbon dioxide and heat. If the silage is packed well and chopped fine, these bacteria will utilize all the oxygen in four to six hours. The heat given off in the process will raise the temperature to the range of 80 to over 100°F.

The second group of bacteria (anaerobic) then take over and work in the absence of oxygen to produce acetic acid. After the second or third day, lactic acid bacteria become active. Production of lactic acid occurs for 16 to 18 days, until the pH drops to between 3.6 and 4.2. At this low pH (high acid) the silage is pickled, and all bacterial activity stops. The silage is now stable and will keep for long periods of time, providing oxygen does not enter the silo.

Having a basic knowledge of the ensiling process fosters an understanding and appreciation of the importance of management practices. Fine chopping and good packing are important to minimize the amount of oxygen that must be eliminated by bacteria before acid production begins. Having a readily available supply of digestible energy for the acid-producing bacteria greatly favors a good ensiling process. This is why corn and other high energy grain crops are excellent silage crops.

The Silo

In addition to preserving silage, silos must protect silage from damage by air, water, birds, rodents, and other animals during storage. Silos can be divided into two basic types — upright and horizontal (**Figure 20.2**). Upright silos include conventional (concrete stave) and oxygen-limiting. Oxygen-limiting silos have higher original and operating costs than conventional, but

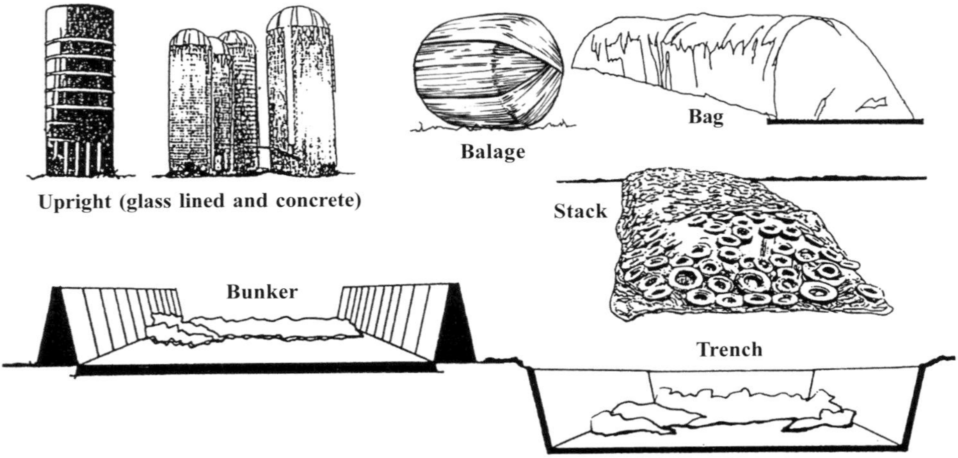

Figure 20.2. Illustrations show several alternatives for silage storage.

offer advantages including bottom unloading, lower storage losses, more flexible use because of the ability to constantly refill, and storage of more than one crop per season.

Horizontal silos include trench (below ground), bunker (above ground with sides), and stacks (above ground without sides). Trenches and bunkers are intermediate in cost to upright and stack silos. Horizontal silos have higher storage losses than upright. Packing is critical with horizontal silos. During filling, silage must be packed constantly. Top spoilage can be excessive if the silage is not covered and sealed to keep out air and water. Packing and sealing are more difficult with stacks since they have no permanent sides. Stacks are usually used for temporary storage or in emergency situations. More losses are usually associated with silage in stacks as compared to other silo types.

An increasingly popular option is commonly referred to as round bale silage or balage. This practice involves cutting the forage crop with conventional hay harvesting equipment, allowing the forage to wilt to between 30 and 60 percent dry matter, then baling it into tight bales and wrapping them immediately. Bales are wrapped mechanically using bale wrapping equipment that tightly stretches four to six layers of plastic around the hay to exclude oxygen and allow proper ensiling.

As compared to hay, round bale silage offers the advantage of avoiding high storage losses usually associated with outside hay storage. In addition, since weather at harvest is less of a factor, it often allows harvest of forage at a stage of higher nutritional value. Another reason why quality is likely to be higher is that harvesting at higher moisture requires less drying time and usually results in better leaf retention. Disadvantages of round bale silage include: 1) need to dispose of used plastic; 2) potential for spoilage when bags get punctured or torn; and 3) less flexibility in moving bales prior to feeding.

Hay-crop silage (haylage) can be harvested and stored in upright airtight silos at a lower moisture content (45 to 55 percent). Less fermentation occurs with low-moisture hay-type plants that contain fewer readily available fermentable carbohydrates, so silage is not fully pickled or preserved.

Alfalfa or alfalfa-grass can be an excellent silage crop. Interest in and use of alfalfa as silage is increasing in the South. Alfalfa can be harvested for silage over a wide range of moisture contents depending on the individual operation and type of silo used for storage.

Equipment is available that permits silage to be harvested, packed into plastic bags, and ensiled. Length of the plastic (silo) can vary to meet individual needs. In addition, plastic bags can be used for non-chopped forage. Forages can be cut, wilted, and harvested in large round bales at high moisture content, placed in individual plastic bags, tied, and sealed.

Factors Affecting Silage Quality

Many factors affect the quality of silage available at the time of feeding. Type of crop stored, stage of maturity, moisture content, and length of chop are all important. With any crop grown for silage, the stage of maturity when harvested has the greatest effect on quality. Guidelines for harvesting various forage crops are provided in **Table 20.2.** As silage plants age or mature, quality declines, resulting in lower animal performance.

Moisture Content

Table 20.2. Usual recommended stage of maturity for silage harvest.[1]

Crop	Stage of maturity
Corn	Kernels will be dented and black layer visible.
Grain sorghum	Late milk to late dough.
Forage sorghum	40 inches or late boot stage.
Sorghum, sudangrass, johnsongrass, millet	40 inches or boot stage, whichever comes first.
Small grains, ryegrass	Boot to early head.
Soybeans	Late bloom, seed forming in pods and before lower leaves fall.
Alfalfa	Bud to early bloom.
Cool season grasses	Boot to early head, first cutting; thereafter at four to six week intervals.
Hybrid bermudagrass	15 inches at first harvest, thereafter at four to five week intervals.

[1]These are guidelines. The quality of feed needed for the type or class of livestock to be fed should also be taken into consideration

Table 20.3. Field technique for estimating moisture content of chopped forage.	
Form a ball of silage in hand, then observe its condition –	Approximate moisture content, %
When the ball holds its shape, and there is considerable free juice	Over 75
When the ball holds its shape, but there is very little free juice	70 to 75
When the ball falls apart slowly, and there is no free juice	60 to 70
When the ball falls apart rapidly	Below 60

Depending on the crop ensiled and the type of silo used, silage can be made over a wide range of moisture contents. If the crop is harvested at a stage when the silage is too dry, extra water must be added to ensure good packing and proper fermentation. Low moisture may allow bacteria, yeast, and molds to become active, thus increasing the silage temperature. Overheating lowers feeding value and increases dry matter loss. Overheated silage will usually be brown to black with a carmelized (burnt sugar) odor. Extreme cases of overheating can result in combustion.

If silage is harvested too wet, excessive seepage will result in loss of nutrients. High moisture may also result in silage being packed so tightly that all the oxygen is used up before the temperature gets to 80°F. Lactic acid bacteria are usually not very active below 80°F. Undesirable (butyric acid) bacteria become active, use carbohydrates, and give the silage a foul odor and a taste similar to rancid butter. Other organisms can break down protein, giving the silage an ammonia odor. This results in unpalatable silage of poor quality with a low feeding value.

When using stacks, trenches, or bunkers, the moisture content of the silage should be about 65 to 70 percent in order to obtain adequate packing. Moisture content can be determined by using a moisture meter or by drying and weighing samples. A field technique for estimating moisture content is offered in **Table 20.3.**

Silage should be chopped at a length of 3/8 to 1/2 inch.

Length of Chop

Excluding air is the first and a critically important phase of the ensiling process. To ensure that this phase is short, it is important to exclude air by fine chopping and packing adequately. The silage should be chopped to a length of approximately 3/8 to 1/2 inch. This helps ensure proper fermentation by releasing plant juices and permits better packing for oxygen exclusion.

Silage Preservatives and Additives

Several materials have been investigated as to their merits for improving silage. Some products have proven to be helpful in certain situations. Products such as enzymes, yeast cultures, and antibiotics continue to be investigated. Acid-forming bacteria have shown promise, especially with early spring- and late autumn-cut haylage.

Careful consideration should be given in selecting silage additives. No additive can substitute for basic silage-making principles such as harvesting at the proper stage of maturity, storing at the proper moisture content, chopping finely, packing well, and covering adequately. Silage can be no better as a feed than the forage plus additives put into the silo.

Silo Gases

Lethal gases may occur in upright silos at any time during and soon after filling, but the greatest danger is from 12 to 72 hours after filling. Silo gases may be present in any ensiled material grown on any type of soil under any level of fertilization.

Two of the most dangerous gases may be recognized by their irritating odor and color. Nitrogen dioxide is reddish brown, and nitrogen tetraoxide is yellow. A third gas, nitric oxide, is colorless and may be present and undetected at lethal concentrations. A few simple precautions will prevent tragedy or injury from silo gases:

1. The blower should be run for 15 to 20 minutes before anyone goes into a partly filled silo. It should be left running as long as anyone is inside.
2. No one should enter the silo for at least one week (preferably two weeks) after it has been filled.
3. The silo room should be ventilated for at least two weeks after filling.
4. The doors between the silo room and barn should be kept closed to protect livestock.
5. If a person in the vicinity of the silo experiences the slightest throat irritation or coughing, he/she should get to fresh air immediately. Also, immediate treatment by a physician is essential.

Feeding Silage

Silage is ready to be fed three to five weeks after it is stored. It can supply some or all of the needs of various classes of livestock. Feeding can be mechanized for convenience and efficiency. In order to have an efficient silage feeding program, sufficient bunk space must be provided to accommodate the animals.

Likewise, nutritional needs of animals must be known. Once the animal class and desired level of performance are known, the amount of silage along with needed supplementation can be determined. To calculate the level of supplementation needed, quality of the silage must first be determined. A forage (silage) sample should be collected and analyzed for nutrient levels.

Corn silage is a mainstay in dairy production.

Considerable variation can exist in silages. In general, corn silage is low in protein and must be supplemented for growing or milk-producing animals. On the other hand, alfalfa and other forage crop silages may be low in energy. A combination of high-energy (corn or sorghum) and high protein (alfalfa) forage has the potential for nearly balanced, home-grown rations.

Feeding losses are usually low in silage feeding programs. Feeding daily the amount that will be consumed prevents unused silage from spoiling in the bunk. This is especially important during warm weather. SF

Minimizing Stored Feed Requirements

One of the most expensive and burdensome aspects of owning forage-consuming livestock is meeting their nutritional requirements during times when inadequate pasture is available. Hay is usually the most logical stored feed, but time, labor, machinery, fuel, and storage costs associated with producing (or procuring) and feeding hay make it expensive.

Feeding hay or other stored feed causes animals to spend considerable amounts of time in the feeding area. The result is that manure will need to be periodically removed from a stable or feedlot. Otherwise, hay feeding areas in pastures can suffer stand losses. Furthermore, nutrients from dung and urine are concentrated in pasture feeding areas, thus often reducing the environmental soundness of the livestock operation (see Chapter 32).

It is not unusual for stored feed to account for 25 to over 30 percent of livestock production expenses. It usually costs at least two to three times as much per day or per animal to meet animal nutritional requirements with hay, haylage, or silage as with pasture. As hay or other stored feed is replaced with pasture, the profitability of a livestock operation will generally improve. Therefore, a basic objective of most livestock producers should be to minimize the amount of stored feed needed. Appropriate techniques vary with location, but several strategies to accomplish this will be discussed in this chapter.

Use of Warm Season and Cool Season Perennial Grasses

Due to lower establishment costs, perennial forages are generally cheaper to grow than annuals, and therefore most livestock operations in the Southern U.S. are based on the use of perennial species (primarily grasses) for pasture. Perennial forages are either warm season species that make most of their growth in summer or cool season species that make most of their growth in cooler weather, mainly spring and autumn (see **Figures 4.4** to **4.7**).

On many farms in the Southern U.S., it is possible to have some acreage of both warm season and cool season perennial grasses. This is an important advantage because it extends the grazing period over more of the year, thus reducing the number of calendar days during which stored feed must be provided.

Because of cooler average temperatures and soils with better moisture-holding capacity, cool season perennial grasses are best adapted and easiest to grow in the upper South. Tall fescue is widely grown in Zones B, C, and D. In addition, orchardgrass can be grown in Zones C and D and the upper portion of Zone B, and timothy and Kentucky bluegrass are grown in the upper portion of Zone C and in Zone D.

Several warm season grasses can be grown in these zones as well. Winterhardy varieties of bermudagrass are grown in Zone B and to a limited extent in Zone C. In addition, dallisgrass can be grown on soils with good moisture-holding capacity in Zone B, and some bahiagrass varieties are adapted in the lower portion of Zone B. The native bunchgrasses such as switchgrass are generally adapted in Zones A, B, C, and D, but are not widely used for pasture. Forage options vary, depending on site, soils, and location, but many producers whose pastures consist primarily of cool season perennial species could benefit from having some acreage of warm season perennial pasture.

Nature often assists in stretching pasture forage availability. In Zone B, many pastures originally planted to tall fescue or orchardgrass contain a substantial amount of volunteer warm season grasses, especially common bermudagrass. Dallisgrass or bahiagrass often volunteer in (or can be planted into) tall fescue in some areas of Zone B, resulting in a longer grazing season than tall fescue alone.

Depending on the site, soil, and temperatures, mixed warm season and cool season grass stands can sometimes be maintained over long periods of time with proper management (see Chapter 15). If cool season perennial grass pastures are thinned by drought or overgrazing, crabgrass (a summer annual) often volunteers and provides substantial summer nutrition for grazing livestock.

On Coastal Plain soils in Zone B and especially Zone A, the best-adapted perennial grasses are bahiagrass and bermudagrass. In this area most producers could benefit from having additional pasture acreage of tall fescue (the only cool season perennial grass that might persist). Unfortunately, the opportunity for growing this grass is limited in most of Zone A. Nonetheless, there are a few sites and soils in Zone A with good year-round moisture availability in which tall fescue is adapted, and producers who have such sites would likely benefit from having some acreage.

Within the warm season and cool season grass categories some species have a different distribution of growth than others. For example, dallisgrass and switchgrass make more early spring growth than bermudagrass. Bahiagrass lags a bit behind these two grasses in spring, but is still earlier than bermudagrass, and it continues growing later in autumn. Tall fescue has more autumn growth than orchardgrass. Thus, having some acreage of different perennial grasses can extend pasture forage availability, even if they are in the same (cool or warm season) growth category.

Use of Perennial Legumes

In most areas in which tall fescue, orchardgrass, or dallisgrass are adapted, white clover or red clover can be grown in combination with the grass. In addition to improving forage quality and providing biological nitrogen, these clovers (especially red clover) can provide a better distribution of forage growth than the grass alone and may increase total forage yield as well.

Grazing-tolerant alfalfa varieties provide an option that many producers should consider. Tall fescue can be suppressed with a herbicide followed by no-till planting of alfalfa, resulting in a tall fescue/alfalfa mixture. It is easy to no-till plant alfalfa into warm season perennial grasses in late autumn, but managing such a mixture to maintain stands is extremely difficult and thus is generally not feasible.

Grazing-tolerant alfalfa can also be planted into a prepared seedbed and used to extend the total number of calendar days of grazing available on a farm. The long growing season of alfalfa can provide emergency pasture during drought periods in the mid to upper South when cool season grasses are non-productive, or provide additional high quality pasture in the lower South to complement warm season grasses, especially in early spring and autumn. Grazing-tolerant alfalfa is actually a dual-purpose crop that can be grazed when needed or used for hay when convenient and when the weather permits.

Alfalfa can be no-till seeded into herbicide-suppressed tall fescue. Though alfalfa may dominate initially, by the second year there is usually a good mixture of the two species.

Sericea lespedeza produces good forage yields in late spring and summer, but is dormant during late autumn, winter, and early spring. A tall fescue/sericea mixture can produce more total forage and provide a better distribution of growth than sericea alone. However, the mixture must be fertilized with nitrogen for good production, as sericea provides little nitrogen to associated grasses (**Table 21.1**). Sericea has poor seedling vigor, so it is difficult to establish in an existing tall fescue stand. Tall fescue can be drilled into an established sericea stand with high probability of success.

Variety Selection

Within a given forage species, some varieties have a different distribution of forage growth than others. For example, Tifton 9 bahiagrass usually provides a longer growing season than Pensacola or Argentine; AU Triumph and other winter-active tall fescue varieties make more winter growth and

Table 21.1. Three-year average forage yields of Serala sericea/tall fescue mixtures as affected by rate of nitrogen in north Alabama.

Forages	Nitrogen lb/A/yr	Dry forage yield, lb/A: March-April	May-Sept.	Oct-Nov	Total
Sericea	0	50	8,120	0	8,170
Sericea/fescue	0	530	8,210	150	8,890
Sericea/fescue	80	1,370	8,180	350	9,900
Sericea/fescue	160	2,404	8,770	610	10,950

Adapted from: C.S. Hoveland, W.B. Anthony, E.L. Carden, J.K. Boseck, and W.B. Webster. Ala. Agric. Exp. Sta. Cir. 221.

head earlier than other tall fescue varieties; and some annual ryegrass varieties persist longer in spring than others. Distribution of forage growth is usually not the primary criterion for variety selection, but it may be worthy of consideration when making decisions among otherwise comparable varieties.

Other Complementary Plantings

Other forage species can also be planted, either alone or in mixtures, to complement the pasture forage availability provided by perennial grasses. In some cases these forages may be planted directly into a perennial grass stand, while in other situations a special planting may be made on a prepared seedbed in a separate field to which livestock can be moved as additional pasture is needed.

Winter annuals can provide additional days of grazing on many farms, particularly in areas in which perennial pastures are dominated by bahiagrass or bermudagrass. Overseeding winter annuals can extend the grazing season in such areas by as much as two to three months at relatively low cost (**Table 12.3**).

Furthermore, overseeded annual ryegrass and/or winter annual legumes can be managed for reseeding, thus enabling more than one year's production from a single planting. The main requirement for successful reseeding is to either remove livestock for several weeks during the seed production period or keep the stocking rate low, thus allowing many or most plants to make seed.

Yields of legumes reseeded in a bermudagrass sod in an Alabama test that simulated total utilization of forage produced is provided in **Table 21.2**. Managing for reseeding will result in less utilization of the forage and thus lower animal production as compared to heavily grazing an overseeded or reseeded winter annual pasture, but may be justifiable in that a substantial quantity of forage can be produced at low cost for more than one year.

The higher cost of planting winter annuals on a prepared seedbed dictates use of such plantings primarily by animals having high nutritional requirements (i.e. stockers or dairy animals). But it may be justifiable for beef cows when hay is in short supply, especially if limit grazed. Winter

Table 21.2. Forage yield of legumes from natural reseeding on Coastal bermudagrass sod in northwestern Alabama.

	Dry forage yield, lb/A			
Legume	April 4	April 27	May 16	Total
Yuchi arrowleaf clover	1,620	690	1,100	3,410
Autauga crimson clover	2,100	80	0	2,180
Ball clover	840	770	480	2,090
Hairy vetch	340	770	410	1,560

Source: C.S. Hoveland, E.L. Carden, G.A. Buchanan, E.M. Evans, W.B. Anthony, E.L. Mayton, and H.E. Burgess. Ala. Agric. Exp. Sta. Bull. 396.

The contrast between overseeded rye, ryegrass, and arrowleaf clover (foreground) and dormant bahiagrass (background) in south Alabama provides impressive visual evidence of the ability of overseeded winter annuals to extend the grazing season.

annuals are also often planted on a prepared seedbed for the purpose of producing high quality hay, haylage, or silage.

Knowledge of the distribution of growth of winter annuals is important when making decisions as to which species to plant. Annual ryegrass is generally the single most productive winter annual, but it makes most of its growth in late winter and spring. Small grains make more autumn growth than annual ryegrass and thus are useful in mixtures with annual ryegrass planted on a prepared seedbed in early autumn. In areas within 75 miles or so of the Gulf Coast, ryegrass is more productive in autumn and winter, decreasing the need for a companion small grain.

The growth distribution of clover species also differs considerably as evidenced by three years of testing at four sites in south Alabama. In this study, five annual legumes (arrowleaf clover, ball clover, berseem clover, crimson clover, and subterranean clover) and two perennial legumes (red clover and white clover, treated as annuals in this test) were planted on a prepared seedbed each autumn, and spring forage yield was measured as early, mid, and late season production (**Table 21.3**). Clearly, the decision as to which clover(s) to plant has a major effect on the timing of forage growth.

Overseeding of winter annuals is not limited to perennial grasses. As discussed elsewhere in this book, alfalfa is a cool season perennial best suited to productive, well-drained soils, while sericea lespedeza is a warm-season perennial that tolerates low fertility soils where other forages, especially legumes, produce poorly. Once a stand of either of these two legumes is established, winter annuals can be drilled or broadcast-seeded into them to extend the grazing season and increase total production.

In central Alabama, rye sod-seeded into sericea lespedeza and fertilized with 100 lb of nitrogen/A increased total forage yield by 2,000 lb/A as

Table 21.3. Mean yields (lb/A/yr) of seven clovers grown in south Alabama for three years.

Clover	Feb-Mar	April-May	June-July	Total
Crimson	1,871	1,698	0	3,569
Berseem	1,359	2,327	589	4,275
Red	254	2,188	1,455	3,897
White	407	1,612	1,202	3,221
Arrowleaf	425	2,525	522	3,472
Ball	530	2,099	134	2,763
Subterranean	646	1,214	0	1,860

J.F. Pedersen and D.M. Ball. Ala. Agric. Exp. Sta. Circular 307.

compared to sericea alone. Rye extended the productive season by about two months. Seeding rye had no adverse effect on sericea stands.

Even on farms where cool season perennials such as orchardgrass or tall fescue are the dominant pasture species, having some acreage of winter annuals can provide additional days of grazing. This is because winter annuals make more growth than cool season perennials during cold weather (**Figure 21.1**). However, the cost of planting winter annuals versus the cost of providing hay or using other strategies for reducing stored feed requirements should be calculated and taken into consideration.

Several species of brassicas, including turnips, rape, and kale, are sometimes planted for forage. These are winter annual forbs, rather than grasses or legumes, that produce lush high quality forage when planted in a prepared seedbed in late summer or early autumn. Livestock will consume the tuberous roots as well as the top growth. Yields vary greatly.

Compared to winter annuals, warm season annual grasses are more expensive to grow, more difficult to manage, and forage quality is lower. Though their usefulness is much more limited than winter annuals, they can provide grazing when a shortage of perennial grass pasture forage is expected. Pearl millet, sorghum-sudan hybrids, and sudangrass produce the highest forage yields in most situations. These grasses should normally be planted on a prepared seedbed rather than being drilled into perennial pastures. Reseeding crabgrass can be a low cost summer annual grass pasture option, especially when managed to volunteer after winter annuals.

Forage chicory (see Chapter 8) is a forb that appears to have promise for providing high quality forage at strategic times in certain situations. In a Georgia study,

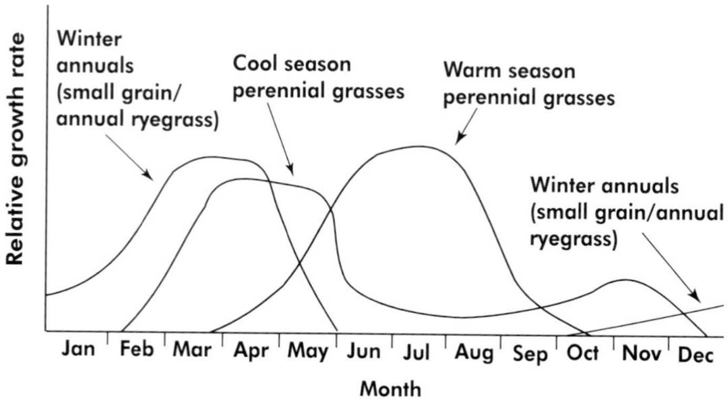

Figure 21.1. Growth curves for cool season perennial grasses, warm season perennial grasses, and winter annuals.

forage chicory, tall fescue, or rye were drilled into bermudagrass in autumn to determine the effect on forage yield and distribution. In this test, 60 lb nitrogen/A was applied in February, April, and September, and forage was harvested monthly. Rye was far superior to chicory or tall fescue during winter, but during spring the chicory mixture equaled tall fescue/bermudagrass and was superior to tall fescue/bermudagrass or bermudagrass alone in summer (**Figure 21.2**).

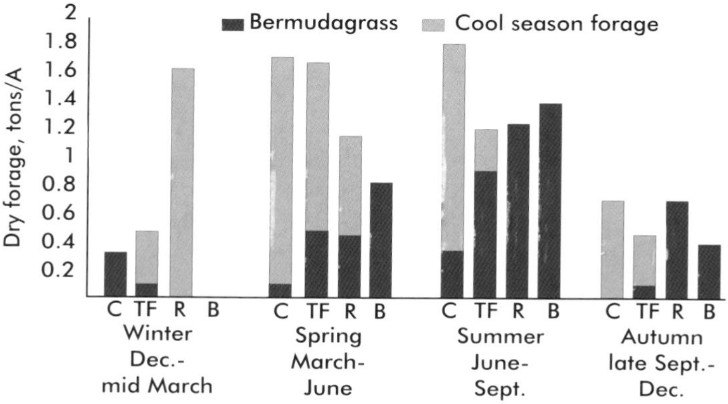

Figure 21.2. Seasonal forage production of chicory (C), tall fescue (TF), and rye (R), no-till planted in bermudagrass (B), two-year average. Central Georgia Branch Station.
Source: C.S. Hoveland and R.G. Durham, The Georgia Cattleman.

Use Grazing Management to Maximize Benefits from Pastures

There are numerous potential benefits to be gained from exercising good pasture management (see Chapter 25), but two deserve mention in this discussion. First, when pastures are grazed appropriately for the forage species they contain, the plants will be healthier and more productive over a longer period of time. If pastures are grazed too closely, the food-producing capacity of the plants is reduced, resulting in lower production and weakening of plants due to depletion of food reserves. Some forages are much more sensitive to this than others.

In a Georgia study, the impact of two clipping heights on forage yields of endophyte-infected and endophyte-free Kentucky 31 tall fescue and AU Triumph (endophyte free) fescue was evaluated. Plants were clipped every three weeks for a total of 10 times each year until November, in an attempt to simulate rotational stocking. The benefit of avoiding excessively close defoliation was especially evident in a dry summer, as there was good autumn growth on both varieties with a 3-inch cutting height, but not at a 1.5 inch cutting height (**Figure 21.3**).

Good grazing management also reduces forage waste. If pastures are undergrazed (which often occurs with poorly managed continuously stocked areas), losses due to trampling and fouling of forage can be substantial. The use of limit grazing, strip grazing, or rotational stocking can reduce these losses, often resulting in utilization of 20 to 30 percent more of the forage produced, and lengthening of the grazing period.

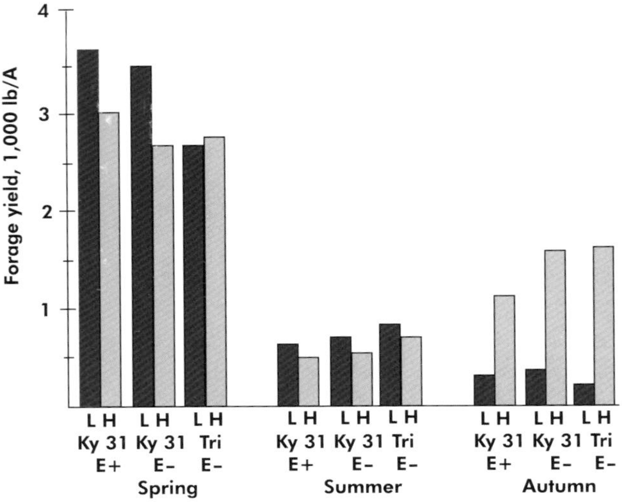

Figure 21.3. **Seasonal forage production of endophyte-infected (E+) Ky 31, endophyte-free (E-) Ky 31, and AU Triumph (Tri) tall fescue cut every three weeks at low (L, 1.5-inch) and high (H, 3-inch) cutting height in north Georgia, dry year.** Adapted from: C.S. Hoveland, R.G. Durham, and J.H. Bouton. Agron. J. 89:119-125.

Nitrogen Fertilization

A number of nutrients are required to be present in adequate quantities in order to obtain good forage production (see Chapter 9). The level of nitrogen fertilization is a particularly important determinant of the yields of forage grasses and forbs, with some species requiring higher levels of nitrogen than others. However, the timing of nitrogen fertilization can also have an important impact on the distribution of pasture forage availability.

Moisture availability and temperature, two factors that cannot be controlled, also greatly affect plant growth distribution. Therefore, the natural fluctuations in pasture growth can be mitigated to some extent by proper timing of nitrogen fertilization. Soil test recommendations provide guidelines for timing of nitrogen fertilization, but when there is a surplus of pasture growth, there obviously is no need to stimulate more growth unless deficits are anticipated in the foreseeable future.

Some producers seem to have excessive concern about loss of nitrogen if fertilizer is applied to pastures too early. However, with the exception of urea applied on alkaline soils or during hot weather, or denitrification in cool, wet soils, there is little nitrogen volatilization loss from applied fertilizer. Loss of nitrogen from runoff or leaching can occur, but these are usually not serious problems.

Perhaps the most important consideration regarding timing of nitrogen fertilization is to make certain there are adequate amounts available in early spring at the beginning of the growing season of perennial grasses. Failure to have adequate nitrogen available when perennial grasses begin to grow can delay pasture growth, and the result is extension of the winter hay feeding period by one or more weeks. It is likewise important to provide adequate nitrogen on a timely basis to cool season annual grasses in late winter to stimulate a vigorous spring flush of growth.

Graze Perennial Hay Fields

In the Southern U.S., summer droughts often occur. The result is inadequate available forage, especially if pastures are dominated by cool season perennials. When pasture growth is limited, it may be advantageous to graze a hayfield.

Table 21.4. Approximate feed value of selected crop residues.

Residue	Percent dry matter[1]	Digestible nutrients[1]	Percent protein[1]
Barley straw	87	44	4.1
Cotton field residue	92	41	6.2
Cotton gin trash	90	45	7.4
Field corn (stalk)	77	50	4.8
Oat straw	89	46	4.2
Peanut residue	91	58	5.5
Sorghum straw	85	50	5.3
Soybean stubble	88	36	5.1
Wheat straw	88	44	3.6

[1]Revised from National Research Council (NRC) nutritional data.

The logic of this practice is that the amount of stored feed needed in winter may be less than expected, especially if strategies such as culling of animals or planting winter annuals to reduce stored feed needs are possible. Meanwhile, the expense of hay harvesting has been avoided, and therefore purchasing hay or other stored feed may be no more (or even less) expensive than producing hay would have been.

Graze Crop Residues

Livestock producers who have diversified farm operations often can reduce hay requirements by grazing crop residues. Crop residue yields vary, but as an example, a 100 bu/A corn crop will often produce 2 to 3 tons of dry matter residue. Other crop residues typically provide 1 to 2 tons of grazable residue.

The quality of crop residues is not high, but can come close to meeting the nutritional needs of some livestock classes. However, supplementation may be required for most classes of livestock (**Table 21.4**). Weathering, mainly influenced by the amount of rainfall after crop harvest, impacts fairly quickly on the energy value of crop residues. Immediately after grain harvest, corn residues usually have about 48 to 50 percent total digestible nutrients (TDN), while 40 to 60 days later the TDN level may be only 36 to 38 percent. The protein in corn residue, though low, generally does not decline prior to utilization by grazing.

Due to a rapid decline in feeding value, crop residues should be utilized soon after harvest. Unless fields are small, it is best to use an electric fence to allow strip grazing to minimize waste. Before grazing or feeding any crop residue, it is important to make certain that any pesticides used in the field do not prohibit consumption by livestock. In addition, it is important to remember that in certain situations nitrate poisoning can be a problem with some crops and that prussic acid poisoning can occur with plants in the sorghum family (see Chapter 22).

Table 21.5. **Yield and crude protein content (DM basis) of Kentucky bluegrass and tall fescue produced from August 15 to December 1 under different levels of nitrogen fertilization at Lexington, KY. Average of three years.**

Nitrogen applied, lb/A	Kentucky bluegrass Yield, lb/A	Kentucky bluegrass Protein, %	Tall fescue Yield, lb/A	Tall fescue Protein, %
0	700	12.8	1,700	11.1
45	1,600	15.5	2,800	11.8
90	2,100	19.1	3,900	14.8

Source: T.H. Taylor, and W.C. Templeton, Jr., Agron. J. 8:235-239.

Stockpiled Forage

Stockpiling, which is simply the process of allowing forage to accumulate for grazing at a later time, offers an excellent opportunity to substantially reduce the winter hay-feeding period. This technique can help compensate for inadequate winter pasture growth, and thus the varying amount of forage available for livestock at different times.

Tall fescue is by far the best-suited grass for stockpiling in the Southern U.S. It normally makes a substantial amount of growth just prior to winter, which is the time when pasture growth is most limited. The forage quality of stockpiled tall fescue is better in autumn than at any other time of year. Finally, tall fescue holds its forage quality over time better than most other forage crops.

Stockpiling tall fescue in autumn is a simple process. The steps required are: 1) graze or mow the grass down to 2 to 3 inches by late summer; 2) when tall fescue growth begins in autumn apply nitrogen at a rate of 40 to 80 lb/A, along with any other nutrients and lime that a soil test indicates may need to be applied; and 3) keep the animals off the pasture and allow the forage to accumulate until hay would otherwise need to be fed.

Properly fertilized autumn stockpiled tall fescue forage will usually contain 14 percent crude protein (CP) and over 60 percent digestible dry matter, maintaining this high nutritive quality well into the winter (**Table 21.5**). Unfortunately, stockpiled endophyte-infected tall fescue will still have toxic properties, although at a lower level than in spring. Kentucky bluegrass is higher quality, but yields are lower. Orchardgrass is less well suited to stockpiling, as it makes less autumn growth and deteriorates more rapidly in winter.

The amount of accumulated forage in a stockpiled field is dependent on autumn rainfall and level of nitrogen applied, but often amounts to 1 to 2 tons of dry matter per acre. Depending on yield and stocking rate, in some years and locations this technique may allow delaying of feeding hay until February or later.

Assuming 1.5 tons of hay equivalent are available per acre of stockpiled tall fescue, that each cow will eat about 25 lb of forage daily, and that 70 percent of the forage will be utilized, it will take 40 cows about two days to graze an acre. Cattle can access stockpiled forage even when it is covered with a few inches of snow.

Warm season forages, including bermudagrass and bahiagrass, can be

Table 21.6. Crude protein percentage of winter stockpiled Midland bermudagrass.[1]						
Forage portion	Dec.	Jan.	Feb.	Mar.	Apr.	Avg.
Leafy portion—grazed	11.4	10.5	13.2	14.0	10.2	11.8
Stemmy portion—residue	7.8	7.0	10.8	7.7	No data	8.3

[1]Two years of averaged data from paddocks being grazed at sampling. Nitrogen at 100 lb/A applied from April to June.
Source: R.L. Dalrymple, Noble Foundation publication NF-FO-00-16, Ardmore, OK.

autumn stockpiled as well, though the nutrient content of autumn forage of these species is lower (8 to 12 percent CP and around 50 percent digestible dry matter), and it does not maintain forage quality as well as tall fescue. In one Oklahoma study, stockpiled bermudagrass CP content was adequate; in another study, digestible dry matter was too low for dry pregnant beef cows (**Tables 21.6** and **21.7**). In such situations, supplemental energy must be provided unless animal body condition is good enough to furnish adequate energy from stored fat.

The forage quality of the leaf material was significantly better than the stem material, a factor that must be considered in determining how closely to graze stockpiled warm season grasses. Livestock should not be forced to graze the low quality stem material. Stockpiled crabgrass will normally be slightly higher in quality and contain less stem material than bahiagrass or bermudagrass.

Another possibility is to stockpile corn, sweet sorghum, or hybrid sorghum that has a sorgo parent. This is a technique that has been little used, but has potential, especially in areas in which there is good soil moisture or where irrigation can be used. For example, sweet sorghum planted in mid summer could produce 5 to 8 tons of dry forage before frost in many areas.

There are two important points pertaining to stockpiling forage that must be considered in order to be successful. First, the forage must be rationed to the animals rather than giving them access to all of it at one time; otherwise, much of it will be wasted by trampling and fouling. Strip grazing in which animals are given access to only a one- to three-day supply of stockpiled forage at a time works best. This can be accomplished by moving a single strand of electric wire across the pasture at various time intervals.

Secondly, if low quality forage has been stockpiled, supplemental feeds

Table 21.7. Percentage of in-vitro digestible dry matter of winter stockpiled Midland bermudagrass.[1]					
Percentage	Nov.	Dec.	Jan.	Feb.	Overall
Low to high ranges	37-54	34-50	31-51	35-42	31-54
Average	49	42	43	39	43

[1]Average of eight research locations, bermudagrass summer-fertilized at 160 to 300 lb nitrogen/A.
Source: C.M. Taliaferro, S.W. Coleman, and P.L. Claypool. Crop Sci. 27: 1285-1290.

will be required to meet the nutritional requirements of the animals. Supplemental feed in the form of range cubes, liquid protein supplements, cottonseed, or cottonseed meal can be used to accomplish this. The amount of supplement provided should be based on forage tests and ration balancing.

In essence, stockpiled forage amounts to standing hay, but livestock do the harvesting rather than the producer. Stockpiling is a simple process, but can be of great economic benefit to many livestock producers, especially those who have tall fescue pastures.

Irrigation

Since drought is one of the primary factors limiting forage growth at certain times of the year, irrigation is a tool that obviously has potential for increasing and extending pasture production. Unfortunately, the cost of irrigation for pasture production is prohibitive for most livestock producers, but there are some situations in which it can be feasible. In particular, fields in which irrigation equipment has been installed for row crop production can be planted with winter annuals to provide early autumn grazing. This can be economically attractive in a stocker beef operation as it normally allows early purchase of weaned calves at lower prices, regardless of autumn drought. In addition, if effluent from a feedlot, dairy, or other source can be sprayed on fields, planting forage crops adds little to the disposal cost.

Minimize Hay Losses

The ideal situation would be to totally eliminate the need for stored feed. However, most producers will need to feed hay during some periods of the year, especially winter. Given the expense of hay, it makes sense to protect any that has been purchased or produced so as to minimize the total amount needed.

A number of factors affect hay storage and feeding losses (see Chapter 19). However, hay that is stored outside unprotected for several months in the Southern U.S. often loses 30 percent or more of its dry matter during storage. In addition, the forage quality of the remaining hay is lower, plus hay feeding losses of weathered hay are much higher due to lower palatability.

Numerous approaches can be used to lower hay losses during storage, many of which cost little or nothing to implement. However, many producers can justify the cost of building a barn to store hay rather than allow substantial losses (see **Appendix A.35**).

Match Hay Quality With Animal Requirements

The objective in feeding livestock is to meet their nutritional requirements without spending any more money than necessary. Therefore, the most efficient way to use hay is to have forage analyses run on various lots, then feed in balanced rations. This ensures both good animal performance and obtaining maximum benefit from the hay. SF

Common Forage-Livestock Disorders

Toxic substances or mineral imbalances in forages and weeds consumed by livestock may result in reduced productivity, visible symptoms of ill health, or even death of grazing animals. In the South, one of the most common ailments is fescue toxicity (see Chapter 24). Several other disorders are also potential problems for Southern livestock producers.

Bloat

Cause. Bloat can be a serious problem in cattle grazing pastures dominated by certain legumes. Other ruminant and non-ruminant animals can be affected, but appear to be less susceptible than cattle. Bloat is caused by formation of a stable foam in the rumen that prevents eructation (belching) of gases produced by microbial fermentation of forage. As a result, the gases normally lost by eructation are retained. The pressure in the left side of the rumen then increases, resulting in the eructation mechanism being inhibited. When this occurs, the animal's oxygen supply is reduced or cut off, eventually causing it to suffocate. Animals affected will swell rapidly, and in acute cases, death can sometimes occur within an hour. Individual animals differ in susceptibility to bloat, and chronic bloaters should be removed from pastures where there is a danger of bloat.

Persian, ladino or white clovers, and alfalfa are examples of plants that have bloat potential. However, other legumes, including birdsfoot trefoil, sericea lespedeza, annual lespedeza, crownvetch, arrowleaf and berseem clovers rarely or never cause bloat. This is probably because leaf tannins within these plants act as protein precipitants that aid in breaking up the stable foam in the rumen. Likewise, tropical legumes such as kudzu, cowpea, perennial peanut, and alyceclover rarely or never cause bloat. Occasionally, bloat occurs on lush pastures of ryegrass or small grains, usually in spring. Feedlot bloat in beef cattle fed high grain diets that may or may not contain legume forage occurs rather infrequently.

Control. Hungry animals should not be turned into a lush legume or winter annual grass pasture. Dry hay should be fed before allowing animals to graze such a pasture. Do not place animals on lush forage wet with dew or that has just received a frost. Limited hay feeding during the initial days of grazing can also reduce the incidence of bloat. Cattle placed on legume pastures should be checked frequently and removed quickly if bloat

Animal in early stages of bloat. Note that the animal's left side is especially distended.

develops. The first signs will be swelling of an animal's left side.

Bloat hazard is greatly reduced when at least 50 percent of a pasture is grass. Providing ready access to salt and water when grazing a legume pasture is also helpful. Bloat potential is greatest during rapid growth periods in spring, declining during the summer months. In most of the South, the period between mid March and mid May is when bloat is most likely to occur.

An effective method of bloat prevention on legume pastures is providing salt-molasses blocks containing surfactants, detergent-type compounds that reduce development of stable foam in the rumen. Although surfactant blocks are relatively expensive, they can prevent animal deaths. Generally, the need is greatest in early spring. Blocks may not be needed as the grazing season progresses. Feeding an ionophore (several types are commercially available) can also reduce the potential for bloat.

Nitrate Poisoning

Cause. Nitrate poisoning in livestock is primarily caused by the consumption of pasture or hay containing high levels of nitrate-nitrogen. During periods of low soil moisture or low humidity, nitrates can accumulate in plants heavily fertilized with nitrogen. Hay cut during or just after a drought period is suspect, especially if nitrogen was applied just prior to hay harvest. Shading by other plant species, cloudy weather, and frost may also increase nitrate levels in plants. The application of nitrogen fertilizers during cool, wet, cloudy weather may also result in nitrate poisoning. Nitrates in hay are stable and can cause deaths months after harvest. Nitrate levels usually decline somewhat when forage is ensiled.

Some forage plants are more likely to accumulate nitrates than others. Plants known to have considerable potential for accumulation of toxic levels are: sudangrass, sorghum-sudan hybrids, pearl millet, corn, wheat, and oats. Certain weeds may also accumulate toxic levels of nitrates and thus pose a threat, especially in hay. Examples are pigweed, smartweed, ragweed, lambsquarter, goldenrod, nightshades, bindweed, Canada thistle, and stinging nettle. In addition, the application of some herbicides (for example, 2,4-D) can increase nitrate levels in plants.

Nitrates present in forages may be reported by laboratories as nitrate, nitrate-nitrogen, or potassium nitrate. Plants containing more than 1.5 percent nitrate [15,000 parts per million (ppm)] are highly toxic to many classes of livestock (see **Appendix A.39**). The reason for the toxicity is that nitrates are reduced to nitrites in the digestive tract. Nitrites then oxidize the iron in blood hemoglobin and prevent adequate oxygen transport. Animal symptoms are labored breathing, muscle tremors, and a staggering gait after which the animal collapses, gasps for breath, and dies. The membranes of the eyes and mouth are bluish, indicating a lack of oxygen. The blood is chocolate-brown, but turns a brighter red when exposed to air.

Control. Animals grazing heavily nitrogen-fertilized pastures of suspect plant species during drought, or wet pastures during cool cloudy weather,

Cow affected by nitrate toxicity on sorghum-sudan pasture.

should be carefully watched for symptoms. Prompt medication with a 4 percent solution of methylene blue supplied intravenously using 100 cc per 1,000 lb of body weight can sometimes prevent death. However, it is rare that the problem is diagnosed quickly enough to administer this treatment. Supplemental grain feeding can reduce risk through a dilution effect.

Hay well fertilized with nitrogen and produced during drought periods should be analyzed for nitrates in a laboratory. Hay containing up to 2,500 ppm nitrate is usually safe to feed. At levels of 2,500 to 5,000 ppm, feeding caution is suggested. Levels of 5,000 to 15,000 are considered dangerous and require feeding restrictions. Levels over 15,000 are considered toxic to most classes of livestock and should not be fed free choice. The danger does not decrease with time. Toxic hay may be ground and mixed with other materials if the nitrate-containing hay is no more than 15 percent by weight of the total ration. Non-protein nitrogen sources such as liquid feeds containing urea should not be fed with hay containing high levels of nitrates.

Animals can tolerate low levels of nitrates, but problems quickly develop when threshold levels in the blood are exceeded. Use of large round bales or stacks increases the danger of nitrate toxicity because the animals are likely to have the opportunity to consume more hay and thus get a larger total amount of nitrates in their bodies within a short period of time. Also, large bales and stacks may contain concentrated spots of nitrates. When nitrate poisoning occurs, it often kills many animals in a herd because each has the same opportunity to gorge itself on high nitrate forage.

Prussic Acid

Cause. Naturally occurring glycosides may form prussic acid, also called hydrocyanic acid or HCN, which can build up to toxic levels in leaves of a number of plants including johnsongrass, sorghum, sudangrass, sorghum-sudan hybrids, and wild cherry. Pearl millet does not produce prussic acid. Prussic acid is most likely to build up to dangerous levels immediately after a frost. Also, tender young growth occurring immediately after a long drought can be potentially toxic. Young, tender, fast-growing plants are more likely to be toxic than older, more mature plants. Herbicides, including 2,4-D, may also temporarily increase prussic acid levels.

Prussic acid causes death by interfering with the oxygen-transferring ability of the red blood cells, causing animals to suffocate. Symptoms include excessive salivation, rapid breathing, and muscle spasms, and may occur within 10 to 15 minutes after the animal consumes prussic acid-containing forage. Animals may stagger, collapse, and eventually die.

Prussic acid and nitrate poisoning are not the same. Toxic levels of nitrates result from heavy nitrogen fertilization followed by severe drought stress. Unlike nitrates, prussic acid deteriorates with time. If forage having high levels of prussic acid is ensiled, it will usually be safe to feed within three weeks after silo fill. Hay that has dried enough to be safely baled (18 to 20 percent moisture) will not contain toxic levels of prussic acid. Standing plants killed by frost are normally safe after about one week. However, in some instances only plants in certain portions of a field are initially killed, and subsequent frosts create danger spots in other areas.

Control. A producer should know which forage crops have the potential for prussic acid buildup. Grazing should be avoided until at least a week after the end of a severe drought or when frost is possible. Once frost occurs, grazing or feeding greenchop should be avoided for at least a week after the last green material has been frosted. Hungry cattle should not be turned into potentially toxic pastures or those containing wild cherry trees. Livestock should never be given access to limbs trimmed from wild cherry trees.

Grass Tetany

Cause. Grass tetany is associated with low levels of magnesium in the blood of cattle and sheep grazing ryegrass, small grains, and cool season perennial grasses in late winter and early spring. It is mostly confined to cows and ewes in early lactation and often affects the highest-producing animals in a herd or flock. It results from animals grazing plants grown on soils low in available magnesium, causing them to be deficient in this element, especially when lactation requires a substantial quantity of magnesium.

Wet soils, low in oxygen, may prevent plants from taking up sufficient magnesium regardless of the soil magnesium level. Grass tetany is more likely to occur on soils low in phosphorus but high in potassium and nitrogen because this combination tends to inhibit magnesium uptake. This can be a problem with cool season grass forage fertilized with high rates of broiler litter. Generally, forage containing 0.2 percent magnesium or more is unlikely to cause tetany.

An animal going into tetany initially is nervous, exhibits muscle twitching, staggers when walking, and later goes down on its side, with muscle spasms and convulsions. If not treated, death will occur.

Control. Pastures deficient in magnesium should be limed with dolomitic limestone, which contains this element. However, magnesium fertilization cannot be expected to always prevent tetany as grass plants may not take up sufficient magnesium on waterlogged soils, which are common in late winter and early spring. Phosphorus fertilization may also be helpful on some soils. Legumes are high in magnesium, and pastures containing sufficient legume forage will normally offset the problem. However, legume growth is often limited in winter, so most of the early season forage may be grass. The most dependable control is supplemental feeding of magnesium-fortified mineral mix during the potentially dangerous tetany season. In much of the South, grass tetany is most likely to occur during the period from mid February to mid April on pastures of tall fescue or small grains.

Other Disorders

Acute bovine pulmonary emphysema (ABPE) is a respiratory disorder that may occur when cattle are abruptly shifted from dry feed to lush pasture or from grass pastures to those with a high percentage of legumes. Cows that have recently calved are especially susceptible. The disorder is characterized by acute respiratory distress, labored breathing, frothing at the mouth, and grunting while exhaling. Occasional coughing and a frothy nasal discharge have been observed. A slight elevation in body temperature may be present. ABPE can be fatal, and death can occur within 12 hours of onset of symptoms. The best prevention is to avoid sudden changes in diet. If an outbreak occurs, quickly remove animals from pasture and feed grass hay.

Ergot poisoning is caused by a parasitic fungus that grows in the seed heads of small grains, ryegrass, bahiagrass, and especially dallisgrass. A toxin produced by the ergot interferes with circulation, resulting in reduced blood flow to extremities of the limbs and tail. Lameness is often an early symptom, with sloughing of the tail tip and possibly feet if cattle continue to be exposed to ergot. Other symptoms include stimulation and depression of the central nervous system, elevated body temperature, and increased respiratory or pulse rate. Since ergot grows in seedheads, clipping of pastures can reduce the danger by limiting seedhead development. Cattle should be changed immediately to an ergot-free diet.

Bermudagrass staggers (bermudagrass tremors) is a nervous disorder of cattle caused by alkaloids from fungal infection of bermudagrass. Outbreaks of the disorder are rare. The problem may occur when cattle are grazing tall, mature bermudagrass pastures during autumn and winter following a period of cloudy, damp weather that promotes the growth of toxin-producing fungi. Hay cut from these pastures has remained toxic for up to two years.

Symptoms are similar to ergot poisoning. Infected cattle twitch, tremble, become stiff-legged in the hind quarters, weak in the front legs, and are poorly coordinated. Cattle may fall to their knees when excited. Animals usually recover rapidly when removed from toxic pasture and given an alternative feed source. This problem can be prevented by keeping pastures in a young vegetative stage and not grazing tall, mature, matted bermudagrass. SF

Poisonous Plants

Many plants contain compounds that can be harmful to livestock. Poisoning normally does not occur as long as the animals have access to adequate amounts of good quality forage. When pastures are short and animals are hungry, they will often eat plants they would otherwise avoid. In addition, some plants may become attractive to livestock during certain stages of growth, after a herbicide application, or when animals have access to wilted leaves of plants that have been cut or blown down.

Space does not allow discussion of all Southern plants that may be toxic. However, this chapter provides basic information regarding a few of the plants most frequently responsible for livestock poisoning. Some plants discussed can also be toxic to humans. Symptoms of poisoning listed are not all-inclusive and may vary in different types of animals. Zones referred to under Adaptation headings are identified in **Figure 3.2.**

Courtesy of Dr. Tom Powe

Black Locust

(Robinia pseudoacacia)

Description: Small, thorny, leguminous tree with dark-colored rough bark and white flowers. Often, trees form a thicket. Individual trees rarely exceed a height of 50 feet.

Adaptation: Found throughout the South, especially in Zones B, C, and D.

Poisonous Principle: Robinin (a phytotoxin) and robitin (a glycoside).

Symptoms of Poisoning: Weakness, nervousness, nausea, vomiting, diarrhea, bloody feces, posterior paralysis, and pounding heartbeat.

Other: All of the above-ground portions of the plant can cause poisoning, especially during the warmer months of the year. Horses are more sensitive than cattle, and the most commonly encountered problem results from horses chewing the bark of trees. Usually not fatal.

Courtesy of Dr. Tom Powe

Bracken Fern
(Pteridium aquilinum)

Description: Herbaceous fern, usually no more than 2 to 3 feet tall, and having stout, dark-colored underground roots, the primary way the plant spreads.

Adaptation: Widely adapted in the South and can be found in Zones A, B, C, and D. Most common in the Coastal Plain or dry or gravelly upland areas in the Piedmont or upper South.

Poisonous Principle: In monogastric animals, thiaminase (an enzyme) and possibly unidentified compounds. In ruminants, prolonged ingestion produces bone marrow suppression, possibly due to unidentified toxins.

Symptoms of Poisoning: In monogastric animals, weight loss, lethargy, convulsions, and death. In ruminants, bloody feces, difficult breathing, failure of blood to clot, bleeding from all body openings, elevated temperature, and death.

Other: The entire plant is toxic, either in green or dried form, but especially young green material. Death is more likely in cattle or horses than in sheep. Poisoning is most likely in late summer or autumn in years or situations in which little other feed is available. Symptoms may not appear for several weeks after consumption.

Courtesy of Dr. Tom Powe

Buckeye or Horsechestnut
(Aesculus species)

Description: Trees or shrubs, most having red, yellow, or yellow-green to white flowers, and large (approximately 1 inch diameter) brown seeds or nuts.

Adaptation: Various species are adapted throughout Zones A, B, C, and D. Most commonly found along streams or the edges of woods.

Poisonous Principle: Aesculin (a glycoside) and possibly other unidentified agents.

Symptoms of Poisoning: Weakness, muscle spasms, vomiting, dilated pupils, and paralysis.

Other: All types of livestock may be poisoned by eating young sprouts or tender leaves in the spring or by consuming seed in autumn or early winter. Not likely to be fatal.

Courtesy of Dr. Tom Powe

Castorbean or Mole Bean
(Ricinus communis)

Description: Upright herbaceous summer annual with large leaves and reddish or purplish stems, sometimes reaching 12 feet in height.

Adaptation: Can be grown throughout Zones A, B, C, and D. Usually planted as an ornamental, but occasionally escapes and volunteers in old fields, waste places, or along roadsides.

Poisonous Principle: Ricin (a phytotoxin).

Symptoms of Poisoning: Vomiting, diarrhea, trembling, sweating, convulsions, and death.

Other: Both leaves and seed can cause poisoning of all classes of livestock, but horses are particularly sensitive. Ricin is a deadly poison. Poisoning most frequently occurs as a result of grains or ground feed becoming contaminated with castorbean seed.

Jimsonweed or Thornapple
(Datura stramonium)

Description: Herbaceous summer annual 3 to 5 feet tall with white or purplish flowers. The fruit is a spiny capsule 1 to 2 inches long.

Adaptation: Zones A, B, C, and D. A common weed in waste places, barnyards, disturbed areas, and cultivated fields, especially in the Coastal Plain.

Poisonous Principle: Hyoscyamine, atropine, and possibly other alkaloids.

Symptoms of Poisoning: Vomiting, dilated pupils, slow respiration, intense thirst, frequent urination, convulsions, and death.

Other: All parts of the plant are toxic, but especially the seed. Dried plants mixed in hay can also be toxic. All types of livestock can be poisoned, but most cases occur with cattle. Poisoning by this plant is fairly uncommon, but can occur in summer or autumn if little other forage is available.

Lantana *(Lantana camara)*

Description: Herbaceous perennial shrub that may reach 5 feet in height. Flower color varies greatly.

Adaptation: Occurs wild in South Florida (lower portion of Zone A), but commonly grown as an ornamental throughout the South. Occasionally escapes to roadsides and waste areas or may be present around old houses.

Poisonous Principle: Lantanin (a triterpenoid).

Symptoms of Poisoning: Vomiting, bloody and watery diarrhea, lesions around the mouth and nose, weight loss, and death. Also causes photosensitization (tissue death and/or lesions), especially in light colored animals.

Other: All parts of the plant are poisonous, but especially the fruit. All types of grazing livestock can be affected. Usually not fatal.

Courtesy of Dr. Ron Shumack

Mountain Laurel, Ground Ivy, Bush Ivy *(Kalmia latifolia)*

Description: Evergreen woody shrub or small tree with showy white, pinkish, or purplish flowers.

Adaptation: Usually found in heavily wooded areas (often around spring heads and small streams) in the mountains or other woodlands in the upper part of Zone B and in Zones C and D.

Poisonous Principle: Andromedotoxin (a resinoid) and possibly other toxic compounds.

Symptoms of Poisoning: Excessive salivation, frequent swallowing, vomiting, frequent defecation, staggering, coma, and death.

Other: All kinds of grazing livestock may be poisoned, but sheep seem to be particularly sensitive. Poisoning usually occurs in late autumn, winter, or early spring when little else is available for animals to eat. Otherwise, animals normally avoid the plant. Several related species in the genera *Rhododendron*, *Leucothoe*, and *Lyonia* may also be toxic. Goats are especially fond of ornamental azaleas.

Courtesy of Dr. Tom Powe

Courtesy of Dr. Ron Shumack

Nightshades *(Solanum* species)

Description: Annual or perennial herbs, some species covered with spines.

Adaptation: Various species are common in pastures, waste areas, or cultivated fields throughout Zones A, B, C, and D.

Poisonous Principle: Solanine and other alkaloids.

Symptoms of Poisoning: Excessive salivation, drowsiness, trembling, vomiting, diarrhea, dilation of pupils, paralysis, and death.

Other: Poisonous or potentially poisonous species include deadly nightshade (*Solanum americanum*), horsenettle or bullnettle (*Solanum carolinense*), and black nightshade (*Solanum nigrum*). The leaves and especially the unripe fruit (berries) are poisonous to cattle, horses, and sheep. Apparently, numerous environmental factors, plant maturity, and possibly animal genetics influence susceptibility. In some cases animals have been known to selectively graze nightshades.

Oaks *(Quercus* species)

Description: Trees or woody shrubs, usually deciduous, the fruit or nut being an acorn.

Adaptation: There are many species of oaks, and there are numerous adapted species in Zones A, B, C, and D. Most species are best adapted to rich, well-drained soils.

Poisonous Principle: Tannins and possibly other unidentified compounds.

Symptoms of Poisoning: Constipation followed by bloody diarrhea, poor appetite, weakness, rough appearance, thirst, and excessive urination.

Other: Poisoning of all types of livestock may result from consumption of leaves or acorns. Poisoning is unlikely unless there is little else for animals to eat, but once symptoms are observed death is likely even with treatment. Some of the more common species are white oak (*Quercus alba*), Southern red oak (*Quercus falcata*), black oak (*Quercus velutina*), post oak (*Quercus stellata*), water oak (*Quercus nigra*), and blackjack oak (*Quercus marilandica*).

Courtesy of Dr. Tom Powe

Oleander *(Nerium oleander)*

Description: Evergreen shrub or small tree with leathery leaves and reaching a height of up to 25 feet. Flowers white, yellow, pink, or red in clusters on stem tips.

Adaptation: Used as an ornamental primarily in the Coastal Plain (Zone A). May also be found around old buildings or growing wild in fencerows, along the edges of woods, or in waste places in some areas along the coast.

Poisonous Principle: Various glycosides and possibly other toxic compounds.

Symptoms of Poisoning: Vomiting, trembling, weakness, bloody diarrhea, and death.

Other: Leaves and twigs can cause poisoning of all types of livestock. Poisoning usually occurs when animals have access to clippings. Dried or green foliage or other plant parts can be highly toxic. Smoke from burning plants can produce toxic symptoms.

Courtesy of Dr. Tom Powe

Perilla Mint *(Perilla frutescens)*

Description: Herbaceous annual with small whitish or purplish flowers and usually no more than 1 to 2 feet tall.

Adaptation: Common throughout Zones A, B, C, and D in pastures, waste places, and along roadsides.

Poisonous Principle: Unknown.

Symptoms of Poisoning: Difficult breathing, nasal discharge, and death.

Other: Apparently, all aboveground portions of the plant can be toxic. Poisoning is most common in cattle or horses, usually in late summer or autumn.

Courtesy of Dr. Tom Powe

Poison Hemlock
(Conium maculatum)

Description: Herbaceous warm season biennial resembling wild carrot. Stems hollow except at nodes. May reach a height of 6 to 8 feet.

Adaptation: May be found in wet-natured waste areas or ditches throughout Zones C and D.

Poisonous Principle: Several alkaloids, especially coniine and N-methyl coniine.

Symptoms of Poisoning: Bloody feces, vomiting, convulsions, paralysis, and death.

Other: All portions of the plant are toxic. Toxicity increases as the plant matures, but decreases as it dries after being cut or frosted. If poisoning occurs, it is usually in the autumn. Grazing animals generally avoid it unless little other feed or forage is available.

Courtesy of Dr. Tom Powe

Pokeweed
(Phytolacca americana)

Description: Upright perennial herb, reaching a height of up to 10 feet.

Adaptation: Common throughout Zones A, B, C, and D in waste areas, along roadsides, or adjacent to wooded areas.

Poisonous Principle: Phytolaccotoxin (a saponin) and possibly other unidentified compounds.

Symptoms of Poisoning: Vomiting, convulsions, and death.

Other: The leaves, berries, and especially the roots are toxic. Cattle and occasionally horses are poisoned, but poisoning is fairly rare. Poisoning most commonly occurs during hot, dry periods in summer or autumn. Cattle have reportedly aborted after eating this plant.

Courtesy of Dr. Ron Shumack

Rhododendron
(Rhododendron species)

Description: Woody evergreen or deciduous shrub or small tree up to 15 feet tall. Flowers showy and may be white, rose or pink.
Adaptation: Grows mainly at higher elevations in the mountains or the upper Piedmont in Zones C and D. Usually found in moist soils in heavily wooded areas.
Poisonous Principle: May contain at least two toxic compounds: andromedotoxin (a resinoid) and arbutin (a glucoside).
Symptoms of Poisoning: May include nausea, vomiting, incoordination, paralysis, and death.
Other: Flowers, leaves, and young stems may be toxic to cattle, sheep, or goats. Poisoning from plants in pastured areas usually occurs during winter or spring. However, due to the ornamental nature of the plants, trimmings or cuttings used for decorations can also be a source of toxicity. Related species in the genera *Kalmia*, *Leucothoe*, and *Lyonia* may also be toxic.

Courtesy of Dr. Mike Patterson

Showy Crotalaria
(Crotalaria spectabilis)

Description: Herbaceous summer annual legume with bright yellow flowers, usually no more than 2 to 3 feet tall.
Adaptation: Widely adapted in the South, but most common in the Coastal Plain or dry upland areas in the Piedmont (Zones A and B).
Poisonous Principle: Monocrotaline (an alkaloid).
Symptoms of Poisoning: May be acute or chronic. Excessive salivation, nasal discharges, bloody feces, lethargy, weight loss, aimless walking, head pressing, and death.
Other: All types of livestock can be poisoned by any portion of the plant. The seed are especially toxic. If mixed in hay, the dried plants and/or seed can cause poisoning months after baling. The onset of symptoms may occur several weeks to months after consumption. This plant produces very hard seed, and volunteer stands can occur when soil is disturbed after many years with no evidence of the plant. Several other species in the genus are also believed or known to be toxic.

Wild Cherry or Wild Black Cherry *(Prunus serotina)*

Description: Woody shrubs or trees, usually small, with white or pink flowers. The fruit usually has a fleshy outer layer with a single hard stone in the center.

Adaptation: Commonly found in fencerows, borders of woods, and in waste places throughout Zones A, B, C, and D.

Poisonous Principle: Hydrocyanic (prussic) acid.

Symptoms of Poisoning: Labored breathing, spasms, and death. Low level poisoning may cause abortions.

Other: All types of grazing animals are susceptible. Many environmental factors may influence hydrocyanic acid levels, including drought and frost. However, most poisoning occurs when animals gain access to the wilted leaves of plants recently cut or blown down. There are many related species in this genus also presumed to be potentially toxic, but wild black cherry is considered the most dangerous.

Yellow Jessamine or Carolina Jessamine *(Gelsemium* species)

Description: Perennial trailing woody vine with fragrant yellow flowers, vegetatively resembling honeysuckle.

Adaptation: Common in the Coastal Plain and Piedmont (Zones A and B). Usually found in thickets, along the edges of woods or stream banks, or in fencerows.

Poisonous Principle: Gelsemine, gelseminine, and gelsemoidine (alkaloids).

Symptoms of Poisoning: Weakness, slow breathing, dilation of pupils, convulsions, and death.

Other: All portions of the plant are toxic to all types of livestock. Poisoning normally occurs only in winter or early spring in situations in which little other forage is available and when large quantities are consumed.

Courtesy of Dr. Tom Powe

Yew *(Taxus* species)

Description: Evergreen shrubs or (usually) small trees having needle-type leaves, reddish-brown bark, and reddish or scarlet berries.

Adaptation: Found primarily at higher elevations in Zones C and D. Also commonly used as an ornamental.

Poisonous Principle: Taxine (an alkaloid).

Symptoms of Poisoning: Staggering, muscular incoordination, and death.

Other: The bark, leaves, and seed are poisonous to all types of livestock. Highly toxic, but rarely eaten. Most poisoning occurs when cuttings are thrown into pastures or when plants in pastures are cut or blown down.

Summary

Although numerous plants commonly found in the South can be toxic, including many not mentioned in the preceding discussion, poisoning is fairly uncommon. The keys to reducing risk are to: 1) reduce access of livestock to potentially poisonous plants or 2) prevent the conditions under which certain plants can become dangerous. The following steps can be taken:

- Learn to recognize common poisonous plants and eliminate them from areas to which livestock have access. This includes poisonous plants just outside a pasture that animals can reach through a fence.
- Use fencing to prevent access of animals to areas where they do not belong. Many livestock poisonings occur when animals are given access to old home sites, trash dumps, or waste areas.
- Lack of adequate quantities of good forage is the primary factor that causes livestock to eat poisonous plants. If drought or other conditions severely limit forage production, alternate feed sources should be provided.
- Don't allow poisonous plants to be baled in hay. Some plants that animals would selectively avoid in a pasture situation may be consumed if mixed with other plants in hay.
- Do not allow livestock access to freshly cut plants, especially species known to be potentially toxic.
- The seed of many weeds is especially toxic, so taking care to prevent livestock from having access to seed screenings or weed seed from other sources is highly advisable.
- Immediately call a veterinarian if poisoning is suspected. SF

Fescue Toxicity

Tall fescue, grown on more than 35 million acres, is the most important cultivated pasture grass in the U.S. Since the late 1930s, this cool season perennial grass has been widely planted in an area from the lower Midwest to eastern Oklahoma and central Georgia. Its rapid acceptance was due to many attributes, including ease of establishment, long grazing season, tolerance to environmental stress, and pest resistance. Over 8.5 million beef cows and about 700,000 horses are maintained on tall fescue pastures.

Chemical measures of forage quality such as digestible dry matter, crude protein, and mineral levels suggest that tall fescue forage has potential for high quality and should give good animal performance. In spite of this, tall fescue gained a reputation for poor gains and reproduction problems in cattle. Mares grazing tall fescue would often abort, produce dead foals, have foaling difficulties, or fail to develop udders.

Fescue Toxicosis Syndromes in Cattle

There appear to be three separate syndromes associated with tall fescue. A brief description of each follows.

1. **Fescue foot.** The clinical signs are elevated respiration rate, vasoconstriction at the extremities, tenderness of legs, and gangrene that results in loss of hooves and/or portions of ears or tails. Fescue foot occurs mainly in winter and is mostly confined to the upper South. It is serious, but occurs relatively infrequently in relation to the large acreage of tall fescue.

2. **Bovine fat necrosis** is characterized by the presence of hard masses of fat in the adipose tissue, primarily in the abdominal cavity. Necrotic fat lesions are most common in the fat surrounding the intestinal tract all the way to the rectum. This syndrome, with upset digestion and difficult births, is reported to be associated with high rates of nitrogen fertilization from either mineral fertilizers or poultry litter.

3. **Fescue toxicity or summer slump** is characterized by poor animal gains, reduced conception rates, intolerance to heat, failure to shed the winter hair coat, and elevated body temperature. Though visible symptoms are most evident in warmer areas, this syndrome occurs throughout all tall fescue-growing regions of the U.S. The term summer slump has been applied in the northern tall fescue growing regions where it is most noticeable in summer, but the adverse effects occur throughout the year. Fescue toxicity is by far the most common and economically important syndrome in cattle on tall fescue.

Fescue Toxicity Syndrome in Horses

Fescue toxicity causes serious reproduction problems with mares. Specific problems are abortions, prolonged gestation, dystocia (difficult birth), thick placenta, foal deaths, retained placentas, agalactia (little or no milk production), and sometimes death of mares during foaling.

Cause of Fescue Toxicity

For many years, perloline and several other alkaloids occurring in tall fescue were suspected to cause the syndrome, but this was never proven. In 1977, several scientists at the USDA Russell Research Center, Athens, Georgia, reported a fungus inside the grass that was suspected to be associated with the syndrome. This was confirmed in grazing trials in Alabama where excellent animal gains and no evidence of toxicity were obtained on fungus-free (endophyte-free) tall fescue. The fungus associated with the toxicity is an endophyte (lives within the plant) and is called *Neotyphodium coenophialum*. The fungal endophyte produces ergot alkaloids that can be highly toxic to livestock.

Animal Response

Beef steer daily gains on endophyte-free tall fescue are typically 50 to 100 percent more than on grass with high rates of endophyte infestation. Steer daily gains are typically 1.5 to over 2 lb per day on endophyte-free grass, compared to around 1 lb or less on highly infected grass. Steers on endophyte-free grass are tolerant of heat, graze throughout the day, shed their winter hair coats in spring, and are more active than steers on endophyte-infected grass. Visible signs of the syndrome increase with higher temperatures, but poor gains occur throughout the year on endophyte-infected tall fescue.

Beef steers grazed from November to May on infected (left) and endophyte-free (right) tall fescue in the Black Belt of Alabama. Steers grazed on endophyte-free tall fescue gained more weight and had a slick hair coat.

Beef cows and calves maintained on endophyte-infected tall fescue pasture were thin and retained their winter hair coat even in May (Black Belt of Alabama).

Beef cows on endophyte-infected tall fescue are often thin and in poor condition, caked with mud, and spend excessive amounts of time in shade or water. Conception rate of beef cows (especially first-calf heifers) may also be reduced, often to 50 percent or less. Calf weight gains are decreased, a result of both reduced milk production by cows and consumption of toxic tall fescue forage by calves. Milk production of beef cows on endophyte-infected grass can be reduced by 30 percent or more.

Lactation of dairy cattle is also sharply reduced on endophyte-infected tall fescue. However, milk production of dairy cows grazing endophyte-free tall fescue has been similar to that on orchardgrass.

Horses are quite sensitive to infected tall fescue. Mares grazing the grass during the last two to three months before foaling are likely to abort or have dead foals and produce little or no milk. The evidence is overwhelming that these problems are associated with the endophyte.

Endophyte-infected tall fescue hay and seed also contain the toxic substance and can cause poor animal performance. Hay from endophyte-infected fields has remained toxic even when stored for two years.

Biology of the Fungal Endophyte

The fungus lives its entire life cycle within the plant, thus being called an endophyte. Unlike most fungi, it is not visible externally on the tall fescue plant. Infected grass appears the same as endophyte-free tall fescue, and the only way the presence of the fungus can be detected is by laboratory examination.

All evidence indicates that the endophyte is spread only through infected seed. This is important because it means that tall fescue pastures free of the endophyte will remain that way for a long time if well managed. However, invasion of an endophyte-free pasture can occur from introduction of infected seed in hay or by cattle that have previously grazed infected tall fescue. Pastures having a low or intermediate level of infection can be expected to increase in percentage of infected plants, due to the higher stress tolerance (competitive advantage) of infected plants.

Storage of infected seed under normal temperature and humidity conditions in the southeastern U.S. generally results in death of the endophyte after one to two years. Thus, planting old seed of endophyte-infected tall fescue can result in an endophyte-free pasture. However, seed germination and vigor also decline with storage time. Viable endophyte infection level of the seed should be tested prior to planting to be certain of its status. Planting of vigorous, new crop, endophyte-free seed from clean seed fields is the best way to obtain an endophyte-free pasture.

Benefits of the Endophyte

The endophyte does not appear to be harmful to the tall fescue plant. In fact, the endophyte and the grass derive mutual benefits from their association. The benefits for the endophyte include food, protection within the tall fescue plant, and dissemination through the seed. In return, the tall fescue plant obtains many benefits from the fungal endophyte that make it better able to survive and compete with other plants in stressful environments **(Figure 24.1).**

Endophyte-infected plants are more drought tolerant than endophyte-free plants, probably due to greater root depth and volume that increase water uptake over a longer period of time, resulting in better survival under moisture stress. Endophyte infection increases seed germination rate, seedling vigor, tiller growth rate, seed production, and mineral uptake. Resistance to some diseases, insects, and nematodes is better in endophyte-infected plants, as is tolerance to close continuous grazing. Thus, the overall result is that the endophyte makes tall fescue more persistent and competitive with other plant species in a pasture.

Endophyte-Free Tall Fescue

Planting endophyte-free tall fescue seed ensures excellent animal performance and eliminates all endophyte-related toxicity problems **(Figure 24.1)**. Unfortunately, such a pasture lacks the benefits conferred by the endophyte. Endophyte effects on stress tolerance of tall fescue have impor-

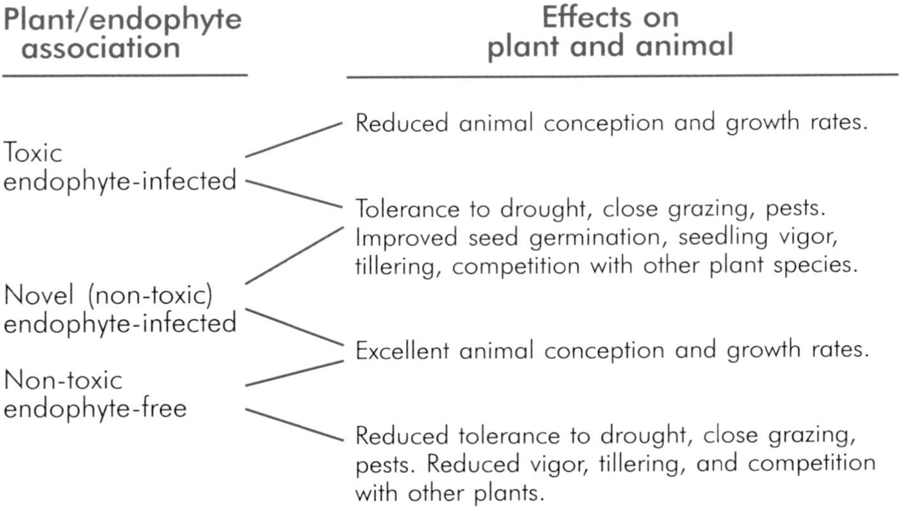

Figure 24.1. Effect of endophyte infection on tall fescue characteristics.

tant implications for livestock producers. More precision is required in establishment of endophyte-free tall fescue pastures. This includes careful attention to soil fertility, as well as planting date, rate, and depth. It is difficult to establish and maintain endophyte-free tall fescue pastures in stressful areas where this grass is only marginally adapted.

Endophyte-free tall fescue stands can be weakened by overgrazing and drought to a greater extent than infected tall fescue. The high palatability of endophyte-free tall fescue may contribute to stand losses due to overgrazing, especially during summer. Thus, endophyte-free tall fescue pastures require better grazing management to maintain stands and productivity.

Endophyte-free tall fescue pastures, planted in autumn, should not be grazed until plants are well established in late spring. Close grazing of a newly established pasture in summer weakens plants and reduces production the next autumn. In the southern area of tall fescue adaptation, environmental stresses are greater than farther north, making it even more important to avoid overgrazing endophyte-free stands.

Novel (Non-Toxic) Endophyte Tall Fescue

Novel (non-toxic) endophyte technology offers a unique solution to tall fescue toxicity problems in livestock. Some endophyte strains do not produce toxic alkaloids, but generally furnish the same benefits to the plant as toxic endophyte strains (**Figure 24.1**). These novel or non-toxic strains can be inserted into endophyte-free tall fescue varieties. There are many strains of non-toxic endophytes, and they vary in their ability to work effectively with different tall fescue varieties, making lengthy testing necessary to determine the stress tolerance of a particular endophyte/tall fescue variety combination.

Grazing trials with lambs, beef steers, beef cows, and horses have shown that animal performance on novel endophyte tall fescue can be excellent and similar to that on endophyte-free tall fescue. Beef steers on novel endophyte tall fescue gained about 0.9 lb/day and 200 lb/A more than those grazing toxic grass in two Georgia experiments during three years. The same gain advantage over toxic tall fescue carried through in the feedlot. Thus, animals grazed on non-toxic endophyte tall fescue reached desirable slaughter weight sooner than animals grazed on toxic grass. With beef cows, calf weaning weights on non-toxic endophyte as compared to toxic tall fescue were 75 lb higher for steers and 60 lb for heifers. Grazing comparisons with pregnant mares on novel endophyte tall fescue in Mississippi gave results similar to mares on endophyte-free tall fescue.

Of great importance, novel endophytes appear to give the tall fescue plant benefits such as improved vigor, pest resistance, and drought and grazing tolerance similar to that of toxic endophyte tall fescue. In tests with severe overgrazing in bermudagrass sod under drought conditions, stand persistence of novel endophyte was superior to endophyte-free tall fescue. Endophyte strain combinations with different tall fescue lines vary in their tolerance to stress, so testing over a number of years is essential to determine the value of a successful novel endophyte/tall fescue variety combination.

Pasture Endophyte Infection Level

Surveys in several states indicate that most tall fescue pastures are endophyte-infected at levels averaging 60 percent to over 80 percent. The widespread infection can be attributed to the seed increase and subsequent planting of fresh Kentucky 31 fescue seed that originated from one heavily endophyte-infected seed source in Kentucky.

Not all tall fescue pastures are infected with the endophyte, so it is important to determine the level of infection. If there is a question about infection level, each field should be tested. Several public and private laboratories will test forage or seed for endophytes.

A common question is why livestock on some farms seem to have fewer fescue toxicity problems than those on other farms, even though all the tall fescue pastures are heavily infected with endophyte. Generally, reduced toxicity symptoms are a result of toxin dilution by other forage species or weeds. Farms that maintain good clover stands in pastures have fewer problems. Tall fescue pastures mixed with bermudagrass or palatable weeds are likewise less likely to have animals showing serious symptoms. Crabgrass and winter annual weeds also dilute the forage available, reducing intake of toxic tall fescue. However, even under these conditions, cattle with few visible fescue toxicity symptoms often have reduced conception rates and lower calf weaning weights that impair overall productivity. The reason is that adequate dilution does not occur throughout the grazing season, resulting in periods when the animal diet is mainly toxic tall fescue.

Practical Solutions to the Toxicity Problem

Various solutions are now available, ranging from relatively inexpensive to expensive. The choice depends on the type of livestock operation, producer expectations, and management expertise. A number of low-cost management practices are available to beef cow-calf producers that will help alleviate but not eliminate toxicity problems. These practices are often adequate for beef cows where toxic pastures are diluted with other forage species and livestock toxicity problems are not pronounced.

- Management of pastures to favor other grasses such as Kentucky bluegrass, orchardgrass, or common bermudagrass in the sward to dilute the toxic tall fescue. Early and close grazing of tall fescue in spring prevents shading of other grass species. Summer application of nitrogen favors summer-growing grasses such as bermudagrass and crabgrass.
- Keeping toxic endophyte-infected pastures grazed relatively closely, as opposed to allowing forage to accumulate, may improve animal performance. Also, mowing of seed heads in spring will reduce intake of the highly toxic seed by livestock.
- Seeding of legumes such as alfalfa, annual lespedeza, red clover, or white clover into pastures will dilute the toxic fescue and improve animal performance. For many producers, this is an especially feasible option.

- Feeding of hay other than toxic tall fescue, such as endophyte-free tall fescue, bermudagrass, orchardgrass, timothy, alfalfa, red clover, or sericea lespedeza, greatly reduces the toxicity problem in winter. Feeding grain has been beneficial to cattle consuming toxic tall fescue, but has not been of benefit to pregnant mares.
- A more expensive solution is available for treatment of pregnant mares grazing toxic tall fescue. Domperidone is a commercially-available compound that can be administered to mares and allow them to carry foals to term without losses. This is unlikely to be useful for cattle as the cost is high, and the effects are short-lived.
- If tall fescue pastures on a farm have a history of beef cows with poor pregnancy rates, low calf weaning weights, and visible toxicity symptoms, then replanting of the pastures with endophyte-free or novel endophyte tall fescue seed will likely improve animal performance and profitability. This is a major decision, as it involves the cost of completely destroying existing pastures and replanting them.

When grazing young beef animals, as in a stocker operation, it is essential to obtain high gains for profitability. Young steers and heifers are highly sensitive to fescue toxicity, with daily live weight gains being reduced by about 0.1 lb for each 10 percentage units of endophyte frequency in pastures. Thus, replanting pastures offers attractive economic returns. Yearling beef animals perform better if a good dewormer is used while they are grazing infected tall fescue. Dewormers probably do not act as an antidote, but they are believed to avoid an interaction effect between internal parasites and the fungal toxins. Dairy and horse producers should consider replanting toxic infected pastures since performance may be affected, even at low levels of endophyte infection.

Replanting Infected Tall Fescue

Replanting infected pastures requires considerable capital outlay along with good establishment techniques, and may take pastures out of production for up to a year. Also, better grazing management is required to achieve the full benefits of these non-toxic pastures. Either endophyte-free or novel endophyte seed can be planted, but the superior stress tolerance of the latter offers extra benefits.

To successfully establish non-toxic tall fescue pastures, the old sod must be completely killed. On land suitable for crops, tillage and cropping in summer before autumn planting tall fescue are generally effective. However, many tall fescue pastures are too hilly for tillage, and severe soil erosion would result if they were tilled. In addition, tillage is expensive. An attractive alternative is killing the endophyte-infected tall fescue with herbicides and drilling endophyte-free or novel endophyte seed with a sod-seeder.

Renovation must begin in spring of the planting year. Seed production should not be allowed during the calendar year of conversion from toxic to non-toxic tall fescue. Herbicide should be applied to the closely grazed pasture in spring before seed head emergence to kill the tall fescue and other vegetation. A summer annual grass can be sod-seeded into the dead tall fescue and grazed, then mowed closely in early autumn and herbicide applied again to kill any remaining tall fescue, summer annual grass, or other plants. Tall fescue can then be drilled into the dead sod. Rye, wheat, or annual ryegrass should not be planted with tall fescue when establishing stands as these species are very competitive and will have an adverse effect on newly established tall fescue plants. The new stand should not be grazed until the next spring to allow good root establishment. To prevent introduction of toxic seed, animals should never be moved from toxic tall fescue pasture without a three-day wait on another forage. For the same reason, toxic tall fescue hay should never be fed on endophyte-free or novel endophyte pastures.

The Fescue Endophyte: Present and Future

Annual losses from reduced beef cow conception rates and calf weaning weights caused by fescue toxictiy are estimated at over $600 million in the U.S. Serious losses are also encountered in horses from abortions and foal deaths. Consumption of toxic tall fescue also adversely affects reproduction in a number of wildlife species.

The toxic endophyte problems with livestock can be alleviated to a considerable extent by management, especially by dilution of pastures with other grasses and legumes. The most dependable long-term solution is replanting toxic pastures with novel endophyte tall fescue seed. This involves more cost and a higher level of management, but it provides the full benefits of excellent animal performance and plant persistence similar to toxic tall fescue.

It is likely that numerous novel endophyte tall fescue varieties will become commercially available, some of which will be superior to others. Producers need to study research trial results to select the best one for their area.

It is also possible that there may eventually be a reasonably priced antidote for the animal that will offset the toxins produced by the toxic endophyte. The discovery of the fungal endophyte as the cause of fescue toxicity and the development of a number of ways to minimize or avoid the problems caused by toxic endophyte have been major advances in grassland research. SF

Grazing Management

Management of pasture plants is unique. While most crop plants are grown for their fruit or seed, it is the leaves or photosynthetic area of pasture plants that are removed, continually or frequently, and this occurs throughout the grazing season. This places great stress on the plants, making them dependent on ungrazed leaves and stored food reserves in the roots, rhizomes, stolons, or stem bases to fuel regrowth after grazing (see Chapters 14 and 15).

How Animals Graze

The grazing animal is a remarkable forage harvesting machine. In one day, a mature cow may consume up to 20 percent of her weight in fresh forage. To achieve this, she moves slowly over the pasture and takes successive bites (30 to 60 per minute) by drawing forage into her mouth with her tongue. With the forage firmly held between her upper dental pad (gums) and lower incisor teeth, she then pulls or tears it from the plants.

Sheep and goats have smaller mouthparts with which they nibble forage, achieving a higher frequency of biting, and may bite rather than tear the selected material by cutting it between the lower incisor teeth and the dental pad of the upper jaw. The biting action and small mouths of sheep and goats allow more selective and closer grazing than the tearing action of cattle. Horses are highly selective grazers and prefer closely grazed forage. They often heavily graze some spots in pastures while not grazing others, and these patches may be overgrazed from year to year unless forage availability is greatly restricted.

Cattle normally graze for six to 11 hours per day, usually in two major periods, just before dusk and just after dawn, with shorter periods during the day or at night. After a grazing period, the ruminant animal rests and

The grazing animal is a remarkable forage harvesting machine.

ruminates, regurgitating the forage, chewing, mixing it with saliva, and swallowing it again. Rumination time ranges from five to nine hours daily.

Pasture Growth

High pasture leaf production over an extended period of time depends on a number of factors, including:

- effective light interception and high photosynthetic efficiency,
- low extent of leaf aging and decomposition of leaves,
- maintenance of a vigorous tiller or shoot population for regrowth,
- maintenance of adequate levels of carbohydrates in plant food storage structures.

Balancing these factors to achieve high forage productivity and animal performance may appear complex, but can be done when the dynamics of pasture growth are understood. Pasture yield potential depends on the amount of light intercepted by the leaves. Considering a leaf area unit of 1 as one layer of leaf tissue covering an equivalent land area (i.e. leaf area equals soil surface area), pasture yield potential increases as leaf area increases until leaves intercept about 90 percent of the light (**Figure 25.1**).

Cool season grasses such as tall fescue generally reach this point at about 6 to 7 leaf area units, while some warm season grasses such as pearl millet with more upright growth allow more light to penetrate the canopy and may attain up to 10 or 12 leaf area units. Legumes such as white clover with horizontal leaves intercept more light per leaf and cause greater shading of other leaves, thus reaching the forage production potential plateau at about 3 to 4 leaf area units. The practical significance of this is that an overgrazed grass pasture will have a greatly reduced leaf area of perhaps 1 or 2 leaf area units and thus is not able to utilize sufficient light to reach its yield potential. Close grazing has a less harmful effect on some clover species than on some erect-growing grasses and legumes.

In consideration of the leaf area concept, it might seem desirable to manage a pasture to maintain a large amount of leaf tissue so as to stay at a high forage production potential plateau. Unfortunately, pasture leaf tissue cannot be stored over long periods of time because individual leaves have a limited life span of only about 30 to 60 days. Aging leaves decline in ability to utilize sunlight and finally die. Over time, the rate of leaf tissue loss to aging and decomposition increases, leaving a high proportion of dead leaves in an undergrazed pasture (**Figure 25.2**).

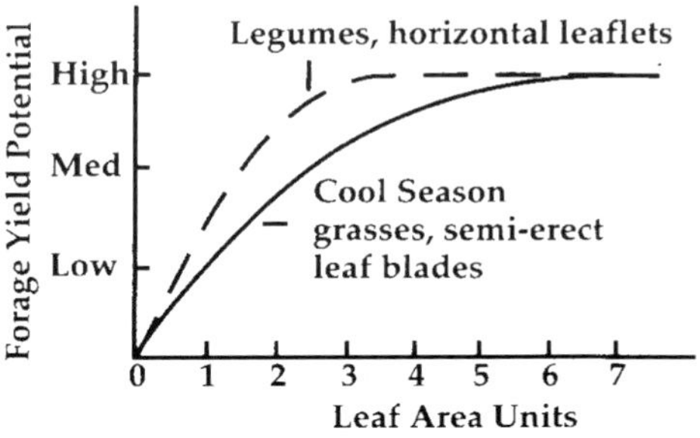

Figure 25.1. **Forage yield in a pasture increases as leaf area increases until leaves intercept about 90 percent of the light.** Adapted from: R.E. Blaser, Virginia Agric. Exp. Stn. Bull. 86-7.

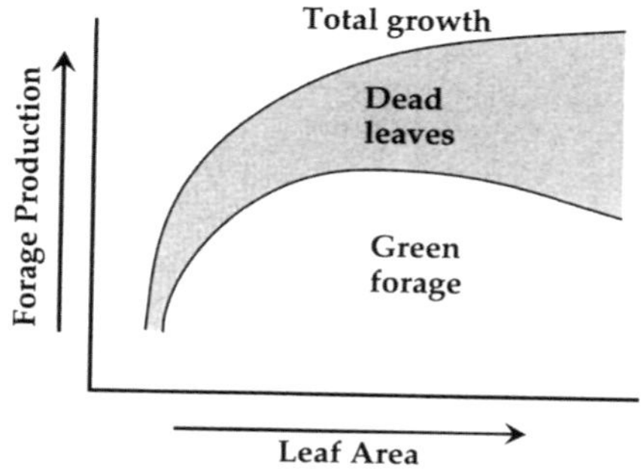

Figure 25.2. Over time, the proportion of dead leaves increases in a pasture at high leaf area levels. The need for removal of leaves by grazing is apparent.

Grazing animals find dead leaves less acceptable and are likely to avoid them when other forage is available. Leaf growth in a pasture needs to be utilized fairly promptly, or much of it will be utilized at a less-than-optimum quality stage. Young leaves are higher in protein and digestible energy than old dying or dead leaves. Thus, in order to manage a pasture well, it is necessary to at least periodically graze off most of the leaves to improve light penetration, which stimulates growth of new leaves. Sufficient light is needed to maintain an adequate number of basal buds to develop young tillers or shoots on both grasses and legumes.

Undergrazing results in heavy shading, which depresses tiller development and reduces subsequent forage production. This often occurs during the peak growth period of tall fescue pastures in spring or of bermudagrass and bahiagrass pastures in summer. Shading of one pasture species by another greatly increases competition. Tall growing grasses such as rye, wheat, oats, tall fescue, or orchardgrass can shade out shorter grasses and clovers if they are undergrazed for long periods of time. For example, gross undergrazing of a small grain/annual ryegrass mixture in autumn and early winter can reduce ryegrass production in late winter and early spring. On the other hand, undergrazing of overseeded annual ryegrass in late spring delays bermudagrass bud development and growth, reducing stand density and allowing more weed growth in summer.

Good pasture management requires compromises with regard to plant height and closeness of grazing to achieve reasonable production of palatable and nutritious forage over a long period of time. This can be done by manipulation of stocking density according to available forage, harvesting surplus forage for stored feed, and timely fertilization. Forage crops differ in their ability to tolerate heavy or light grazing, and thus optimum pasture height varies with species (**Appendix A.53**).

Effects of Grazing Animals on Pastures

The productivity and populations of various species in a pasture can be rapidly and substantially altered by grazing animals. The effects of a particular grazing regime may be harmful or beneficial, depending on the plant species present. Grazing animals defoliate and trample plants and excrete dung and urine on a pasture. The interrelations of animals and plants in a pasture are complex, and the effects of grazing differ greatly from hay harvesting.

Defoliation. The removal of plant shoots or leaves by grazing affects pastures differently depending on: 1) the species present; 2) the extent of

Overgrazing (left) adversely affects forage growth, water and soil conservation, and pasture plant persistence. Undergrazing (right) results in forage waste, reduced nutritive quality, reduced tiller development, loss of legumes, and less subsequent growth.

selective grazing of different plant species; 3) the frequency of removal; 4) how much plant material is removed versus how much remains; 5) the stage of plant development; and 6) weather conditions at time of defoliation. Defoliation is the most important influence of grazing animals on a pasture. Grazing reduces leaf area, thus affecting plant food production and storage, shoot development, leaf and root growth, light intensity in the lower portion of the forage canopy, soil temperature, and soil moisture. Defoliation effects are a result of grazing pressure by livestock, as illustrated in the photos.

Close grazing when grass growing points are being elevated prior to flowering may be especially harmful to certain grasses such as orchardgrass. With tall-growing forage species, continued overgrazing generally results in weakened plants with reduced root systems, lower forage yield, greater soil erosion and water run-off, thinned forage stands, and more weeds. The closeness and frequency of defoliation often determine which forage species and weeds dominate a pasture. For example, continuous close grazing favors bahiagrass or common bermudagrass over taller bermudagrass hybrids such as Coastal. Also, close grazing favors white clover growing in association with tall fescue. Low stocking rates or intermittent grazing allows the survival of tall species such as johnsongrass or switchgrass, neither of which is tolerant of close continuous defoliation.

Undergrazing also has undesirable effects on a pasture. Wasted forage and reduced overall nutritive quality are most obvious, but there are other negative effects. Undergrazing grass-clover pastures generally decreases clover stands because the taller-growing grass(es) shades the lower-growing legume(s). For example, undergrazed tall fescue or orchardgrass will shade out white clover. Red clover, under these conditions, is more competitive with grasses because it has a more upright growth habit.

Clovers differ in their tolerance to shade. For example, crimson and subterranean clovers are more shade tolerant than arrowleaf clover. Arrowleaf clover is particularly sensitive to shading because this reduces development of buds near the stem bases for initiation of new leaves. Therefore, considerable grazing is required to maintain good arrowleaf clover growth in late spring.

Heavy spring growth of cool season perennial grasses is frequently under-utilized, resulting in shading of tiller buds. When growth slows in summer due to heat and/or drought, these pastures are often overgrazed, but recovery after rains is poor because of insufficient tillers and leaf area. Patch grazing by cattle is a result of understocking, and is usually not a problem when pastures are grazed to maintain a height of 3 to 6 inches. Some general principles regarding species responses to grazing are listed below.

1) Tall upright plants are easily defoliated by grazing and usually depend on food reserves in roots, rhizomes, and/or stem bases for regrowth and persistence. Rotational stocking with a rest period, or continuous stocking at a rate low enough to leave a higher stubble is required for species such as red clover, most alfalfa and sericea lespedeza varieties, kudzu, pearl millet, sorghum, johnsongrass, big bluestem, indiangrass, and switchgrass.

2) Semi-erect species, or those having food storage areas and buds near the ground, are fairly tolerant of close grazing except under stress conditions. Species in this group include tall fescue, arrowleaf clover, and to a lesser extent orchardgrass.

3) Prostrate species that are extremely tolerant of close grazing include bermudagrass, bahiagrass, Kentucky bluegrass, white clover, and subterranean clover.

Treading. Pugging or pressure by hooves of grazing animals injure plants and compact the soil, reducing pasture production. As with other stresses, pasture plants respond differently to treading damage. Ryegrass, tall

Cattle hooves on wet pasture damage plants, compact soil, and reduce water infiltration on clay soils.

fescue, Kentucky bluegrass, bermudagrass, bahiagrass, and white clover are more tolerant of treading than small grains, orchardgrass, or red clover. Pasture treading damage is greater on wet than dry soils, on clay than sandy soils, on recently-tilled than settled soils, and with short forage as opposed to taller forage. Treading of cattle on wet clay soils substantially reduces water infiltration, resulting in less benefit from rainfall. Removing cattle from pastures during extremely wet periods can greatly reduce treading damage.

Excretion. Cattle, sheep, and goats normally defecate 10 to 18 times and urinate six to 11 times daily. Losses differ for various nutrients (see Chapter 9). Under continuous stocking, excretion concentrates nutrients on only about 20 percent of the pasture and reduces the amount of grazable forage due to cattle avoiding dung and urine patches. Stock camps (water, shade, salt areas) further concentrate the excreta. Locating water, salt, and shade in separate areas can reduce the problem.

Pasture Stocking Rate

The effect of a grazing system on animal productivity is strongly influenced by grazing pressure (animals per unit of forage available) and stocking rate (animals per acre). Stocking rate and its relationship to available forage are the most important management factors influencing the output of animal product from a pasture, plant persistence, and productivity of a given forage species. Thus, determining appropriate stocking rate and varying the stocking density to utilize the forage on a farm impact economic returns. Several major factors influence the optimum stocking rate.

1) Forage production. With improved forage species and good levels of fertilization, the amount of forage produced increases, creating a need to increase stock numbers in order to utilize the forage growth. At a low stocking rate, available forage and productivity per animal tend to be high, but output per acre is low (**Figure 25.3**). When pasture quality declines due to accumulation of stems and dead forage, dry matter intake by animals decreases, lowering animal output.

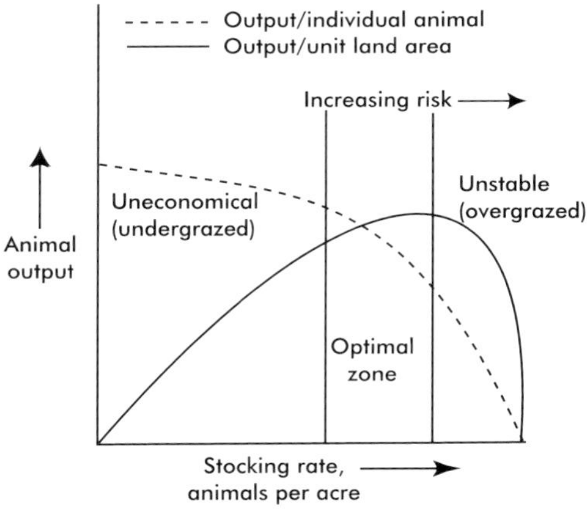

Figure 25.3. Relationship of animal output (per animal and per unit of land area) and pasture stocking rate. Adapted from: G.O. Mott. p. 606-611. Proc. 8th Int. Grassland Congress, Reading, England.

As stocking rate is increased on a pasture, less forage is available per animal. Individual animal output decreases as animals compete for forage and have less opportunity to select green, leafy forage. However, due to increased forage utlization, animal output per acre increases with stocking rate until individual animal gains are depressed to the point that the additional animals carried do not compensate for the loss. At very high stocking rates, photosynthesis is reduced due to insufficient leaf area, plants are weakened, and forage growth is depressed.

Productive pastures must have sufficient leafy, green forage available to allow the animals to quickly satisfy their appetites by selective grazing. This will require about 1,200 to 1,500 lb/A of dry forage on tall fescue and 1,500 to 1,800 lb/A for hybrid bermudagrass. To maintain these amounts of forage under continuous stocking will require plant heights of about 4 to 6 inches for both grass species.

In cool, moist climates or in mountain areas of the Southern U.S., a good grazing recommendation for cool season grasses is to maintain a forage height of 3 to 4 inches. This encourages new leaf development and results in high quality forage. However, in most of the Southern U.S. where late spring, summer, and autumn drought can occur, most beef cow-calf producers prefer to maintain pastures at a somewhat greater height to have reserve forage for drought periods.

Stocking a pasture below the optimum rate for output per acre results in a higher rate of production per animal due to selective grazing. As stocking rate is increased, the opportunity for selection of high quality leafy forage is less than in pastures having a lower stocking rate. Closely grazed pastures may also have more internal parasites and if seriously overgrazed, less forage production, further reducing production per animal.

2) **Accessibility of forage to animals.** Insufficient watering points or shade may cause animals to spend most of the time in certain areas and thus may effectively reduce forage available to animals by causing overgrazing, trampling damage, and stand degradation in portions of a pasture. Rotational stocking or separating shade, mineral, and water locations will improve utilization of the entire pasture.

3) **Nutritive value of pasture.** Animals improve their diets by selectively grazing certain species such as clover, by choosing green leaves over dead leaves, or by selecting leaves rather than stems of grasses. On high quality winter annual or cool season perennial grass-legume pastures with adequate available forage, selectivity is generally not a problem. Growth of new leaf tissue of grasses, especially of warm season perennials, can be stimulated by nitrogen fertilization and periodic mowing of uneaten stems.

4) **Species composition of pasture.** Heavy stocking rates that result in very close grazing can reduce production and the stand of some desirable forage species, allowing encroachment by weeds. For example, close grazing of orchardgrass may result in invasion by less desirable species. At the southern edge of its adaptation zone, tall fescue is often invaded by bahiagrass or bermudagrass when grazed closely in summer. This problem is more serious for endophyte-free than endophyte-infected tall fescue. However, heavy stocking may improve summer animal performance by increasing the amount of crabgrass or white clover in endophyte-infected tall fescue pasture.

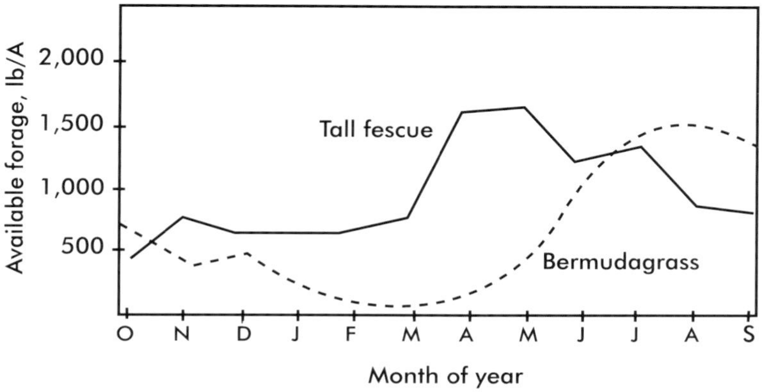

Figure 25.4. Available forage in mixed tall fescue-bermudagrass pasture grazed year-round with beef cows and calves, central Georgia. Source: C.S. Hoveland, M.A. McCann, and N.S. Hill. J. Prod. Agric. 10:245-250.

Stocking rate can be a highly useful tool for changing pasture composition. Close grazing of bahiagrass or bermudagrass in autumn makes it easier to establish annual forage crops, either by sowing or natural reseeding, thus furnishing higher quality forage and an extended grazing season. Broadcast seeding of red clover or white clover into a dormant tall fescue pasture in late winter, followed by heavy stocking of 10 to 20 animals per acre for a week or two, can result in establishment of a clover stand (see Chapter 12).

5) Seasonal variations in forage production. Pasture production varies greatly over the year and dramatically affects potential stocking rate (**Figure 25.4**). Stocking rate adjustment is essential if forage is to be efficiently utilized and animal production maintained over a long period. Surplus forage can be harvested as hay from ungrazed pastures during peak seasons of growth. Regardless of grazing management, stored feed will likely be needed during periods of limited growth. The requirement for stored feed can be reduced by having both a cow-calf and a stocker operation. This situation gives more flexibility because, if necessary, animals can be bought or sold to increase or lower stocking rate. However, prices are often depressed during periods of low forage growth. Astute timing in purchase or sale of cattle is a critically important profit factor.

Grazing Methods

Several grazing methods have been developed to accomplish various objectives. Low cost, high voltage electric fences have made it much more feasible to implement a variety of grazing methods that reduce pasture waste, conserve surplus forage as hay or silage, and possibly increase forage quality for the grazing animals. It should be remembered that the method of grazing used generally has less influence on livestock production than the stocking rate. The objective of a grazing method should be to manage the pasture and other feed inputs to efficiently produce animal products. Effectively managing forage quantity and quality over the grazing season is of

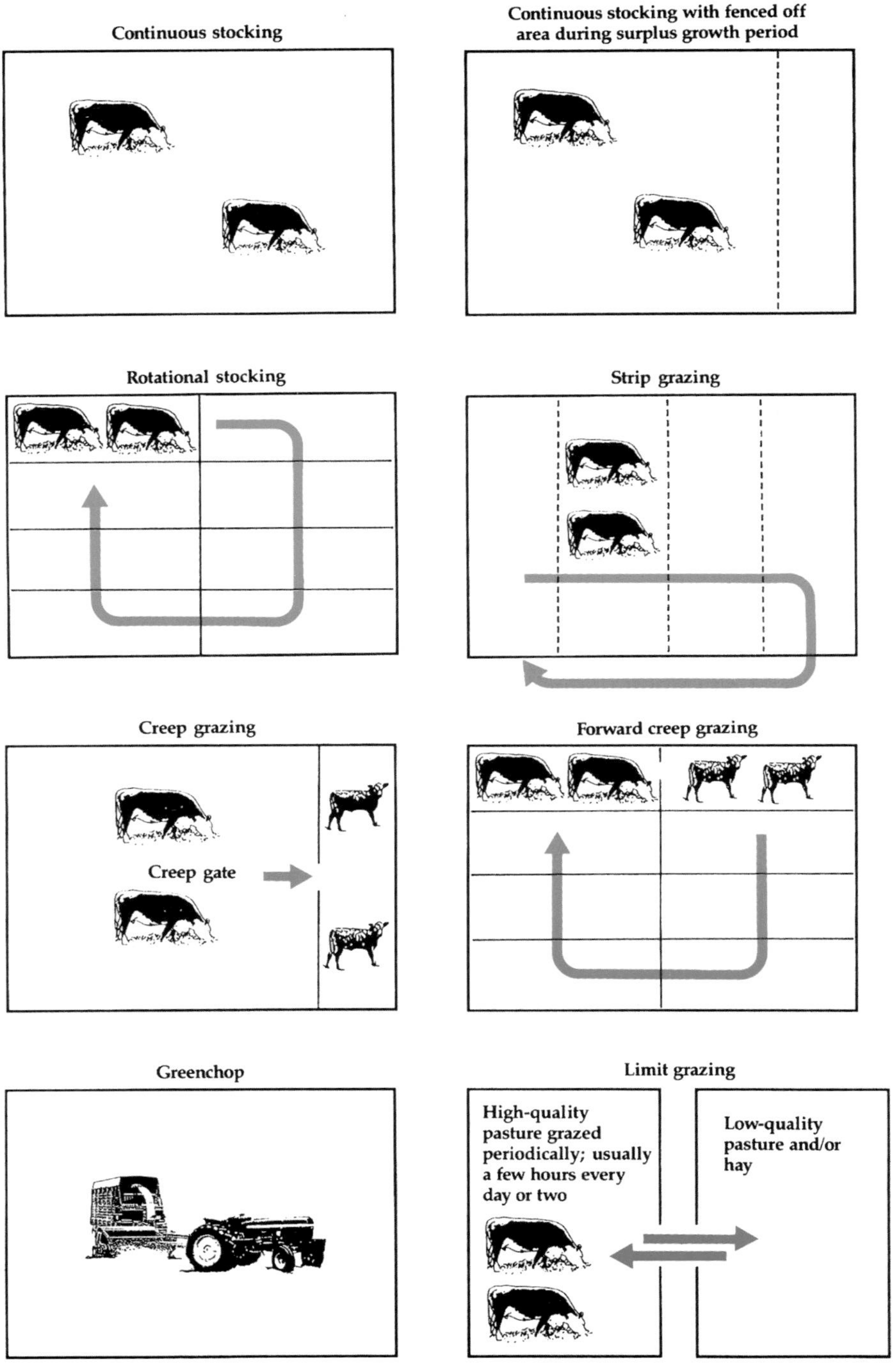

Figure 25.5. A variety of grazing/harvest methods may be used successfully.

much greater importance than which grazing method is employed.

Grazing methods are of two general types: continuous and several variations of intermittent grazing. They vary from simple to complex (**Figure 25.5**).

Continuous Stocking (often referred to as continuous grazing). Animals are maintained on a single pasture unit during the grazing season. This method allows animals to selectively graze unless the stocking rate is too high. If animal numbers or pasture size are not adjusted as pasture conditions change, this method may result in some plants being undergrazed and others being overgrazed. Also, without adjustment, the stocking rate may be near ideal part of the time and too high or low at other times during the grazing season. Pastures may be set-stocked with a fixed number of animals, or numbers may be adjusted to fit the feed supply over the grazing season. Adjustment of the stocking rate as needed greatly improves forage utilization. A temporary fence is sometimes used to close off part of a continuously stocked pasture during periods of surplus growth. This allows accumulated forage to be harvested for stored feed.

Continuous stocking has often been incorrectly equated with overgrazing and poor management. A continuously stocked pasture can be just as productive and efficient as any other method provided that available forage is controlled by adjusting stock numbers as needed. Continuous stocking can encourage a high number of grass tillers to maintain pasture stability and production over a long period of time.

Certain plant species such as johnsongrass, big bluestem, indiangrass, and switchgrass are not suited to continuous stocking unless the stocking rate is low enough to maintain 6 to 8 inches of leaf tissue. Stands of conventional hay-type alfalfa varieties will weaken and die under continuous close stocking. However, grazing-tolerant alfalfa and sericea lespedeza varieties will persist under moderate continuous stocking, though rotational stocking will provide increased forage utilization and lower the likelihood of weed encroachment.

Creep Grazing. This method allows young animals to pass through a fence opening or creep (**Figure 25.6**) to a special small pasture of higher quality forage (such as pearl millet, small grains, chicory, clover, or alfalfa) than the lower quality pasture where their mothers are maintained. This is particularly effective in summer when low forage availability restricts gains and when nutritive quality of a perennial grass pasture is low (**Table 25.1**).

Table 25.1. Creep grazing of beef calves on pearl millet from June-September (104 days) when cow-calf pairs were maintained on tall fescue pasture in northern Alabama.

	Control	Creep grazing
Calf weight gain, lb	144	219
Calf average daily gain, lb	1.38	2.10
Cow weight change, lb	-60	+27

Source: E.E. Thomas, J.T. Eason, D.M. Ball, and B.G. Ruffin. Alabama Agric. Exp. Stn. Highlights Agric. Res. Vol. 30, No. 2.

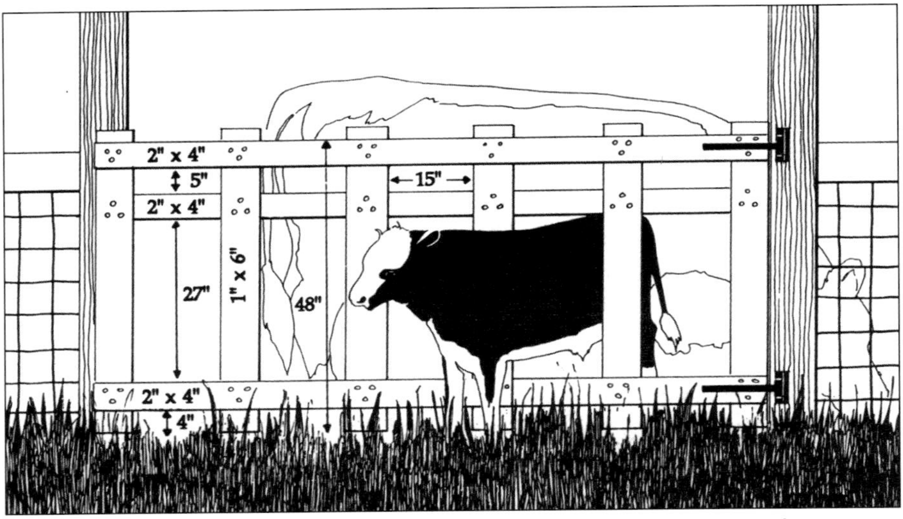

Figure 25.6. A creep gate allows calves, but not their mothers, to have access to higher quality pasture.

With beef cattle, calf gain increases and cow condition is often improved with creep grazing. This is a relatively inexpensive system as it requires only a small area of high quality pasture for the young growing animals. Creep pastures should be close to water or loafing areas so calves will utilize the high quality forage.

Forward Creep Grazing. This method allows calves or lambs with a high nutrient requirement to pass through an opening in the fence to graze fresh ungrazed pasture ahead of their mothers in a conventional rotational method. A creep gate or a single strand of electric fence positioned at the correct height to allow calves, but not cows, access to a higher quality paddock can be highly effective in creating a creep pasture.

Strip Grazing. Movable electric fence is used ahead of and sometimes behind the animals to ration daily forage. This method results in high forage utilization and is most effective with excellent pasture during cool weather when nutritive quality declines slowly. With low-quality forage, animal daily gains may suffer with strip grazing because of reduced selectivity. This method is especially valuable for minimizing waste when grazing stockpiled tall fescue during late autumn and winter.

Limit Grazing. Maintaining livestock on lower quality pasture, but allowing them access to a high quality winter annual pasture for a few hours each day or every few days, can reduce waste from trampling. This method is often used in the lower South where beef cows are kept on frosted bermudagrass or bahiagrass pasture during winter and fed low-quality hay, but allowed periodic access for a few hours each day or every few days to high-quality rye, wheat, and/or annual ryegrass pasture as a protein supplement. This provides good nutrition at relatively low cost as the area needed for winter annual pasture is relatively small.

Greenchop. Green forage is chopped mechanically and fed to livestock. This method reduces waste by grazing animals so that more animals can be fed per acre, but forage selectivity is reduced, and individual animal output is often lower. Equipment costs are high with this method. Forage often is not harvested at optimum growth stage, lowering nutritive quality. Also, daily harvesting can be difficult, especially in winter when rain results in wet soils and poor field conditions.

Deferred Grazing or Stockpiling. This is an excellent way to reduce hay feeding costs by grazing during early and mid winter the grass that was left ungrazed during autumn. For example, tall fescue fertilized in late summer or early autumn can be allowed to grow and accumulate forage until needed. Stockpiled tall fescue will usually contain 14 percent crude protein and over 60 percent digestible dry matter and maintains this high nutritive quality well into the winter. Unfortunately, stockpiled endophyte-infected tall fescue will still have some toxic properties, but the effect on animals is less severe during cool weather. Orchardgrass is less well suited for stockpiling as it makes less autumn growth and deteriorates more in winter. Warm season grasses such as bermudagrass or bahiagrass can also be stockpiled and grazed after frost, but nutritive quality is lower than tall fescue, and leaf quality deteriorates more quickly. Continuous stocking of stockpiled grass will result in a high percentage of the forage being trampled and wasted. Strip grazing with a movable electric fence is a useful way to ration daily forage for cattle and reduce waste.

Rotational Stocking (often referred to as rotational grazing). The pasture is subdivided into several paddocks and for a particular subdivided area, a rest period follows each grazing period (**Figure 25.5**). The number of paddocks may vary from only a few to 12 or more. A high stocking rate is imposed on a paddock for a short time, generally no more than seven to 10 days. Animals are then shifted to another paddock.

During periods of surplus growth, one or more paddocks may be harvested for hay, haylage, or round bale silage while animals are rotated

Rotational stocking of endophyte-free tall fescue can improve stand persistence, give better control over the pasture, and should reduce forage waste.

through other paddocks more quickly. When grazing animals are given access to a fresh pasture, the best quality forage is consumed first. Therefore, moving animals more quickly when pasture growth rates are high provides top quality forage to the livestock while helping to prevent excess forage accumulation in any of the paddocks.

A major advantage of rotational stocking often is increased carrying capacity, which may be 20 to over 30 percent higher than obtained with continuous stocking. This is mainly a result of less wasted forage from trampling as well as increased leaf growth. Some studies have shown little or no increased production as a result of rotationally stocking winter annuals. However, when high quality wheat-annual ryegrass no-till planted in bermudagrass was grazed during the cool season in Arkansas, steer gain/A was increased about 40 percent as a result of improved carrying capacity, while steer average daily gain was not affected (**Table 25.2**). In this case, three- and 11-paddock systems gave similar results. However, during the warm season on bermudagrass there was no improvement in gain per acre with rotational stocking. Average daily gain trended downward. Rotational stocking often reduces the opportunity for animals to select only the leafiest forage, thus decreasing the overall quality of forage ingested and sometimes lowering individual gains. This is especially true on low-quality warm season perennial grasses such as bermudagrass and bahiagrass. Small grains and annual ryegrass are highly palatable. Their nutritive quality remains high over the grazing season, allowing animals to maintain high performance, regardless of grazing method, if stocking rate is appropriate.

A variation on rotational stocking is to give first access in a paddock to animals having high nutritional requirements such as growing steers or lactating dairy cows, followed by animals with lower nutritional requirements. This is referred to as **forward grazing**. For example, steers or heifers with high potential for gain can be allowed to graze a paddock first, followed by beef cows that utilize the remaining lower-quality forage. This method maintains high gains on the young animals and removes the old residue to stimulate new growth of high-quality leafy forage while the pasture is rested. This approach can also be used with lactating dairy cows

Table 25.2. Beef steer performance and stocking rate on no-till planted wheat-annual ryegrass (cool season) on Midland bermudagrass (warm season) pasture as affected by rotational stocking in northwest Arkansas, two-year average.

Grazing method	Stocking rate, lb body wt./A		Avg. daily gain, lb		Steer gain/A, lb	
	Cool season	Warm season	Cool season	Warm season	Cool season	Warm season
Continuous stocking	1,460	2,220	2.07	1.45	430	310
Three-paddock rotational	1,880	2,050	2.36	1.37	600	270
11-paddock rotational	2,030	2,230	2.21	1.21	620	254

Source: G.E. Aiken. J. Prod. Agric. 11:185-190.

Table 25.3. Effect of year-round continuous vs. rotational (12 paddocks with cattle rotated every two days) stocking of endophyte-free tall fescue and common bermudagrass mixed grass pastures in the Piedmont of Georgia, three-year average.			
	Continuous	Rotational	Change, %
Stocking rate, cow-calf units/A	0.50	0.69	+38
Calf weaning weight, lb	490	486	0
Total calf gain/A, lb	243	334	+37
Cow pregnancy rate, %	93	95	0
Hay fed/cow, lb	2,430	1,680	-31
Source: C.S. Hoveland, M.A. McCann, and N.S. Hill. J. Prod. Agric. 10:245-250.			

followed by dry cows or replacement heifers.

Benefits of Rotational Stocking. Having more control over the grazing animals through rotational stocking allows the manager to better utilize the supply of forage when it is abundant during periods of fast growth in the spring. This can stretch or extend pasture forage availability as growth slows during summer. Healthy, properly grazed and rested pasture plants usually grow longer in the early stage of drought and come back quicker after rain. Having more than one pasture also gives the manager greater control. With only one pasture and continuous stocking, the animal makes the decision as to where to graze, when to graze, where to excrete dung and urine, and where to congregate, ruminate, and socialize. With rotational stocking, control and decision making are switched from the animal to the manager. Greater control through rotational stocking offers opportunities for several benefits in addition to increased carrying capacity when proper management is employed.

1) **Calmer livestock when proper management is employed.** Animals are often more docile and easier to handle.

2) **Better persistence and productivity of pasture plants that are sensitive to close continuous grazing.** For this reason, plants such as alfalfa, sericea lespedeza, and endophyte-free tall fescue will usually benefit from rotational stocking. When a mixture of endophyte-free tall fescue and common bermudagrass was grazed year-round with beef cows and calves in Georgia, rotational stocking maintained better stands and productivity of the tall fescue, improving carrying capacity and calf gain per acre and decreasing the amount of hay fed in winter by 31 percent (**Table 25.3**).

3) **Improved utilization of more species in the pasture.** When rotational stocking is used, in many cases weeds are eaten more than would otherwise be the case, favoring dominance by desirable species.

4) **Less forage wasted by trampling.** Smaller paddocks are more uniformly grazed, and during periods of surplus growth, unneeded paddocks can be harvested for hay.

5) **Better distribution of dung and urine.** In continuous stocked pastures, more dung and urine are concentrated around water and shade areas.

6) **Environmental benefits.** Proper fencing that keeps cattle from standing and loafing in ponds and streams will give access to drinking water only from selected and protected water points. This will improve water

quality by reducing the concentrations of nutrients and bacteria from animal waste and soil particles resulting from stream bank erosion (see Chapter 32).

7) **Facilitation of management.** If various pasture areas are dominated by different forage species, fencing them separately allows for more optimum management. For example, if a bottomland area is mostly tall fescue and white clover while the adjacent upland area is dominated by bermudagrass, it is impossible to exercise appropriate grazing management when both areas are grazed simultaneously. In addition, separating the areas will allow overseeding the bermudagrass with winter annuals or planting of clover in tall fescue. Also, concentrating animals in smaller areas for short periods allows successfully trampling in broadcast-seeded clover.

8) **Better overall management.** Moving livestock from one paddock to another generally causes the producer to observe livestock more frequently and more carefully evaluate pasture species and productivity, thus becoming a better manager.

Concerns with Rotational Stocking

Sometimes, rotationally stocked pastures do not provide any benefits and may even give poorer animal performance than continuous stocking. There are a number of reasons why this may happen, and it is important to recognize them before making investments in this stocking method.

1) **Unproductive or low quality forage species, poor forage stands, low fertility, and soil acidity.** The benefits of rotational stocking are more likely to be realized with high-quality cool-season perennials than with warm-season perennials such as bahiagrass or bermudagrass. In general, rotational stocking offers the most potential with animals having high nutritional requirements such as stocker cattle or lactating dairy cows. Pastures must have good stands and be adequately fertilized; otherwise, cross fences will provide few benefits.

2) **Unsatisfactory layout.** This may be a result of either very wet and dry soil areas being present within the same paddock or long narrow paddocks that make it difficult to control grazing.

3) **Overstocking.** With more forage normally available on rotationally stocked pastures, there is a temptation to increase stocking rates to such an extent that grazing pressure results in lower forage available for good selectivity of leaves by the animals (**Figure 25.3**). Lower daily gains by growing animals on rotationally stocked as compared to continuously stocked pastures would indicate that stocking rate was too high. Forcing high-producing animals to overgraze a paddock will result in poor animal performance. Concentrating too many animals on a paddock during wet weather may result in damaged forage stands (especially with legumes) and increased soil erosion and compaction. In addition, if paddocks are grazed too closely, internal parasites may be more of a problem.

4) **Rest period too long.** When rotationally stocked pastures have too long a rest period between grazings, available forage becomes over-mature, and animals do not have sufficient selectivity of young green leaves. This is

an especially serious problem with warm season perennial species such as bermudagrass where digestibility drops rapidly with maturity, particularly during hot summer weather. Another problem with long rest periods and accumulated forage is that more waste will occur. During periods of surplus growth, unneeded paddocks in the rotation can be skipped and harvested for hay. Warm season perennial grasses such as bermudagrass need adequate nitrogen fertilization, frequent rotation, and short rest periods to maintain young leaves with higher quality if better animal performance is desired.

5) Cost. There is substantial cost involved in converting existing pastures to rotational stocking. Planning the layout of paddocks, building new fences, and providing a watering system for cattle in each paddock involve considerable cash outlay. Frequent moving of animals is initially viewed as an additional chore, but is often seen later as a benefit.

Getting Started with Rotational Stocking

As the discussion has indicated, rotational stocking has advantages and disadvantages. It offers numerous potential benefits, but may or may not be the best approach for a given situation. Furthermore, if improperly managed, initiation of rotational stocking may actually result in more harm than benefits. Proper rotational stocking, especially if numerous paddocks are to be involved, requires more knowledge and a higher level of management by a livestock producer. Therefore, a discussion of how to initiate rotational stocking is appropriate.

Getting started in rotational stocking can vary from simple to complex. The greatest success occurs when producers progress at their own pace until they are comfortable with the overall management system. It is important to stay flexible and be willing to fine tune overall grazing management as experience, resources, and environmental conditions dictate. Improvements can be made with minimum inputs and effort. For example, one can often make a lot of progress just by closing the gate between two pastures. If one large field is divided in half, an important step has been made toward improving management of pasture growth and utilization.

Fencing. Livestock producers realize the necessity and importance of fencing. However, fencing is usually viewed as a tool for animal management. Typically, it is seen as being useful primarily for the purpose of keeping animals on the property, out of crop fields, away from roads or other dangerous areas, and as a means of keeping certain animals separated.

Although fencing is important for these and other animal management reasons, it is also necessary for good forage management. However, importance of fencing as a forage management tool is often overlooked. The potential of fencing is frequently not fully appreciated, and its configurations often contribute to inefficient animal production and/or forage utilization.

The first major requirement in developing a rotational stocking program is to have a good boundary fence that will keep grazing animals on the farm or in the area to be pastured. A cautious approach in getting started with rotational stocking is to rotationally stock only part of the herd on a small part of the farm. The system can be expanded as one gains confidence and experience.

Temporary or interior fencing will be required to keep grazing animals in the subdivision or paddock area. In most cases, the fencing system will change as one gains experience. There is no perfect system, and a few mistakes are likely. Lessons learned from any mistake can be easily incorporated into the grazing system.

Electrical powered fencing is usually the most versatile and economical method of subdividing pastures. Considerable technological advances in fence chargers, wire types, and fencing accessories continue to make fence construction simpler, easier, cheaper, and more efficient.

Water. Although fencing is often considered the most important limitation to implementation of rotational stocking programs on many farms, water is actually the most limiting. Water is the most important and often most overlooked nutrient for animals. It is required for almost every bodily function. Animals need a clean, fresh, safe supply of water. Many factors influence amounts required, including animal species, size, stage of production, and temperature (**Appendix A.49**). Water intake influences dry matter intake, and dry matter intake influences animal performance.

Advances in portable watering systems, such as quick couplers and flexible tubing, are making it easier and more economical to have water available in every paddock. When this is not possible, lanes or alleys can provide access to water.

Location of water is quite important. The farther livestock have to travel to water, the more energy and time are utilized, and performance is likely to be reduced. As travel distances increase, the uniformity of pasture use decreases. In addition, animals often drink alone or in small groups when travel distance to water is reduced, requiring smaller water tanks and reducing loafing time at water points. Providing adequate access to water is important and may be increasingly challenging as the number of animals grazing together increases. Water sources should be positioned on level ground, if possible, to reduce erosion hazards created by hoof action and to minimize the amount of energy the animals have to expend to reach water.

Paddock number, size, and shape. One of the most frequently asked questions by producers wanting to start a rotational stocking program is "How many paddocks should I have?" This is a controversial topic among grazing enthusiasts, and there is no simple answer to this question. The optimum (most profitable) number will vary from farm to farm, depending on the individual circumstances, resources, goals, environmental conditions, and desired level of animal production.

Paddock numbers vary considerably, depending on need, desire, and resources. Dairy producers may need eight to 12 or more paddocks for frequent rotation to provide high quality forage. For most beef operations, five to 10 paddocks may be sufficient. This permits paddocks to be grazed in three to seven days and rested 25 to 35 days. In most cases, five paddocks should be considered a minimum, and there is little economic advantage for most operators to have more than 12. Since single-strand electric wire or tape can be used, fencing can be moved as needed to adjust the system.

Size of individual paddocks depends on several factors, including acres of total pasture, available forage, animal number, production desired, and total number of paddocks. In most cases, it is not practical to make perennial forage paddocks smaller than 1 to 2 acres. Permanent paddocks can be subdivided flexibly with temporary wire to regulate access to pasture forage as plant growth changes over the season. They do not have to be the same size, but it is desirable for each paddock to be similar in the amount of forage available. For help in calculating paddock number and size, see **Appendix A.51**.

Shape of paddocks is important. Within practical limits, square paddocks are more efficient compared to other shapes (rectangles, triangles, pie, etc.). Square paddocks allow the animals to obtain their daily ration of forage with minimum grazing time, animal effort, and trampling damage. Square paddocks are also more economical to construct than other shapes (**Appendix A.50**). Having exactly square paddocks is certainly not necessary or always practical; however, long narrow or pie shape paddocks should be avoided. When possible, it is best to fence along slopes rather than up and down them.

Layout in designing a system is not an easy job, but one that can pay large dividends over time. There are many tools and resources available from universities, governmental agencies, and industry personnel. In developing a system, the following are useful: a good aerial photo, a soils map, soil test results, knowledge of pasture species and productivity, location of water source(s), and animal inventory (number, size, production desired).

This is an area where planning is critically important. The most important advice is to plan and develop a system that is right for the resources, land capability, and farm goals. It is critical to remain flexible and be willing to continually adjust the grazing system as information, circumstances, resources, climatic changes, and/or goals change.

Movement of animals among paddocks should be flexible so that rotation is not based on a fixed time schedule but rather on available forage, rate of forage growth, and animal requirements (**Table 25.4**). During periods of surplus growth, one or more paddocks may be harvested for hay, haylage, or round bale silage while animals are quickly rotated through other paddocks. With experience, a manager can use forage height to estimate the amount of forage available (**Appendices A.28** and **A.52**) and subsequently calculate how long a paddock will provide feed for animals to be grazed. Forcing high-producing animals to overgraze a paddock will result in poor animal performance.

Estimating Available Forage

Effective management of a rotationally stocked pasture requires knowing how much forage is available in a paddock. This information, along with the estimated daily consumption by the grazing animals, allows

Table 25.4. Deciding when to move animals to a fresh paddock.
Look down. Has the present paddock been grazed adequately, or is there too much forage left? Most new graziers tend to allow their animals to overgraze paddocks. Move often enough to leave a little more forage than seems necessary.
Look ahead. Is the next paddock ready for grazing? What is the pasture growth rate? Rapid growth may indicate the need to speed up the rotation or harvest some paddocks for hay. Slow growth signals the need to lighten stocking rate, provide access to additional acres of pasture, or feed hay.
Look at the animals. Do they appear hungry and are they in good condition? Livestock can let a manager know when they want to move, but their desire to move may be too soon for high utilization. High-performing animals should be moved more often.
Look behind. How fast is the last paddock regrowing? During slow growth it may be necessary to slow the rotation, reduce stocking rate, or feed hay. Slowing the rotation (more days per paddock) makes animals graze closer and gain less. Regrowth from closely grazed paddocks may be slower.
Look at the weather. Approaching rain can signal the need to move from pure legume to grass-based pastures to reduce pugging of the soil and stand damage. Animals should be removed from johnsongrass, sorghum, sudangrass, and sorghum-sudangrass pastures prior to frost.
Finally, look at the calendar. During the active growing season, residual forage height should be managed to allow fast regrowth. On strip-grazed autumn and winter stockpiled pasture, each strip should be grazed closely to utilize forage that otherwise will be lost during the winter.
Adapted from: J.C. Henning, G.D. Lacefield, et.al. Rotational Grazing. Kentucky Coop. Ext. Serv. ID-143.

the manager to calculate how long animals can remain on a paddock before they should be moved to the next one. There are a number of ways to estimate the amount of forage in a paddock:

Harvested, dried, and weighed forage. A square frame 18 x 18 inches (2.25 square feet) is dropped on an area that is representative of the pasture. All the forage inside the frame should be harvested to the same stubble height to which the animals will graze and then placed in a bag. This should be repeated at several places in the pasture. The forage can be dried in an oven or microwave (**Appendix A.37**) and weighed. The pounds of available forage per acre = dry sample weight x (43,560 square feet divided by 2.25 square feet).

Pasture probe. Electronic instruments are available that can be inserted into the pasture canopy to estimate instantaneously the amount of forage dry matter. Many estimates can be made in a short time period, and some probes keep records of multiple sampling in several paddocks. Accuracy depends on several factors, including the number of samples made in the pasture, forage species, stand density, amount of dead forage, and dry matter percentage.

Forage height measurement for estimation of forage available. Measurement of height is fast and easy. Many readings can be made in a pasture. A rough estimate of the pounds of forage available per inch of height can be obtained from **Appendices A.28 and A.52**. However, it varies greatly depending on forage species, stand density, growth stage, and season of the year. This is a crude way to measure forage available, but it can be helpful. With experience, a livestock producer generally becomes adept at visually estimating forage available and when to move animals to the next paddock to provide an adequate quantity of forage of the quality needed.

The Challenge

Much skill is required to obtain optimum or near optimum animal production from pastures. It is one thing to produce forage, but efficient utilization is usually a greater challenge. In order to provide adequate quantities of good quality forage and economically convert it to animal products, good grazing management is essential. It involves frequent observation of pasture height, forage available, and periodic adjustment of stocking rate or movement of animals as needed.

The choice of grazing method to be used depends on the individual farm and the livestock producer. Continuous and some form of intermittent stocking such as rotational or creep grazing may be used on the same farm for different livestock enterprises or at different seasons of the year. Different methods are not mutually exclusive, and one is not necessarily superior to another.

A grazing method is a tool that allows a producer to efficiently and profitably harvest the forage with livestock and maintain the pasture in a productive state. Each method requires management control to be successful. This involves variable stocking rates that may be achieved by altering animal numbers per acre, altering the size of the land area to a fixed number of animals, harvesting surplus forage as hay, haylage, or round bale silage, and/or mowing excess growth in a pasture.

Each grazing method has advantages and disadvantages. A producer must select the one(s) that best suits a particular situation. This varies, depending on the type and class of livestock, pasture species, resources available, and objectives of the operation. SF

Forages for Beef Cows and Calves

Beef cattle production in the South consists primarily of commercial and purebred cow-calf operations. Commercial cow-calf producers normally sell calves at weaning that are subsequently transported to other areas of the U.S. where they are pastured and then finished in a feedlot. However, an increasing number of Southern producers are purchasing weanling calves or retaining calves from their cow-calf operations for stockering on high quality pasture to benefit from the attractive profit potential from sale of feeder calves.

There are over 12 million beef cows in the South, including eastern Texas and Oklahoma. Most of the herds are small, often part-time operations or associated with crop farming. A common problem is uncontrolled breeding, resulting in calves being born throughout the year. Due to this and other poor management practices, calf death rates are increased, and calf weaning weights are low, often much less than 500 lb. Poor quality forage during much of the year also contributes to low calf weaning weights and reduced cow reproduction (see **Table 26.1**).

Nutrient Needs

The primary objectives in efficient cow-calf production should be to: 1) maintain the cow as cheaply as possible; 2) obtain good reproduction; and 3) attain high calf weaning weights. To achieve these objectives, it is necessary to produce forage in pastures and hay fields at low cost and of sufficient quality to meet the needs of the animals with little supplemental feeding.

A controlled breeding season is necessary to ensure adequate nutrition

Crossbred cows and calves grazing Coastal bermudagrass near Malakoff in east Texas.

Table 26.1. Estimated impact on average calf weaning weights if Southern beef producers used near-optimum management.[1]	
Item	Increase, lb
Nutrition	50-75
Genetics	30-35
Implants	25-30
External parasite control	15-20
Internal parasite control	15-20

[1]Based on estimates by university agronomists and animal scientists.
Source: D.M. Ball

for the cow during early lactation and to match available supplies of high quality pasture to the growing calf. Dry, pregnant mature cows can be maintained on relatively low quality forage having 7 to 8 percent crude protein (CP) and 50 percent digestible dry matter. Lactating cows require a diet furnishing about 10 to 12 percent CP and about 60 percent digestibility.

An important factor affecting cow herd production, rebreeding, and calving percentage is the available energy level during the first three months of lactation (see Chapter 17). Even more important is the condition of the cow or heifer at the time of calving. Cows calving in good body condition usually have no trouble rebreeding and raising a good calf when provided with adequate nutrition. However, cows in thin body condition at calving will have low rebreeding rates, even when fed high levels of nutrients.

Ideally, calving should occur four to six weeks prior to the initial availability of good quality pasture to correspond with peak beef cow nutrient demands and allow nursing calves to use pasture for much of their growth. Thus, the ideal calving period differs in various zones of the South, depending on pasture availability.

Autumn calving is desirable in Zone A (see **Figure 3.2**) where limited small grain or other winter annual pasture is available to cows or creep grazing is available to calves. If only warm season perennial grasses are used, late winter calving is more desirable. In Zone B, where tall fescue-legume pasture is available, winter calving is more suitable, while in Zones C and D, late winter or even spring calving may best match supplies of pasture to animal needs. In any of these areas, summer is generally the single worst time for a cow to calve.

Overfeeding dry cows, with resulting excessive weight gain, can result in decreased fertility and increased calving problems. The period from weaning until calving is the portion of a cow's reproductive cycle during which it is easy to improve her body condition. Her nutrient requirements are low, and she can fatten on late summer-early autumn low quality grass.

Although it is a common practice to provide protein supplement with hay feeding, such supplementation is usually not needed if the hay was harvested at early maturity or if it contains clover, alfalfa, or birdsfoot trefoil. Salt should be provided and supplemental phosphorus may be needed. Most cool season grasses contain adequate phosphorus levels, but warm season grasses may be deficient. When supplying phosphorus, some calcium should be included in the mineral supplement. Some areas in the lower South also are deficient in selenium and thus require supplementation.

Possible Forage Systems

Various pasture-hay systems have been effectively used for feeding beef cow herds (**Table 26.2**). All of these forage systems except endophyte-infected tall fescue plus nitrogen resulted in satisfactory cow pregnancy levels, calf weaning weights, and calf daily gains. The poor performance on endophyte-infected tall fescue in southern Indiana occurred even though winter hay feeding was supplemented with corn silage for about two months after calving and prior to grazing in mid May. Growing clover with endophyte-infected tall fescue resulted in animal performance similar to that on orchardgrass pasture. Endophyte-free tall fescue plus clover pastures with winter feeding of tall fescue plus clover hay in Virginia, or endophyte-free tall fescue/clover pasture plus sericea lespedeza hay in Georgia, both gave excellent calf weaning weights.

Legumes in grass pastures gave high calf weaning weights, although generally requiring more acreage per cow-calf unit than grass-nitrogen systems. Maintaining cows on bermudagrass pasture and hay in Alabama gave good performance at less than one acre per cow. However, it was a costly program since it required high nitrogen fertilization and winter feeding with cottonseed meal supplement because the hay contained only 9 percent CP. A cheaper system of Coastal bermudagrass with arrowleaf clover and no nitrogen fertilizer or supplement resulted in high calf weaning weights in east Texas.

Year-round pasture-hay systems differ considerably, depending on the climatic zone (**Figure 3.2**). Forage system possibilites are outlined for each zone.

Zone A

1. Bermudagrass, bahiagrass, or dallisgrass pastures overseeded with an annual clover, rye, and/or annual ryegrass. Surplus hay harvested from fenced-off areas during late spring and summer. About 1.5 to 2 acres needed per cow if no crop residues are available.
2. Hay or crop residues such as cornstalks, peanut hay, or soybean residue fed in midwinter.
3. Autumn-born calves creep grazed in winter on rye, wheat, or oats, and/or annual ryegrass planted early on prepared land.

Zone B

1. Tall fescue, preferably planted with white or red clover, grazed from early autumn until early summer. A tall fescue/common bermudagrass mixture with nitrogen fertilization in autumn and late winter can provide grazing over most of the year. About 1.5 acres needed per cow. Sericea lespedeza, tall fescue, or bermudagrass hay fed in midwinter. Rye overseeded on bermudagrass or sericea for grazing. Surplus tall fescue hay can be harvested from fenced areas in spring.
2. Sericea or bermudagrass hay harvested in late spring. About 0.5 acre needed per cow. Sericea or bermudagrass grazed during mid to late summer when tall fescue is unproductive.

Table 26.2. Performance of beef cows and calves on year-round pasture-hay systems in the South.

Pasture	Winter hay	Location	Nitrogen fertilizer, lb/A	Land/ cow-calf, acres	Calf daily gain, lb	Calf weaning weight, lb	Calf gain/ acre, lb	Cow pregnancy rate, %
WARM SEASON GRASSES								
Coastal bermudagrass + arrowleaf clover	Coastal bermuda	East Texas[1]	0	1.10	2.70	645	446	95
Coastal bermudagrass + arrowleaf clover	Coastal bermuda + 134 lb/cow of liquid protein	Alabama Piedmont[2]	100	2.00	1.72	594	209	97
Coastal bermudagrass	Coastal bermuda + 294 lb/cow of cottonseed meal	South Alabama[3]	200	0.94	1.53	453	458	95
Dallisgrass + white clover + caleypeas	Dallisgrass	Alabama Black Belt[4]	0	2.00	1.70	484	242	—
COOL SEASON GRASSES								
Endophyte-free tall fescue + ladino clover	Sericea lespedeza	Central Georgia[5]	0	1.75	1.81	499	315	94
Endophyte-free tall fescue + ladino clover	Tall fescue-red clover hay + stockpiled tall fescue-red clover pasture	Northern Virginia[6]	0	1.78	1.83	551	310	94
Endophyte-infected tall fescue	Orchardgrass hay + corn silage	Southern Indiana[7]	100	1.80	1.28	353	—	71
Endophyte-infected tall fescue + ladino and red clover	Orchardgrass hay + corn silage	Southern Indiana[7]	0	1.80	1.83	436	—	92
Orchardgrass	Orchardgrass hay + corn silage	Southern Indiana[7]	100	1.80	1.79	430	—	90

[1]FM. Rouquette, Jr., M.J.. Florence, V.A. Haby, and G.R. Smith. Texas A&M Univ. Overton Res. Ctr. Tech. Rep. 90-1. p.153-165.
[2]C.S. Hoveland, W.B. Anthony, J.A. McGuire, W.A. Griffey, and H.E. Burgess. Alabama Agric. Exp. Stn. Bull. 497.
[3]R.R. Harris, V.L. Brown, W.B. Anthony, and C.C. King, Jr. Alabama Agric. Exp. Stn. Bull. 411.
[4]C.C. King, Jr., W.B. Anthony, S.C. Bell, L.A. Smith, and H. Grimes, Alabama Agric. Exp. Stn. Bull. 424.
[5]J.A. Stuedemann and C.S. Hoveland, USDA and Univ. of Georgia. Unpublished data.
[6]V.G. Allen, J.P. Fontenot, D.R. Notter, and R.C. Hammes, Jr. J. Anim. Sci. 70:576-587.
[7]D.C. Petritz, V.L. Lechtenberg, and W.H. Smith. Agron. J. 72:581-584.

Zone C

1. Tall fescue, orchardgrass, or Kentucky bluegrass with red or white clover, grazed from late winter until late autumn. About 1.5 to 2 acres needed per cow. Surplus growth harvested for hay in spring.
2. Stockpiled tall fescue grazed in early winter. Hay fed in mid winter. About 0.5 acre of sericea per cow could be substituted for part of the grass acreage to provide hay and mid summer grazing during drought.

Zone D

1. Tall fescue, orchardgrass, Kentucky bluegrass, or timothy, each planted with red or white clover or birdsfoot trefoil, grazed from early spring until autumn. About 1.5 to 2 acres needed per cow. Surplus growth harvested for hay in spring.
2. Stockpiled tall fescue grazed in late autumn. Hay fed in winter.

On many farms in all zones, crop residues can be utilized as additional forage for cattle. These materials may reduce the acreage needed for hay production. Normally, winter is the main hay feeding period, but severe summer droughts may require additional feeding. Generally, about 1 to 1.5 tons of hay per cow annually should be adequate for winter feeding.

Sorghum-sudan or pearl millet is sometimes planted as supplemental summer grazing or hay for beef cows and calves. These grasses are much more expensive than perennial pasture and cannot be justified except in emergency situations or as creep grazing for calves.

Summary

Forage systems differ from one zone to another and within zones, depending on land capabilities and type of enterprise. Regardless of the forage system, it is important to determine seasonal distribution of pastures on a farm and adjust calving to match cow and calf needs to forage quality. During periods of surplus growth, cattle should be restricted to a smaller area to allow harvesting of hay at the proper stage of maturity. Pastures should be used as much of the year as possible to reduce the cost of supplemental feeding. SF

Non-toxic tall fescue and white clover make an outstanding pasture for beef cows and calves.

Forages for Beef Stockering

Stocker animals are grazed on high quality pasture from weaning to usually 700 or 800 lb before being sold to feedlots for finishing. However, only an estimated 15 to 20 percent of the calves are retained in the South and grown to these heavier weights. The greatest opportunity for improving profitability in Southern beef production lies in stockering (also referred to as backgrounding) weaned calves on high quality pasture.

Historically, the price of calves is lowest in early autumn when the greatest number of calves are available. This is the time of year when most cow-calf producers wean their calves. Calf prices vary with weight. Usually, lightweight calves are priced higher (in terms of cost per pound) than heavy calves. Prices for calves typically increase in winter and peak in March and April. The price of calves sold in late spring may be slightly lower due to the weight gains on winter pasture. However, the cost of this late spring gain is relatively low, generally making it a profitable enterprise in most years.

The large supply of available calves in the region offers an opportunity for persons wishing to concentrate on this intensive system of livestock production. However, stockering is a high-risk and capital-intensive enterprise compared with a cow-calf operation. Purchasing and selling of cattle, health care, production and grazing management of high quality pastures, and supplemental feeding require a high degree of skill and experience. Generally, only larger operations (usually at least one truckload, about 60 calves) can justify the managerial input required. Economy of size is also needed to spread fixed investments over a large number of animals, acreage of land, and equipment. The investment is large, but profit potential is good for well-managed enterprises.

Beef steers grazing rye, ryegrass, and arrowleaf clover pasture in central Alabama.

Nutrient Needs

Profitable stockering of young, growing cattle generally requires an average daily gain of at least 1.5 lb for the season. High forage quality is essential for high daily gains and profitability of steers. A growing beef steer or heifer requires forage with about 12 percent crude protein and 65 to 68 percent digestibility in order to make such gains (see Chapter 17). If possible, an ionophore should be fed to steers on pasture. These compounds increase daily gains approximately 10 percent and reduce the potential for bloat.

Steer performance varies greatly on different pasture species in the South (**Table 27.1**). In addition to individual daily gain, the carrying capacity and length of grazing season of a pasture system are extremely important.

Warm season perennial grasses such as bermudagrass and bahiagrass have generally furnished poor average daily gains because of low digestible energy. Although excellent daily gains can be obtained on bermudagrass in spring, animal performance declines rapidly during summer. More digestible varieties such as Tifton 85 are better in late summer. Nitrogen fertilization and mowing at intervals to remove stems and old leaves have been helpful in improving forage quality and animal performance of bermudagrass.

Warm season annual grasses such as pearl millet and sorghum-sudangrass are highly productive and allow high stocking rates. But, because of relatively high pasture costs and a short grazing season, stockering of calves on warm season annuals has generally been about a breakeven proposition at best. These grasses can be used if a low-cost, high energy supplement is fed. With such a system, calves are purchased in early spring when prices are normally high and sold in late summer when prices are at their lowest. Unless this fits into a program of retained ownership through a feedlot finishing period, making a profit is difficult.

Small grain (rye, wheat, oats) and/or annual ryegrass pastures have traditionally been used in the lower South for most beef stocker production. Mixtures of rye, ryegrass, and arrowleaf clover can provide high gains over a longer grazing season. However, winter annual pastures are fairly expensive to grow and must be well managed to produce profits. Cost of gains have generally been in the range of $0.25 to $0.40 per lb during normal winters.

Orchardgrass alone, and especially with clover, has furnished high daily gains in areas where it is adapted. However, a problem with this cool season perennial grass is the relatively short stand life under close grazing, particularly in the mid South area.

Tall fescue generally gives low daily steer gains because most pastures are heavily infected with a fungal endophyte (see Chapter 24). Novel endophyte and endophyte-free tall fescue have given excellent steer gains, approaching that of winter annuals. The high daily gains, high stocking rate, and long grazing season of non-toxic tall fescue make profitable stockering possible over much of the South. Even toxic endophyte-infected tall fescue can produce good gains if pastures have abundant clover. With a perennial sod, trampling and mud problems during wet winters will not be as great

Table 27.1. Beef steer performance on pastures in the Southern U.S.

Pasture species	Location	Nitrogen per acre, lb	Average daily gain, lb	Gain per acre, lb	Gain per animal, lb	Grazing season, days
COOL SEASON ANNUALS						
Rye + ryegrass + arrowleaf clover	Alabama Piedmont[1]	100	1.98	442	394	193
Ryegrass + arrowleaf clover	Western Louisiana[2]	178	2.21	520	370	149
Wheat + ryegrass	Central Mississippi[3]	122	2.19	609	404	180
COOL SEASON PERENNIALS						
Tall fescue (endophyte-free)	Alabama Black Belt[4]	200	1.82	426	322	171
Tall fescue (endophyte-infected)	Alabama Black Belt[4]	200	1.00	301	174	171
Tall fescue (endophyte-free) + birdsfoot trefoil	North Alabama[5]	0	2.37	550	384	142
Orchardgrass + ladino clover	North Alabama[6]	0	1.60	576	374	183
Alfalfa	North Alabama[7]	0	2.16	475	349	163
WARM SEASON ANNUALS						
Pearl millet	South Georgia[8]	150	1.26	366	—	86
Sorghum-sudan	North Alabama[9]	100	1.10	210	84	77
WARM SEASON PERENNIALS						
Low-tannin sericea	North Alabama[7]	0	1.65	276	245	139
High-tannin sericea	North Alabama[7]	0	1.39	248	190	139
Tifton 85 bermudagrass	South Georgia[10]	225	1.47	1,080	—	169
Coastal bermudagrass	South Georgia[11]	150	1.08	331	—	131
Pensacola bahiagrass	South Georgia[11]	150	0.95	222	—	131

[1]W.B. Anthony, C.S. Hoveland, E.L. Mayton, and H.E. Burgess. Alabama Agric. Exp. Stn. Cir.182.
[2]C.P. Bagley, J.I. Feazel, and K.L. Koonce. J. Prod. Agric.1:149-152.
[3]E.G. Morrison. Mississippi Agric. Exp. Stn. Inf. Bull. 167.
[4]C.S. Hoveland, S.P. Schmidt, C.C. King, Jr., J.W. Odom, E.M Clark, J.A. McGuire, L.A. Smith, H.W. Grimes, and J.L. Holliman. Agron. J. 75:821-824.
[5]C.S. Hoveland, R.R. Harris, R.L. Haaland, J.A. McGuire, W.B. Webster, and V.H. Calvert II. Alabama Agric. Exp. Stn. Bull. 567.
[6]R.R. Harris, C.S. Hoveland, J.A. McGuire, W.B. Webster, and V.H. Calvert II. Alabama Agric. Exp. Stn. Bull. 563.
[7]S.P. Schmidt, C.S. Hoveland, E.D. Donnelly, J.A. McGuire, and R.A. Moore. Alabama Agric. Exp. Stn. Cir. 288.
[8]G.M. Hill, W.W. Hanna, and H.D. Wells. Proc. 16th Int. Grassl. Cong. Nice, France. pp. 1173-1174.
[9]C.S. Hoveland, R.R. Harris, J.K. Boseck, and W.B. Webster. Alabama Agric. Exp. Stn. Cir.188.
[10]G.M. Hill, R.N. Gates, and G.W. Burton. J. Anim. Sci. 71:3219-3225.
[11]P.R. Utley, H.D. Chapman, W.G. Monson, W.H. Marchant, and W.C. McCormick. J. Anim. Sci. 38:490-495.

Clover can improve the quality of perennial grass pastures for stocker animals.

compared to annual species planted in a prepared seedbed.

Including a legume such as alfalfa, red clover, or white clover with non-toxic tall fescue will further increase gains. Costs are also reduced due to nitrogen supplied by the legumes. If legumes make up a good proportion of the forage, endophyte-infected tall fescue pastures can also produce good stocker gains.

Alfalfa offers potential for stockering of steers during spring, summer, and autumn. Daily gains of 2 lb per day can be obtained on this pasture during spring and summer. Rotational stocking, to allow rest periods for accumulation of root food reserves, is essential to maintain stands and productivity on hay-type alfalfa varieties (see Chapter 25).

Possible Forage Systems

Zone A

1. Rye, wheat, or oats planted on prepared land in September provide grazing from mid October or November until mid April. Adding annual ryegrass and arrowleaf clover can extend the grazing season to June. Annual ryegrass alone can be used in the Gulf Coast area. Well-fertilized crabgrass can supply excellent grazing in this area during summer. Supplemental hay, silage, or other feedstuffs of similar quality should be fed in January when pasture growth is restricted. Stocking rate of one and a half to two steers per acre.
2. Pearl millet or a sorghum-sudan hybrid can be grazed from May or June to September. Stocking rate of four to six steers per acre.

Zone B

1. Non-toxic tall fescue, preferably with alfalfa, or white or red clover, can be grazed from late September to late December and from early March to June or July. Hay, silage, and corn or similar quality feedstuffs can be fed in mid winter to maintain gain at about 1 lb per day. Stocking rate of one to two steers per acre.
2. Alfalfa can be rotationally grazed from April to July or August and again from September to early November. Stocking rate of one and a half to two steers per acre.
3. Endophyte-infected tall fescue can be used if at least 30 percent of the forage is a legume. Grazing period and stocking rate same as with

endophyte-free tall fescue.

Zone C

1. Orchardgrass, with alfalfa, white or red clover, or birdsfoot trefoil, can be grazed from April to July or August. Stocking rate of one and a half to two steers per acre.
2. Non-toxic tall fescue, preferably with alfalfa or white or red clover, can be grazed from April to July and from September to November. Stocking rate of one and a half to two steers per acre.
3. Endophyte-infected tall fescue can be used if at least 30 percent of the forage is a legume. Grazing period and stocking rate same as with endophyte-free tall fescue.
4. Alfalfa, rotationally grazed from late April to September. Stocking rate of two to three steers per acre.

Zone D

1. Orchardgrass, with alfalfa, white or red clover, or birdsfoot trefoil, can be grazed from late April to September. Stocking rate of one and a half to two steers per acre.
2. Non-toxic tall fescue, with white or red clover, or birdsfoot trefoil, can be grazed from late April to September or October. Stocking rate of one and a half to two steers per acre.
3. Endophyte-infected tall fescue can be used if at least 30 percent of the forage is a legume. Grazing period and stocking rate are similar to endophyte-free tall fescue.
4. Alfalfa, rotationally grazed from May to September. Stocking rate of two to four steers per acre.

Grain feeding of steers on high quality pasture during the cool season is generally not recommended as animals tend to substitute grain for forage. This allows higher stocking rates, but gain per day remains about the same unless an ionophore is added. If grain is to be fed, it is best to do so at the end of the grazing season when forage quality begins to decline. Lightweight steers, initially weighing 400 to 500 lb, are best suited for stockering as weight gains are high and more calves can be grazed on a given area of land. In some situations, stocker animals can be finished on pasture and slaughtered at about 1,000 lb for lean beef.

Summary

Stockering offers excellent opportunities for profit when operations are well managed. Several pasture systems are available in each climatic zone of the South. However, good pasture management is essential to maintain high forage quality throughout the season. Adjustment of stocking rate, supplemental feeding, and good health care are necessary to achieve the high gains needed for profitability. SF

Forages for Dairy Cattle

The dairy industry in the South has changed considerably over the past 50 years. Increased mechanization, improved breeding, better feeding, computerized ration balancing, advances in herd health, and better overall dairy farm management have resulted in increased milk production per cow. However, reduced demand for dairy products, economics of production, environmental issues, and other factors have resulted in a dramatic decline in the number of dairy herds in the South.

In the U.S., there were approximately 21 million dairy cows on farms in the early 1950s. By 2000, this number had dropped to approximately 9 million. During that period, herd size and production per cow had more than doubled.

Over the past decade, there has been a sharp reduction in overall milk production in the South. The number of herds has decreased by over 40 percent, cow numbers are down by 25 percent, and total milk production decreased by 12 percent, even though milk production per cow is up 17 percent. Although not as dramatic as the South, the U.S. overall has shown a similar trend, with a 9 percent decrease in cow numbers and a 37 percent decrease in number of herds. Total milk production was up 13 percent and milk per cow up 24 percent in the U.S. over the past decade.

Dairy producers have demonstrated their ability to produce milk efficiently. However, changing diets and lifestyles, availability of dairy substitute products, health concerns, and perhaps other factors have resulted in a decreased demand for some dairy products. As a result, the dairy industry has responded with active promotion programs that bring the importance and value of dairy products to the attention of consumers. The

Milk production per cow has increased in the past decade.

High quality silage is readily consumed by dairy cattle.

industry has also responded to consumer demands for different products such as low-fat milk and convenience food items (sour cream, dips, yogurt, flavored milk, etc.). This provides evidence that the dairy industry is sensitive to needs and demands, and is both visible and progressive.

Another change in some parts of the dairy industry has been a trend toward using pasture to a greater extent in meeting animal nutritional requirements. This has been brought about by economics (equipment, labor, and other costs associated with confinement feeding), environmental issues, advancements in fencing and watering systems, and improvements in forage species. The opportunities for grazing to play an increasingly important role in the dairy industry are great.

A number of forage species are commonly used in dairy pastures in the South. Many producers who have suitable land for growing alfalfa have put grazing-tolerant varieties to good use in recent years, especially in the upper South. Orchardgrass and endophyte-free or novel endophyte tall fescue, often with red clover or white clover as a companion species, make excellent cool season perennial pastures.

Small grains (rye, wheat, and oats) and annual ryegrass are widely used in the lower South, especially in Zone A. Bermudagrass varieties selected for higher digestibility are the best choice of warm season perennial grasses on sandy, Coastal Plain soils, while dallisgrass or non-toxic fescue/clover mixes are a good choice for the heavy Black Belt soils of Alabama and Mississippi.

Corn silage serves as the foundation of rations for lactating cows on many farms in the South. Some varieties of silage corn result in higher quality silage than others. Annual ryegrass or a small grain/legume (clover or vetch) mixture can also be grown for silage and used with great success for lactating animals. Forage sorghum silage, which is slightly lower in quality, is often grown and fed to non-lactating animals.

Feeding Systems

Use of pasture as a major provider of nutrients for dairy cows has varied considerably. In the early 1950s, pasture provided over 30 percent of the nutrients dairy cattle consumed. That figure has fallen to less than 20 percent at present; however, interest in grazing is once again increasing for several reasons. Smaller dairies with sufficient land resources can make valuable use of high quality pasture. As herd size increases and land resources decrease, pastures often are used only for dry cows and replacement animals. Most large dairies do not have sufficient land for pasture and consequently utilize a total dry lot feeding program. A combination of pasture and dry lot systems is also used with success. The use of high quality pasture in conjunction with dry lot feeding can reduce feed costs and improve net profit from milk production on many farms.

The types of forage crops used for dairy pastures varies from one part of the South to another. In addition to being widely used for hay production, alfalfa is used to great advantage as a pasture crop by many dairy producers. In the upper South, orchardgrass-clover is a popular mixture. While endophyte-infected tall fescue is not a good choice, good milk production can be obtained from endophyte-free or novel endophyte tall fescue. In the lower South, mixtures of winter cereals and annual ryegrass are commonly used to provide quality grazing for dairy cattle.

High-Energy, High-Quality Forage Is Necessary

High producing dairy cows require adequate levels of energy, protein, vitamins, minerals, and water in their diet. Energy and protein are of major importance because of the amounts required and the expense of providing them. Feed cost is typically the largest single expense a dairy producer faces. High quality forages are the most economical source of the essential nutrients.

For profitable production, dairy cows must consume large quantities of quality feed for optimum production. A high quality forage is one that results in high intake (is consumed in large amounts), is digestible (capable of supplying large amounts of nutrients), and contains the proper balance of needed nutrients. Forage quality can make the difference between high or low production and between profit or loss in dairy feeding programs.

Feeding high quality forage reduces feed cost, stimulates high milk production, increases dry matter intake, and contributes to health, thriftiness, and productive life of the cow. Conversely, feeding low quality forage can be costly by reducing feed intake and milk production.

Energy. Although corn and other grains supply energy in dairy feeding programs, high-energy grain crops harvested and stored as silage provide the major energy source for most dairy operations in the South (see Chapter 20). Corn is rightfully considered king of the silage crops. It has the potential of producing more energy per acre than other crops.

In addition to corn, sorghum, pearl millet, and small grains are com-

Dairy cattle grazing high quality winter annual pasture near Dothan, Alabama.

monly used for silage. These crops produce good yields, are easily mechanized from standing crop to feeding, and are dependable.

Many factors influence silage yield and quality, including: rainfall, variety, fertility, cultural practices, pests, stage of maturity when harvested, and harvesting and storing conditions. Corn and sorghum have the ability to produce large amounts of energy and nutrients per acre, but crude protein must be supplemented for high milk production.

Protein. Protein is needed for growth, production, reproduction, and maintenance. The amount required in the diet depends on animal size, condition, growth rate, and level of production. Protein content of forage crops varies considerably, depending on many factors, especially plant species and stage of maturity. In general, legumes are higher in protein than grasses.

Legumes harvested at bud to early bloom and grasses harvested at boot stage for first harvest and at a leafy stage for aftermath harvest are usually high in protein. On dairy farms, alfalfa or an alfalfa-grass mixture is an excellent complement to corn silage. Other forages such as red clover grown in association with orchardgrass, endophyte-free or novel endophyte tall fescue, or timothy can provide high quality dairy hay when harvested at the proper stage of maturity. Other cool-season species as well as warm-season species and various by-products can also be used in formulating dairy rations.

Forage Testing. In order to adequately and economically provide a balanced ration to the dairy cow, it is important to know the nutrient content of feed sources to be used. With the wide variety of on- and off-farm feed sources throughout the South and the importance of forage quality to the dairy herd, forage testing is essential.

Forage testing provides the framework for ration balancing. Feed sources should be sampled so that representative samples can be submitted for analysis. The sampling process is critically important, as only a few grams of material submitted for analysis may represent many tons of feed or forage. Results from the analyses can then be used to provide a balanced ration without the extra cost of unnecessary supplements.

Grazing Opportunities. Grazing systems today are more adaptable and easier to implement, primarily as a result of rapid advances in low cost fence and water systems. The high degree of flexibility afforded by this technology allows a grazing system to be implemented quickly. It can be modified easily to minimize the adverse effects of seasonal forage quality and availability and to maximize utilization of forage resources to meet animal needs.

Other incentives for producers to shift to pasture systems include: increased soil conservation, fewer manure management problems, better animal health, and reduced concern about various environmental issues. These are all important; however, a fundamental underlying issue is economics. With the increasing cost of confined feeding systems and with little or no increase in milk prices, dairy producers are anxious to reduce production costs and improve profitability.

Feed comprises over 50 percent of the cost of producing dairy products in a traditional dairy operation. Grazing can mean a feed savings of $75 to over $150 per cow per year. Grazing during only a portion of the grazing season can result in a $1 savings for each 100 pounds of milk. Seasonal grazing of good quality pasture can reduce corn silage usage as much as 80 percent.

There is no specific procedure required for success with grazing of dairy cows. The pasture contribution to overall feed production can vary considerably depending on resources, needs, and desire. Some grazing enthusiasts have switched to a total grazing program with seasonal milk production matched to the main pasture season, while others utilize high quality pastures when available to reduce a substantial amount of stored feed.

In general, high quality pastures (grazing-tolerant alfalfa with adapted grasses, grass-clover mixtures, annual ryegrass, small grain) should be provided in a vegetative stage in adequate amounts for high producing dairy cows. This can generally be best managed with rotational stocking of small paddocks (Chapter 25). Many dairy producers use forward grazing, which allows lactating cows first access to a paddock, followed by dry cows or replacement heifers. This results in animals with the highest nutritional requirements getting the highest quality forage. Grain and mineral supplementation can be adjusted based on pasture supply, quality, and animal productivity.

Concerns often expressed by dairy producers considering grazing for the first time include variation in pasture quality and quantity, bloat, fencing, and water costs, problems with heat stress during summer, and cattle management. Although these factors are of concern; they can be resolved with good management. For example, experienced dairy producers do not consider bloat a major problem when proper precautions are taken

(Chapter 22). Likewise, low cost, portable, and flexible fencing and watering systems can be adapted and implemented to meet individual farm needs. Research has shown that cows can travel up to a mile from the milking parlor to pasture without a loss in production.

In the lower South, irrigation is highly desirable in maintaining quality and quantity of pasture forage. It is also needed in most years to get winter annual pastures established in early autumn when weather is usually dry. Generally, in the lower South winter annual pastures are the most dependable and profitable dairy pastures. Summer pasture is a problem because of heat and drought stress.

Summary

Dairy producers in the South have demonstrated their ability to grow quality products efficiently. Feed cost represents the largest single expense a dairy producer faces. High quality forages are the most economical sources of the essential nutrients needed by dairy cows. Knowing the quality of feed sources available through forage testing permits producers to more efficiently and economically balance rations with off-farm feeds, including by-products from industry.

Research and on-farm demonstrations have shown that pasture systems can be used to advantage by many dairy producers. Survey results, demonstrations, and research confirm that it is possible for experienced dairy producers with adequate resources to save $120 per cow per year or more by adopting grazing programs to supply high quality pasture to meet at least some portion of feed requirements. The extent of such contributions depends on the quality and quantity of pasture available and length of the grazing season. Grazing high quality, high yielding forages such as winter cereals, annual ryegrass, alfalfa, or alfalfa-perennial cool season grass mixtures provides dairy producers an opportunity to reduce the amount of stored feed required and produce milk more economically.

29 Forages for Horses

There are several reasons why horse owners should have some knowledge of forage crops. Horses need forage in their diet because it helps prevent digestive problems. An adequate quantity of good quality forage is also an economical way to minimize feed costs, which normally constitute the greatest expense involved in keeping horses.

In addition, knowledge of certain potential problems that may occur in pasture situations or that can result from feeding an inappropriate type of hay or grazing certain types of plants may enable an owner to avoid injury or death to animals. Horses are also less likely to chew on wood or other objects when in a good pasture. And finally, pastures provide a healthful exercise area for horses while beautifying the landscape.

General Nutritional and Feeding Information

Horses are natural forage eaters as evidenced by the fact that wild horses do quite well in open range situations. Feeding of concentrates becomes necessary only when there are great demands on the animals, such as when they are being worked or when young and growing. The late gestation and lactation periods also require concentrate supplementation to meet nutrient needs. At other times, good quality pastures can totally meet nutrient requirements. If only low-quality forage is available, supplemental feeding may be necessary, especially for young, growing animals or lactating mares.

Pastures such as this Kentucky bluegrass/white clover mixture in central Kentucky provide an exercise area and good nutrition while beautifying the landscape.

Horses are not ruminants. Their digestive system differs considerably from those of cattle and sheep. Instead of having four stomachs, including a large rumen where fermentation and microbial digestion take place, horses have a single, relatively small stomach. However, they do have a well developed cecum just beyond the smaller intestine in which bacteria digest forage somewhat like the rumen of a cow, although less efficiently (see **Figure 16.2**).

The low digestion efficiency in the cecum results in a greater requirement for high quality protein. Much of the protein obtained by cows and sheep is produced by bacteria in the rumen and subsequently digested in the ruminant's true stomach, or abomasum. Since the horse digests forage after materials pass through the true stomach and small intestines where many nutrients are absorbed, less of the protein synthesized in the cecum is available for absorption.

Because of the small stomach size and characteristics of their digestive system, horses need to be fed frequently. Furthermore, they need to consume good quality hay or pasture that will be easily digested and move rapidly through their digestive systems. How a horse is fed will greatly influence its growth, reproduction, speed and/or strength, as well as its appearance. As with any type of animal, the nutritional needs of horses vary depending on size, age, and activity. Diets should be formulated by qualified individuals based on the class of animal and the specific nutrient analyses of materials being fed.

The diets of horses can consist of a combination of pasture, hay, concentrates, and even high quality, well-ensiled silage made from corn or small grains (though silage should not comprise more than about 50 percent of the roughage intake). Once a diet has been formulated, abrupt shifts in feedstuffs should be avoided, especially from very low quality to very high quality. Gradual changes are much less likely to cause digestive upsets or colic.

Hay for Horses

Hay is an important feed for horses. Non-lactating broodmares and idle mature horses can do well on high quality hay alone, while increased activity and reproduction require supplemental feeding. Even when other supplemental feed is being provided, it is desirable to furnish horses with hay because it tends to prevent colic and digestive problems. Horses need to receive about 1 to 2 lb of high quality hay per day per 100 lb of body weight.

Many types of forage can make good horse hay. Legume hays that are often fed in the South include alfalfa, sericea lespedeza, and red clover. Second cutting red clover hay can cause excessive slobbering due to a mold that sometimes is present, but this is mainly a cosmetic problem and normally not dangerous. When red clover is cut at the early bloom stage rather than being allowed to become quite mature, the mold normally does not have time to make any significant growth.

In the lower South, bermudagrass or bahiagrass make good summer pastures for horses.

Among grass hays, timothy has the reputation of being especially good for horses, but other types of grass hay can be equally acceptable. Bermudagrass, ryegrass, and/or small grains, and either endophyte-free or novel endophyte tall fescue all have the potential to make excellent hay if harvested at the proper stage of maturity and not damaged by rain.

Hay and other feed materials should be free of mold; otherwise, digestion may be upset. Dry, dusty hay can also irritate the lungs, resulting in a cough, runny eyes or nose, and possibly pneumonia or an incurable disease called heaves. Good horse hay should be free of weeds and foreign objects. Hay should also be leafy and have a pleasant aroma. Fine-stemmed, soft hay is preferable to coarse, fibrous hay.

A misconception is that good hay will always be a bright green color. Although a bright color is an indication of no rain damage, color alone is a poor way to evaluate hay because low quality hay can have bright color while top quality hay will eventually lose color with time. Hay color makes no difference to horses.

When purchasing hay, it is best to buy it by the ton if possible because it is considerably cheaper when bought in quantity. Also, when purchased by the ton, one does not have to be concerned with variability in bale size, which greatly affects the cost of hay purchased by the bale.

Although visual inspection is quite useful, the best way to evaluate hay quality is by a laboratory analysis. Many reputable hay dealers have their hay tested as a routine practice. Beware of dealers who do not want an analysis of their hay.

Hay belly is a term that some horse producers use to refer to animals having a large, distended digestive tract. This occurs as a result of feeding

Winter annuals make excellent horse pastures.

large quantities of low quality forage. High quality hays do not cause this problem.

Pasture for Horses

Providing pastures for horses is a healthful way to allow them to get exercise while simultaneously furnishing the nutrients they need. The amount of pasture required for a horse will vary depending on factors such as size and age of the horse, pasture species, amount of supplemental feed provided, and soil fertility. However, for most of the South, at least 1.5 to 2 acres of pasture should be provided for each mature animal. Generally a horse will consume about 2 percent of its body weight in dry matter per day.

Mature, non-working horses and well-developed older yearlings can normally be maintained on good pasture with little or no grain supplementation, but should have salt available. Animals with higher nutritional requirements, such as young growing horses or work horses, may need some grain and high quality hay along with pasture, especially at times of the year when forage availability is limited.

Many different forage plants can be used for pasture in the South, and most make suitable pastures for horses. While horses will consume some forage of most legumes, they generally prefer grasses. In most cases, pastures should consist of grasses or of grass/legume mixtures. However, arrowleaf clover and vetch are two annual legumes that are quite unpalatable to horses.

Bermudagrass, bahiagrass, and dallisgrass are often used to pasture horses in the lower South. In the upper South, Kentucky bluegrass and orchardgrass are commonly used for horse pastures. In addition, endophyte-free or novel

Mares often have reproductive problems on endophyte-infected tall fescue, but non-toxic tall fescue pasture or hay is excellent for horses.

endophyte (see Chapter 24) tall fescue makes an excellent horse pasture, but in the interest of long-term persistence, care should be taken to avoid overgrazing. As discussed elsewhere in this book, white clover, red clover, or birdsfoot trefoil can be used as companion species with these cool season grasses. Alfalfa can also provide excellent grazing for horses.

Winter annual grasses (small grain and/or ryegrass) or winter annual grass/legume mixtures make superb horse pastures. These can either be planted on a prepared seedbed or overseeded (or sodseeded) on a warm season perennial grass. Suitable summer annuals include pearl millet, browntop millet, and crabgrass. With management to allow reseeding, crabgrass can be a dependable volunteer species following winter annuals planted in autumn on a tilled seedbed.

Browntop millet makes a good quality, but short-lived pasture. Pearl millet is much more productive, but may be initially unpalatable to the animals. Due to its erratic growth, pearl millet is also difficult to keep stocked properly.

Species to Avoid

Sorghum, sudangrass, johnsongrass, and particularly sorghum-sudangrass hybrids are not recommended for horse pastures. Horses grazing these species may develop cystitis, which results in paralysis and urinary disorders. Hay of these species is safe to feed. German or foxtail millet is also not recommended (see Chapter 5).

Toxic endophyte-infected tall fescue should not be used as pasture for pregnant broodmares, especially during the last three months of gestation (see Chapter 24). It has also been shown to reduce weight gains of yearling horses and may have other effects that have not been documented. Endophyte-free or non-toxic endophyte tall fescue are excellent, but the latter has better grazing tolerance and stand persistence in horse pastures. Either non-infected or novel endophyte tall fescue makes an excellent horse pasture.

Special Pasture Management Considerations

It is not unusual to see horse pastures that are overgrazed, trampled, and unproductive. While a basic problem is often inadequate pasture area, lack of grazing management is also a problem in many cases, even when

Kentucky bluegrass is a commonly-used forage in horse pastures in the upper South.

there is adequate pasture available.

Horses are more selective than cattle and tend to spot graze. In addition, they bite off forage very closely. The result is that, without proper management, some areas in a pasture are heavily grazed while others are left virtually untouched. If this situation is allowed to continue too long, close defoliation may hurt plant vigor and even forage stands in the grazed spots, while much forage is wasted in ungrazed areas.

Periodically moving animals from one area to another can provide the following benefits: 1) increase the vigor of pasture plants by resting them on a regular basis; 2) achieve more even utilization of the forage produced; 3) minimize hoof damage; and 4) reduce parasite problems. Electric fencing, either high tensile wire or electrified tape, is safe and works well with horses, though it is best to condition them by initially providing exposure to only a short strand of electrified wire.

After removing horses from a pasture area, it may be desirable to clip the remaining forage to even out the overgrazed and undergrazed areas and to keep forage plants young and tender. Cattle can also be used to graze down an uneven pasture after horses have been removed. Dragging pastures after horses have been moved scatters dung and, with the possible exception of dragging done in spring, reduces parasite problems.

If pastures are overstocked, horses will not have the opportunity to selectively graze, and nutritional quality will drop. Grazing horses and cattle together is desirable because cattle reduce the effects of spot grazing. Also, horses and cattle will graze around each other's fecal and urine spots, but not their own.

Pastures for horses should be well drained, free of holes or stumps that might cause injury to the animals, and contain no poisonous plants (see

Chapter 23). It is important to have safe fences that will not easily injure the horses. Fertilization should be according to soil test recommendations. There is no need to remove horses from pastures during routine fertilization unless the equipment frightens them (although if a fertilizer spill should occur, it should be immediately cleaned up). Horses need access to shade, plenty of clean fresh water, salt, and a basic mineral mixture. To reduce parasite exposure for yearlings, it is desirable to graze mature horses separately. Horses do not normally bloat on pasture, but may founder on an extremely lush pasture if they are not acclimated to it and are allowed to overeat.

Spraying of horse pastures with an appropriate herbicide to control weeds is highly desirable when weeds are a problem. Any grazing restrictions provided on the herbicide label should be strictly observed.

The hooves of horses can be more damaging to pasture than those of cattle. This is another reason why rotational stocking is desirable, particularly in newly established pastures. Any type of pasture can be damaged if overstocked, but bermudagrass and bahiagrass are more tolerant of treading than most species. Tall fescue is reasonably tolerant as well. Pastures recently planted on a prepared seedbed are especially vulnerable and should be protected until a good root system has developed. It may also be necessary to protect even a well-established pasture by temporarily removing the animals during wet periods when the ground is soft. SF

Forages for Goats, Deer, Sheep, Llamas, and Ratites

Forages are consumed by many animal species other than cattle and horses. They range from exotic animals in zoos and animal parks to species of considerably greater economic importance, such as those discussed in this chapter. In each case, it is important that forage needs of each species are considered on the basis of their respective physiology, seasonal demands, and consumption habits.

Goats

Goats are grown in the U.S. for one of three purposes. Angora goats are grown for mohair. Dairy goats are used for milk production. Meat goat production, once a minor enterprise, more than doubled in recent years. Demand has grown primarily due to the continuing influx of immigrant people who traditionally include goat meat in their diet or utilize it for religious feast days.

Characteristics of goats

Spanish (or bush) goats, commonly grown for meat in the southeastern U.S., will breed any time of the year. Dairy goats are more seasonal, usually breeding between August and March, with a gestation period of about five months. The does usually deliver two or more kids and require little attention during kidding except in cold, rainy weather, when their lack of subcutaneous fat allows them to be easily chilled.

Goats select higher quality leafy forage than cattle in grazing. They readily consume the desirable and more nutritious parts of coarse weeds and brush, as well as grasses and some legumes (see Chapter 25). They consume

Goats thrive on pastures containing shrubs and small trees.

a wider range of plants than cattle and tolerate bitter tastes such as plants containing large amounts of tannin. Although their diets may vary greatly depending on what is available, if given a choice, goats will consume 40 to 60 percent brush, 10 to 30 percent weeds and legumes, and 20 to 30 percent grass. They often ignore clover and high-quality grasses. Goats are adaptive and will consume much larger amounts of grasses in improved pastures. Goats have prehensile lips that allow them to eat around the spines and thorns of brush plants.

Goats have no efficiency advantage over cattle when fed high quality forage. The rate of passage through the alimentary tract is higher in goats than cattle, resulting in the need for a higher forage intake as a percentage of body weight as compared to cattle.

Pasture management for goats

Intensive grazing of goats on high-investment pasture is usually not cost effective. An ideal way to utilize goats is to graze them with cattle in large pastures because in such situations they can be quite effective in controlling weeds and brush. They are effective in eliminating many troublesome plant species that cattle do not consume such as willow, persimmon, multiflora rose, pigweed, thistles, stinging nettle, blackberry, plantain, and curly dock. Goats also consume seed heads of grasses that are often ignored by cattle. Some pasture weeds such as sicklepod, bitterweed, and dogfennel are avoided by goats.

When goats are used to clear pasture areas of weeds and brush, grazing can be prolonged until these species are destroyed. However, if brush, vines, and weeds are to be used as a long-term resource, rotational stocking will be needed to allow these species time to recover.

On most farms, supplemental pasture species will likely be needed to supply adequate forage for meat goats during at least part of the year. It is important to supply a higher level of nutrition, including 14 percent protein, in the diet of does in late pregnancy and early lactation, as well as to growing kids that will be marketed for meat on a target date. Sericea lespedeza is an excellent warm season perennial legume that is readily consumed by goats. They also like bahiagrass, johnsongrass, chicory, and pearl millet, but bermudagrass is less palatable to them. Endophyte-infected tall fescue can be used, but toxicity can be a problem when no other plant species are present in the pasture. Rye, wheat, and annual ryegrass are suitable, but clovers are often ignored. Poisonous plants are usually not a problem for goats with an adequate feed supply.

Problems

Parasites are a major problem with goats in the humid southern U.S. when they are confined to small areas of pasture at a high stocking rate. They can be particularly serious in closely grazed pastures of species such as bahiagrass. Taller growing species such as sericea lespedeza, pearl millet, and kudzu are excellent for goat pasture as they allow the goat less contact with the ground during grazing. The best prevention against parasite infestation is using an appropriate stocking rate and rotational stocking, which allows pastures to rest between grazing periods. A common reason for parasite problems is keeping too many goats on a small land area. A good deworming program is a second line of defense.

Predators can be a major challenge with goats. Coyotes can be particularly harmful, but feral or neighborhood dogs can also kill kids and even adults. Putting goats in pens at night is one option, but another is the use of guardian animals such as donkeys or llamas that will attack predators. Good electric fences also help. Since goats are intelligent, they can be trained to electric fences by placing them in a small pasture enclosed by a five- or six-wire fence with the bottom three wires 6 inches apart and the top one at 4 feet. Once trained, goats are easily contained by three-wire electric fences placed at 10, 20, and 36 inches above ground.

Farmed Deer

Deer farming is the production of venison, antler velvet, or trophy bucks for game ranching from deer maintained on fenced high quality pasture. New Zealand is the major venison producer with well over a million deer on farms. Most of the venison is exported to western Europe and the antler velvet to Asian countries for medicinal purposes. There was little deer farming in the U.S. until the 1990s, when expansion occurred because of the demand for venison and antler velvet. Demand for farmed venison is growing in the U.S., but well over half is still imported from New Zealand. Farm-raised venison is a higher quality meat than wild venison because of better nutrition, health care, and marketing at a young age. It is lower in fat than beef, with a cholesterol level equivalent to skinless chicken.

Red deer, shown here, and fallow deer require high quality pasture in summer for lactating females and during winter and spring for bucks grown for slaughter.

Most venison farms in the U.S. use fallow and red deer. Fallow deer weigh about 110 lb at slaughter, red deer about twice as much. White-tail deer are not well suited for venison production on intensive pastures because they prefer browse, utilize little grass except in winter, and require higher fences. Elk, similar to deer in their diet habits (**Appendix A.54**), are raised mainly for production of trophy animals at hunting preserves.

Considerations in deer farming

Deer offer several advantages over beef cattle. Pastures meet most of their nutrient requirements, so it is an environmentally friendly agricultural system. They mature more quickly than cattle (15 to 20 months) and reproduce longer, up to 20 years. The carcass composition is higher, about 58 to 60 percent, and they produce a higher proportion of prime cuts than cattle. However, there is virtually no twinning in the main farmed deer species.

Cattle have an important advantage over deer in that the breeding season can be adjusted to fit the period of highest pasture quality and thus better match the nutritional needs of the animal for reproduction and growth. In contrast, most farmed deer species do not have this flexibility in adjustment of breeding season because they have a fixed early summer fawning season. Fawning occurs during late May and June, with lactation continuing until weaning in late September. Thus, nutrient needs are highest for lactating deer during summer when perennial grasses generally decline in quality. Ideally, pastures for deer should provide forage with 64 percent total digestible nutrients (TDN) and 16 percent crude protein (CP) from mid April until the breeding season in October. After this, the nutrient requirements drop sharply (52 percent TDN and 10 percent CP) so most perennial pastures or good grass hay are adequate for maintenance of pregnant females. Weaned bucks to be grown out for slaughter have high nutrient requirements similar to lactating females during late autumn, winter, and spring. Selenium requirements of deer are higher than for cattle.

Fence is a major expense. High tensile woven wire is commonly used for pasture perimeter fences with a height of 6 feet adequate for fallow or red deer, but 8 feet is required by law in many states. Electric polywire tape is often used for cross fencing pastures. Another expense is special handling facilities. Deer are usually relatively healthy, but do require minimal worming and vaccinations.

Summer pasture problems and solutions

Perennial grasses are the cheapest summer pastures for deer. In late spring, nutritive quality of cool season perennial grasses such as non-toxic tall fescue, orchardgrass, and smooth bromegrass are certainly adequate for pregnant and lactating deer. The same is true for well fertilized bermudagrass early in the growing season. However, as temperatures increase in summer, forage lignin content increases and reduces digestibility of perennial grasses, so energy and protein supplements will be needed. Toxic endophyte-infected tall fescue reduces animal growth and adversely affects appearance, making it less desirable for deer pasture. Dilution with clover or another grass reduces the problem. In most areas of the South, clover growth declines during hot, dry summer weather and normally provides only limited grazing.

The most dependable summer pasture plant with high nutritive quality over much of the South is grazing-tolerant alfalfa. Pastures should be cross-fenced and rotationally stocked to allow a four week rest period. Chicory is another high quality pasture plant relished by deer. This broadleaf perennial plant has a deep taproot that tolerates acid subsoils, so it can obtain moisture and maintain growth even during relatively dry periods.

In areas dominated by warm season perennial grasses, the summer options are more limited. Management of bermudagrass that includes frequent nitrogen fertilization and close mowing to 2 or 3 inches can enhance new leaf growth, giving satisfactory early season performance with fallow and red deer. The highest quality adapted bermudagrass variety should be planted. As bermudagrass quality declines during summer, corn and soybean supplements should be fed. Cottonseed can reduce antler growth due to the high gossypol content. In high rainfall areas, highly fertilized crabgrass is a summer option. Sorghum-sudangrass can also provide nutrient requirements in summer if managed properly and if care is taken to avoid prussic acid poisoning (see Chapter 22). Pearl millet and browntop millet also are relatively high quality annual grasses, but deer dislike them. Cowpea and forage soybeans are high quality annual legumes that grow well on sandy soils and are palatable to deer. In the lower Coastal Plain, perennial peanut is one of the best choices for dependable high quality deer pasture. It must be planted vegetatively and requires two years to obtain a productive stand, but once established, it survives indefinitely if properly managed.

Winter pastures for growing bucks

In much of the South, novel endophyte or endophyte-free tall fescue can supply the nutrient needs of bucks during autumn and in late winter and spring. During winter, rye, wheat, oats, and/or annual ryegrass are good choices in the lower South. Annual ryegrass is preferred in the Coastal Plain because it tolerates close grazing better than small grains. High gains can be expected on annual ryegrass, so weaned bucks should be able to reach slaughter weight before the ryegrass matures in May. Where winter pasture is not available, high quality hay can be fed along with supplements if needed.

Sheep

Sheep lead all farm animals in the ability to produce marketable products on forage alone. However, successful sheep production requires careful attention to parasite and predator control as well as to births during lambing season. These factors, together with low wool prices, contribute to the continuing decline of sheep production in the humid Eastern U.S. Annual per capita consumption of lamb in the U.S. is only about 1 pound; much of this is imported, mainly from New Zealand.

Winter annuals make excellent pastures for sheep.

Some sheep breeds are better suited than others to the climate of the Southern U.S. These include Suffolk, Dorset, Hampshire, and hair sheep breeds such as Katahdin, St. Croix, and Barbados Blackbelly.

Pastures

A high percentage of the annual feed requirements of sheep can be provided from forage. A profitable sheep operation depends on providing as much grazing through the year as possible. The stocking rate for sheep varies according to forage species and soil fertility, with usually about four to six ewes grazed on the same amount of pasture required for a cow. Usually, 30 to 35 ewes plus a ram are considered to be the minimum economic size for a sheep flock.

Matching breeding season to feed supply

Late pregnancy and early lactation are the times when ewes have the greatest energy requirements. Thus, in most of the Southern U.S., a late winter or early spring lambing program is generally most successful. In such a program, breeding occurs in the autumn, and the pregnant ewes are wintered on hay, silage, or cool season pastures. With such a program, lambs can either be grazed through the spring and early summer on high quality pastures, or they can be weaned at 90 days of age or less and fed out in dry lot. Autumn lambing is a possibility, but less likely to be profitable unless alfalfa or cool season annual grasses are utilized extensively. In such a program, the ewes are bred in late spring and the lambs marketed in mid-spring after having grazed winter annual pastures, non-toxic tall fescue/white clover, or orchardgrass/white clover pastures. Pasture systems in the various climatic zones are similar to those for beef stocker cattle (see Chapter 27). Immediately after lambs are weaned, the nutritional requirements of ewes decrease, and they can be maintained on low quality forages until near the beginning of the breeding season.

Mature llamas manage well on a wide range of pasture grasses.

Special problems

Predators, especially dogs and coyotes, can cause losses, but electric fencing reduces the problem. As with goats, donkeys and llamas bond with sheep and can provide predator control. Guardian dogs can also be used. Internal parasites can be a severe problem for sheep, so control measures are essential. Periodic worming, often monthly, is necessary. In addition, parasite levels can be kept lower by using rotational stocking and moving animals before pastures are grazed closely.

Llamas

There are over 100,000 llamas in the U.S. They are used as pack animals for campers and hikers, as pets, and increasingly as livestock guardians against predators. They are highly territorial animals and bond well with sheep, goats, and fallow deer. Llamas, like alpaca, are camelids native to the high Andes mountains of South America. Their gestation period is about 340 days, which is longer than for cattle or horses. The crias (or young) are weaned at four to five months.

Llamas are modified ruminants, with a three-compartment stomach, and efficiently digest plant material. They consume grasses, weeds, and browse from shrubs and trees, including bark. They eat clover to a lesser extent than sheep and tend to be patch grazers in pastures. Most pastures should allow a stocking rate of four to five per acre. In their grazing habits, they deposit pellets in communal dung piles. Some llama owners collect these pellet piles and sell them as fertilizer to gardeners.

The nutrient requirements for llamas are relatively low. Forage containing 8 to 9 percent CP is adequate for mature llamas, increasing to 10 to 14 percent for lactating females. Minerals important in their diet appear to be calcium, phosphorus, selenium, copper, and zinc. Most fertilized pasture grasses should be adequate for mature llamas. When grass quality is low, limited protein and grain feeding may be necessary during late pregnancy

Ostrich can utilize a large percentage of forage in their diet, but pastures need to be of high quality.

and lactation. There is some indication that llamas are sensitive to toxic endophyte-infected tall fescue. Overfeeding of llamas with high quality forages should be avoided as it can cause obesity, overheating in hot weather, and fertility or birthing problems. For this reason, alfalfa and clovers are not recommended for pasture or hay.

Ratites

Ostrich and emu (originating in Africa and Australia, respectively) are ratites, large flightless birds that are raised mainly for meat production. They produce lean red meat low in fat and cholesterol. It is sold as a specialty meat in Europe, South Africa, and to some extent in the U.S. Body skin is thick and durable, but soft. It is used for clothing, purses, shoes, and boots. Ostrich have been raised on farms in South Africa for about 150 years, producing meat, ornamental feathers, and leather.

Ostrich are seasonal breeders, starting in March and ending in August or September. The egg incubation period is 42 days, with fertility about 60 percent. From time of hatching, growth is rapid, and birds are ready for slaughter at between 10 and 14 months of age. The carcass yield of lean meat is 55 to 65 percent.

Ostrich and emu both consume forage, but ostrich have a larger cecum and slower rate of passage in the gut, so utilize fiber better than emu. The gut of an emu resembles that of a chicken more than an ostrich, requiring them to consume good quality food high in available nutrients. The ostrich digestive tract is more similar to a pig or horse, allowing them to utilize high quality forage to supply 60 percent or more of their nutritional requirements. Thus, pastures need to be of high nutritive quality to achieve this goal or else grain feeding must be increased. Based on grazing experience in South Africa and New Zealand, alfalfa and annual ryegrass make desirable pasture species for ostrich. Other possibilities might be endophyte-free or novel endophyte tall fescue, orchardgrass, chicory, and red clover, while warm season perennial grasses are less desirable pasture species. Adult ostrich are very territorial and best suited to continuously stocked pastures. The calcium requirement of female birds is high for egg production because the shells contain a high percentage of this element. Thus, it is necessary to increase calcium in the diet prior to the onset of breeding to allow normal egg production. Ostrich are afflicted by internal parasites and respiratory infections that are more of a problem in humid than dry environments with low relative humidity. Preventive treatments are necessary in the Southern U.S. SF

Many people are interested in wildlife. Hunting is a popular sport enjoyed by millions, plus many non-hunters enjoy observing wildlife and want to help provide better conditions for them.

Before European settlers arrived on the North American continent, wild game was plentiful. However, as land was cleared and farming practices led to the destruction of wildlife habitat, populations of many wild animals declined. Today many people would like to see wildlife populations increase.

Through the years, many approaches to increasing wildlife numbers have been tried. These have included the release of pen-raised animals into the wild, imposing strict regulations pertaining to hunting, and predator control. Depending on the situation, such techniques may or may not be helpful. Generally, the best method of increasing wildlife populations is to improve the habitat by: 1) increasing the amount of cover and/or 2) improving the year-round food supply available for the animals. Many forage crops can help accomplish these purposes.

Characteristics of Game Animals

Before discussing plants that are useful in feeding or protecting wildlife, it is worthwhile to first consider a few of the habits and characteristics of common game animals. The behavior patterns of animals have a major influence on the appropriateness of growing various crops, as well as how they should be planted.

Deer. The range of white-tail deer can vary widely, but often is an area approximately three-quarters of a mile wide and one and one-half miles long. Usually, a buck will range over about a section (640 acres) of land, and a doe will range over about one-half that. However, deer will travel substantial distances from their normal range to reach a food plot. Bucks are especially likely to range more widely during the rutting season. In many areas, deer populations have greatly increased, so they have become pests, causing damage to crops, vegetable gardens, and ornamentals.

Deer in white clover near Auburn, Alabama.

White-tail deer like a varied diet consisting of numerous items including twigs, acorns, fruits, weeds, grasses, and legumes. They prefer a high percentage of shrubs and trees in their diet. (see **Appendix A.54**), but will graze large amounts of high quality forages when other feed is in short supply. Winter annuals are widely planted for deer because they furnish high quality forage during a time when there is little other green material available, plus much of their growth occurs during deer hunting season, so they can be quite effective in attracting deer for harvest. Usually, several winter annual species are planted in a mixture to provide a long grazing period.

Knowledgeable wildlife managers are interested in providing nutrition for deer as needed throughout the year. Early summer is the time fawns are normally born, and the highest nutritional requirements of does occur during early lactation. The rebreeding of does, the body weights of deer during winter, and antler development of bucks are all affected by nutrition during summer and autumn. Protein is especially likely to be deficient in deer diets at this time.

The high quality perennial legumes—red clover, white clover, and alfalfa, each of which is normally planted in pure stands when established for deer—are excellent. They provide high quality forage over a long period of time and normally last for several years. Warm season annuals commonly planted for deer include soybean, cowpea, and American jointvetch.

Food plots for deer should normally be 1 to 5 acres in size. In predominately forested areas, 1 to 5 percent of the land area should be planted for food plots in order to support a high deer population. Ideally, plots should be long and narrow (as opposed to square) and should be located in sunny areas close to woods or transition zones that provide escape cover. The edges of logging roads, forest openings, utility rights-of-way, and idle crop fields are good places to locate plots.

Doves. Although some mourning doves (commonly called simply doves) stay in much of the South all year, the dove is basically a migratory bird. Millions fly through the South each autumn and spring. In addition, even local doves may range over a wide area in search of food. Non-migrating doves will fly up to 12 miles to reach a feeding field.

Doves have a high mortality rate, with an estimated 70 percent of the population dying from one year to the next. Although it may be important to a local population, hunting pressure has relatively little effect on dove mortality overall. The high rate of mortality is of little consequence because doves are extremely prolific, often raising four to six broods per year. In addition, some doves hatched early in the year can reproduce before the year end.

Doves can be attracted with food plots, but it may be difficult to hold them in a given area. Their migratory nature and lack of hesitation to abruptly abandon one feeding area for another account for the unfortunate experience many hunters have had of seeing large numbers of birds in a field one day, but none the next when a dove shoot has been arranged. Such rapid movement is often accompanied by a change in the weather.

Probably the best plant species to attract doves are browntop millet, proso millet, and sunflower. A good approach is to plant a small food patch of 2 or more acres in early spring to feed local doves during summer, then make a larger planting in mid to late spring to attract migratory doves. Fields in which dove shoots will be held should normally be at least 5 acres in size.

Doves are poor scratchers and will not dig up buried seed. Also, they usually will not perch on plants to eat from seed heads. They prefer their food lying out in the open on relatively bare ground.

Courtesy Quail Unlimited www.qu.org

Bobwhite quail require nesting cover and food availability to thrive.

Ducks. With the exception of some wood ducks that remain in the South throughout the year, ducks are migratory birds. Food plots are commonly used to attract migrating ducks. In flooding areas, Japanese millet, corn, and grain sorghum are good duck food plants. In other areas, browntop millet is an excellent choice.

Quail. There are several species of quail native to the U.S., but in most of the South, the most common quail is the bobwhite. Other species have similar feeding habits to the bobwhite.

Quail covey ranges are usually fairly small. The size or shape of a range varies, but is usually less than one-half mile in width or length. The requirements of a range are: 1) adequate food availability; 2) roosting sites; 3) nesting cover; 4) escape cover; and 5) protection from bad weather. All of these except nesting cover must be available throughout the year.

Quail eat a diversity of food items. Their diet consists mainly of seeds, fruits, and insects, but they will also eat small amounts of green leaves. Probably the best plants to grow for quail food are annual lespedeza, partridge pea, shrub lespedeza, reseeding vetch, and Egyptian wheat. Millets, corn, sorghum, and alfalfa are also excellent quail plants.

The bobwhite seems to thrive best where there are about equal amounts of cultivated crops, idle fields that have not been under cultivation for 3 to 10 years, woodlands, and areas reverting to woodland. It is best if these are in small, well-scattered tracts.

A one acre food plot for every 12 acres of land should provide adequate food for high quail populations. Food plots should be at least 15 feet wide and a quarter acre in size. Cover plots should be at least one-eighth acre in size. Several one-eighth acre plots are better than one large area. Annual (striate or Korean) lespedeza is probably the single most important winter food of quail in the South.

Rabbits. Rabbit populations are dynamic, and food supplies are critically important in maintaining a high population. Since winter is the time when rabbit food supplies are of most concern, any type of green winter plant (with the exception of endophyte-infected tall fescue) is a good choice for food plots.

When food plots are planted, it is best to place them in narrow strips (approximately 10 feet wide) close to a thicket or other area that provides

Wild turkeys range over a wide area. Winter annuals are good choices for food plots.

cover. This allows the rabbits to feed, but they still have the opportunity to scamper back into the cover if danger threatens. Examples of good plants to grow include various clovers, small grains, and ryegrass. Deer and wild turkeys will also use plantings of these species.

Wild Turkeys. Turkeys range over a wider area than deer and eat a varied diet consisting of insects, seeds of various plants, and a substantial amount of green leaves. Chufa, corn, soybean, cowpea, and any type or mixture of winter annuals are good choices for turkey food plots.

Plants for Wildlife

Plants provide both cover and food for wildlife, but this discussion will center primarily on those that provide food. Although most of the plants discussed are forage crops, a few non-forage species are included.

When considering plants for wildlife food, the first question that comes to mind is, What will wildlife eat? The answer is that wildlife will, if necessary, eat many different things. Dramatic evidence of this is provided by areas that have excessively high deer populations. During periods when there is little plant growth, virtually every bit of green material up to the maximum height that deer can reach will be consumed.

The primary concerns relating to plant selection for wildlife food plots relate to species palatability, nutritive quality, quantity of forage produced, and length of time it is available, especially during periods of critical need. Plants that meet these requirements should be considered for wildlife plantings. The following is a discussion of some plants that have been found to be useful in wildlife plantings or beneficial to wildlife on a farm if planted primarily for other purposes.

Alfalfa. This cool season perennial legume makes excellent high quality forage growth during spring, summer, and autumn. The forage is relished by deer, and it is an excellent source of insects and green material for quail and turkeys. While more management-intensive than most wildlife plants (see Chapter 8), it has a great deal to offer in certain situations. The availability of grazing-tolerant (and thus more persistent) varieties has greatly increased the feasibility of planting the crop in areas where wildlife (especially deer) populations are high.

American Jointvetch. American jointvetch (or *Aeschynomene*) is neither a vetch nor a cool season forage as are other vetches. It is a summer annual legume that is sometimes planted for deer. It is best adapted to fairly moist sites in Zone A (**Figure 3.2**), but can often be successfully grown on well-drained soil. If allowed to make seed, a reseeded stand can normally be obtained by disking the area in spring.

Annual Lespedeza. Annual lespedeza includes both Korean and striate species. Korean lespedeza is best adapted in the upper part of Zones B and in Zones C and D, while striate lespedeza is the best choice for the lower part of Zone B and for Zone A. There are several varieties of each species.

Annual lespedeza is an extremely useful species to plant for quail food. Doves are not particularly fond of it, but will eat it if nothing else is available.

Browntop Millet. Browntop millet is an extremely valuable plant for attracting doves, quail, or ducks. Timing of planting can be an important consideration because seed mature about 60 days after germination. Consequently, if browntop millet is planted too early, all the seed may be gone before dove season begins. It is best to time a planting so that doves have at least two weeks of feeding time to become accustomed to the field before a shoot is held. All plantings need to be made early enough to allow the plants to mature seed before frost.

Chufa. Chufa is a type of giant nutsedge that is a favorite food of deer and especially wild turkeys. It is widely adapted in the South and is easy to grow. It is best suited for use on soils that are sandy or loamy.

Wildlife do not eat the leaves, but they relish the nutlets that grow on the roots. When mature, a few plants should be dug to expose the nutlets. Once wildlife have discovered them, they will dig the rest themselves. Chufa is planted primarily for turkeys. It probably is not worthwhile to plant just for deer.

Chufa will sometimes volunteer if the area in which it was grown the year before is disked well in spring, but it is not as aggressive as many other types of nutsedge. Therefore, it is not likely to be a weed problem in subsequent years in a field where other crops may be planted.

Cowpea. Cowpea, also called southern pea, is well-adapted to many areas in the South. It makes a substantial amount of summer growth that can provide forage for deer, cover for quail, and seed that can be consumed by various types of birds. If all the seed are not consumed, cowpea has the potential to reseed. Reseeding can be facilitated by disking a seed-containing area in the spring.

Several varieties of cowpea are available, including some selected specifically for wildlife purposes. The plant is easy to grow, soil pH is not critical, and the crop does well with minimal fertility. However, the seed should be inoculated with cowpea inoculant prior to planting.

Egyptian Wheat. Egyptian wheat is a type of grain sorghum. It is not an outstanding grain yielder, but it has loose heads, allowing birds easy access to the grain.

Egyptian wheat is an especially good choice for quail. The seed shatter over a fairly long period of time, thus providing an extended period of food availability. Furthermore, the 6- to 10-foot stalks tend to lodge easily, providing cover for quail while they are feeding. This gives the birds a sense of security and protection from avian predators. Also, as compared to some food plants used for quail, deer are not likely to consume large quantities of Egyptian wheat.

Florida Beggarweed. Florida beggarweed is always in demand as a quail feed. Because it has a long growing season, plants may be killed by frost prior to making seed if grown too far north, so its usefulness is limited to Zone A. It is best adapted to fertile, moist, sandy soils. Seed need to be scarified before planting, a normal practice for commercially available seed. Several species of beggarweed are native to the South.

Foxtail Millet. Foxtail millet is infrequently planted, but also makes good food for birds. It is best adapted in Zones B, C, and D, normally producing mature seed about 75 days after germination.

Grain Sorghums. Although Egyptian wheat is one type of sorghum commonly planted for wildlife food plots, grain sorghum is also often used. Most modern sorghum hybrids will provide excellent high energy food for quail and doves. If sorghum is planted over a large area, strips should be mowed through the food patches at one-month intervals during the fall and winter to give the birds access to the grain. Sorghum is quite sensitive to soil acidity. If the pH is lower than 5.6, lime should be applied and worked into the soil before planting.

Japanese Millet. Japanese millet can be grown for all game birds, but it is especially well suited for ducks. It can be grown successfully on well-drained soil in all zones, but it can also tolerate flooded soil as long as a part of the plant is protruding from the water. Most varieties mature within 80 to 90 days, but it is possible to obtain varieties that mature in about 120 days.

Lablab. Lablab (*Dolichos lablab*) is a viny summer annual legume sometimes planted for deer. It has good nutritive value and a growth habit similar to that of cowpea. It is best suited to well-drained, fertile soils in Zone A.

Native Grasses. Any of several native grasses, including eastern gamagrass, big bluestem, and switchgrass (see Chapter 5), can be beneficial to wildlife, especially to provide nesting habitat for quail and wild turkey. When planted in a strip up to 100 feet wide along a stream, these species can also serve as a buffer zone that slows water runoff. This can help to protect stream banks from erosion and reduce contamination of surface water by soil particulate matter and/or nutrients from cropland or pastures.

Partridge Pea. Partridge pea is one of the most widely planted quail food plants. It is tolerant of a wide range of soil types and soil fertility conditions, but is especially well adapted to clay soils in Zones A and B. Seed of this summer annual legume are usually both in demand and expensive.

Partridge pea produces a large quantity of hard seed. Once a stand has been established in an area, there will usually be a good deal of reseeding year after year. This is especially true if the soil is disturbed in late spring. When partridge pea is first established, scarified seed should be used. In order to obtain reseeding, the area should be disked or burned in late winter or early spring. Because of its hard, durable seed, partridge pea provides food for quail over a long period of time.

Proso Millet. This is another summer annual grass that is quite attractive to doves and quail. There are white proso and red proso millet types, with white proso being especially useful. Proso millet matures in about 90 days. It has the potential of producing a higher seed yield than browntop millet.

Sericea Lespedeza. Quail will eat sericea lespedeza seed, but its primary value for quail is as a cover. Deer will readily eat the forage of low-tannin sericea lespedeza, but are not fond of high-tannin varieties. Sericea lespedeza is infrequently used in wildlife plots, but is often of benefit to wildlife when planted for pasture, hay, or conservation purposes.

Sesame. Sesame or benne is highly palatable to both quail and doves. Most varieties shatter easily. The seed are produced in great quantities in autumn, but they are soft and deteriorate quickly. This species is widely adapted throughout the South. It is an excellent source of feed for both game and non-game birds.

Sesbania. Sesbania is an excellent quail food plant that can also be used by doves. Once a stand has been obtained in an area, it is likely to volunteer in subsequent years (perhaps being a serious weed problem if the area is row cropped). It is best adapted to wet, clay soils in Zone A. The seed are not highly palatable, but it is an important food source because the seed remain in good condition until late winter when a food shortage often exists. Sesbania should be planted in early spring.

Shrub Lespedeza. Bicolor lespedeza is often planted along field borders or in small patches to attract and feed quail. A related species is Thunberg (*Lespedeza thunbergii*). Both of these are long-lived perennial shrubs that produce large quantities of seed. Thunberg lespedeza is recommended in areas having high deer populations, since deer are less likely to consume this species. It is also less invasive than bicolor lespedeza.

Shrub lespedeza can grow so thick that it hinders dog handling and shooting. To avoid this, it is best to plant it in strips between fields or along the borders of woods. Both species can be established from either seed or seedlings, but survival and establishment are usually best with seedlings. Seed should be scarified.

Many people have found that patches of shrub lespedeza may help them locate quail easily. Quail are fond of the seed and also feel protected from avian predators by the upper portions of the plant. Therefore, during the winter, they often spend much of their time in or near patches of shrub lespedeza. A hunter can move from patch to patch with a fairly high probability of finding many of the coveys in an area.

Shrub lespedezas are best suited for soils of medium texture and good drainage. Every three to five years the plants should be mowed to a 4- to 8-inch height in late winter in order to thicken the stand and prevent it from becoming too tall.

Sunflower. Sunflower is highly attractive to doves and other game birds. Several small-seeded, high oil varieties have been developed primarily for wildlife purposes, but any sunflower variety is acceptable. Most varieties mature in about 100 days. Sunflower is pollinated by bees, so a good bee population is necessary to obtain good seed set.

Velvetbean. Many years ago velvetbean was commonly planted with corn as a livestock feed in the lower South. Corn ears were harvested by hand before allowing livestock access to a field to enable them to eat the fodder and velvetbean. In recent years, there has been a revival of interest in growing velvetbean and corn as a summer deer food. Although normally not a high priority crop for deer, it is an option.

Winter Annual Forage Crops. Winter annual forages make excellent green fields for deer. Many winter annual species can be used in various combinations, but a particularly popular mixture is to plant 90 to 120 lb/A of small grain (rye, wheat, and/or oats) plus 20 to 30 lb/A of crimson clover. Such fields provide cover, seed, and a source of insects for both game and non-game wildlife species.

All species of vetch produce seed that make good bird food. However, seed is mostly available in summer when there is usually plenty of other food available. Hairy vetch is adapted throughout the South, but several varieties of common vetch are adapted only in Zone A. Vetch can be used to provide winter and spring green feed for deer or turkey.

Reseeding common vetch is also an excellent plant to attract insects for feeding by turkeys or quail in early spring. Since quail need high protein insects for their breeding season, vetch can thus play a vital role in reproduction.

Wildlife Plant Establishment

There are limited data available on the amount of money and energy spent on establishing wildlife plantings in the South, but it is certainly many millions of dollars annually. It is probable that the greatest amount of money is spent on plantings for deer, followed by quail, and then doves. However, interest in establishing plants to provide food and cover for wildlife is increasing for all game wildlife species.

As with any crop, it is important to follow recommended planting procedures when establishing a wildlife crop (see Chapter 11). Otherwise, results are likely to be disappointing. Fertilization and liming should be according to soil test recommendations. General guidelines regarding planting dates, seeding rates, and seeding depths for plants discussed in this chapter are provided in **Table 11.1** and **Table 31.1**. Some characteristics of selected wildlife plants are given in **Appendix A.55**.

Summary

It is likely that there will be continued and even increased interest in planting food and cover plots for wildlife in the future. Many people have the financial resources to join hunting clubs or lease private land for hunting. In addition, there is increased interest among landowners in alternative enterprises, including catering to hunters.

Wildlife is already a big business and will probably continue to grow in importance. It is likely that many forage crops, as well as other plants, will be used to an even greater extent for wildlife purposes in the future.

Table 31.1. Seeding rates and usual planting dates (Zone A used for example) for some species commonly planted for wildlife purposes.[1]

Plant	Seeding rate, lb/A[2]	Planting dates
American jointvetch	B: 20-30	4/1-6/30
Annual lespedeza	B: 25-35	2/15-3/31
Beggarweed	D: 7-8	2/15-3/31
	B: 12-16	
Browntop millet	D: 15-20	4/1-8/15
	B: 25-30	
Cowpea	D: 30-40	5/1-6/15
	B: 100-120	
Chufa	B: 30-50	4/1-6/30
Proso millet	D: 15-20	4/1-8/15
	B: 25-30	
Egyptian wheat	D: 5-8	4/1-5/30
	B: 15-20	
Foxtail millet	D: 12-15	4/1-8/15
	B: 25-30	
Grain sorghum	D: 5-8	After frost
	B: 15-20	
Japanese millet	D: 15-20	4/1-8/15
	B: 25-30	
Lablab	D: 40	5/1-6/15
	B: 50	
Partridge pea	D: 7-8	2/15-3/31
	B: 12-16	
Sesame	D: 8-10	4/1-5/30
	B: 10-12	
Sesbania	B: 15-18	3/15-5/1
Shrub lespedeza	D: 8-10	3/1-4/15
	B: 15-20	
Sunflower	D: 15-20	4/1-6/30
	B: 35-40	
Velvetbean	D: 15-20	3/15-5/15
	B: 50-60	

(Velvetbean is often planted with a low seeding rate of corn)

[1]Seeding rates for other forage plants commonly used for domestic livestock, but that may also be planted for wildlife, are provided in Chapters 5-8.
[2]D = Drilled; B = Broadcast

Forages and the Environment

In recent years, there has been increasing awareness of the importance of preserving our natural resources and the environment. As a result, it has become more important to assess the environmental impacts of agricultural production. Forage agriculture makes numerous positive contributions, but there are also some concerns.

Air Quality

The 'greenhouse effect' is often brought into discussions of ecology and the environment. In simple terms, this refers to more of the sun's energy reaching Earth and being held under a blanket of carbon dioxide and other pollutants rather than being deflected back into space. Increases in the carbon dioxide concentration of Earth's atmosphere from burning of fossil fuels contribute to this effect. Agricultural production consumes significant quantities of fossil fuels.

Fortunately, during photosynthesis, plants consume carbon dioxide and release oxygen. While all types of crop plants perform this important function, the high leaf area of most forage canopies makes them particularly efficient.

Soil Improvement

The soil improvement characteristics of grasslands have long been recognized, but often are forgotten or ignored on many farms. After land has been devoted to perennial forages for several years, the trend is for subsequent arable crops to produce better than would otherwise have been the case.

The use of forages in crop rotations can provide substantial benefits. Forages in rotation with row crops interrupt weed, disease, insect, and nematode cycles, while the deep root penetration of many forage crops into compacted soil layers can leave channels that improve water and air movement and enhance root penetration of subsequent crops. As a result, crops that follow are more productive and healthy.

Perennial grasslands also tend to make the soil more suitable for subsequent arable crops in other ways, including improving soil tilth due to the activity of earthworms, soil insects, and microorganisms. Over time, the nutrient-holding capacity of the soil increases, and various mineral cycles operate to increase nutrient availability in the surface layer. When forage legumes are used in rotations, other crops benefit from substantial quantities of residual nitrogen fixed by the legumes.

Crop rotation is a basic, desirable agronomic practice that enhances long-term soil productivity. Because of numerous potential benefits that can be realized, many arable crops should be grown in rotation with forage grasses or grass/legume mixtures.

Energy Inputs

Energy conservation is also a concern of many environmentally-minded persons. Energy inputs into grassland systems are usually far less than for row crop production. Where perennial forages are grown, fuel-consuming tillage is generally limited to establishment. In many situations, no-tillage planting can be used to establish forage crops (Chapter 12). Nutrient recycling from grazing animals lowers fertilizer inputs as compared to row crop production, and pesticide usage tends to be lower on grasslands than other crop areas.

Animals sold off pasture remove a surprisingly small quantity of nutrients, as their bodies are primarily composed of carbon, hydrogen, and oxygen, which come from air and water (**Figure 9.6**). Thus, conservation of energy is another benefit of grassland systems.

Enhancement of Wildlife

Enhancement of wildlife populations with forage plants began in the Southern U.S. when Indians periodically burned patches of woodlands. The resulting development of open areas and stimulation of native grasses favored many types of wildlife and helped ensure hunting success.

Many of the forage species normally planted for livestock in the Southern U.S. are also commonly planted for game animals (Chapter 31). Deer and wild turkeys consume substantial quantities of green material. Birds consume insects and seed of forage crops, and small animals such as rabbits use forage crops for food and cover.

Game and non-game wildlife benefit from having access to forage crops. Wildlife populations are usually favored when a farm has a mixture of crops, pasture, and woodland. One of the joys of farm life is being able to observe animals and birds that survive and flourish along with agricultural enterprises.

Nonpoint Source Pollution

As has been explained, forage and livestock production is more environmentally friendly overall than many other land uses. However, improper management of pastureland on some farms results in environmental problems, particularly with regard to water quality.

Nonpoint source contamination of water is of increasing concern. This problem arises not so much from a given field or farm, but rather from the collective harm done by improper management of land resources. When pastureland impacts on water quality are assessed from this perspective, it becomes clear that there is much room for improvement.

Pastures occupy more than 75 million acres in the Southern U.S. alone. Given such a large area, the accumulative impact of even small improvements applied broadly can have a large influence on the environment. More specifically, water quality of many wells and surface waters can be ensured or improved by good management practices, many of which are neither difficult nor expensive to employ.

Several factors associated with pastures can lead to water quality problems. These include soil erosion, nutrients in runoff water (especially

Soil erosion can be a serious problem in row cropped areas without proper management.

where animal manure or other organic wastes have been applied), and direct contamination of water sources by animals.

Soil Conservation versus Erosion

It has long been recognized that preserving the soil is extremely important to individual farmers and landowners as well as to our nation. Concern about this problem, heightened by tragic abuses, led to the creation of the Soil Conservation Service [now the Natural Resources Conservation Service (NRCS)], a federal agency that has been remarkably effective in reducing soil erosion. Yet, wind and water erosion remains a serious problem in the Southern U.S.

Soil erosion causes numerous damaging effects. Streams, rivers, ponds, and lakes become polluted with soil sediment, adversely affecting fish and other marine life. Nutrients, both indigenous and applied, are lost along with soil and also contribute to lowered water quality. Gullies and rills are created, making the land more difficult to use for agricultural purposes. Furthermore, when topsoil is lost, the remaining eroded soil is usually lower in organic matter and fertility. It also has a lower capacity for holding nutrients and water, and is therefore less productive and less valuable.

Clearly, humans must take responsibility for soil erosion, because nature endeavors to avoid it. If left alone, with no interference from man, almost any area in the Southern U.S. will soon develop a vegetative cover that protects the soil from erosion. Unfortunately, while nature will protect the soil, it does not normally generate food and profits to the extent that humans need and expect.

One solution to this dilemma is to use proper tillage methods for crop production in areas not subject to severe erosion and to use more erodible areas for other purposes, thus allowing economic production without risking excessive erosion losses. Most farms in the Southern U.S. have significant acreage that should either not be tilled or be tilled only infrequently. For millions of acres of highly erodible land, growing forage crops is an alternative to row crop production.

Perennial grass sods are particularly effective in reducing soil erosion losses (**Table 32.1**). Even if a given field is used for row crop production, forages may be used to reduce erosion. Grassed waterways, grassed terraces, strip cropping, and long-term rotations utilizing forages are good examples. Many people do not fully realize the potential damage of unchecked erosion. Once serious erosion damage has occurred, productivity will be greatly reduced for many years.

Table 32.1. Estimated average annual sheet and rill erosion on non-federal land in selected states.[1]

	Erosion loss, tons/A	
State	Cropland	Pasture
Alabama	6.0	0.5
Arkansas	3.4	1.1
Florida	1.2	0.1
Georgia	5.2	0.4
Kentucky	3.4	2.0
Louisiana	3.2	0.2
Mississippi	5.0	1.2
North Carolina	4.6	1.7
Oklahoma	2.8	0.6
South Carolina	3.0	0.4
Tennessee	5.6	0.8
Texas	2.6	0.5
Virginia	3.9	3.3

[1]Source: Summary Report, National Resources Inventory, USDA-NRCS.

Many industrial construction sites, roadbanks, parks, landfills, mine reclamation sites, and portions of golf courses are seeded to forage crops. Initially, these sites are likely to be devoid of topsoil, inherently low in soil fertility, and often have high soil acidity. Along with the application of lime and fertilizer, mixtures of annual and perennial grasses and legumes are often seeded together to quickly stabilize the soil until the best adapted perennial forages have an opportunity to dominate. With time and proper management, most disturbed or critical areas can be stabilized. Eventually, the soil is improved with the addition of organic matter, and a former eyesore often becomes an attractive area due to the beneficial effects provided by forages.

Erosion is most likely to occur on slopes greater than 5 percent, especially if the soil is fine-textured. Unfortunately, many pastures are located in areas that fall in this category and thus have high erosion potential. Sheet and rill erosion can result from large quantities of water flowing across pasture areas with thin vegetation. Gullies form when concentrated water eats away at erodible soil.

If allowed to do so, livestock form traffic paths in which no plants can survive, thus creating a place where erosion can begin. Even in areas in which there are no traffic paths, erosion may be excessive if there is a poor forage stand, if the soil is infertile and plant vigor is low, or if a pasture, or portions of a pasture, are overgrazed. Keeping a thick, vigorous stand of forage plants and a substantial amount of accumulated plant material on the soil surface minimizes the erosion hazard, even on steep slopes.

Riparian areas (the transition zone between streams and the surrounding areas), are environmentally sensitive. This is partially because livestock traffic can lead to excessive bank erosion (especially if trees are present that provide shade for the animals) and also cause the enhanced likelihood of

Courtesy of Morris Gillespie

Strip cropping with forages helps protect water resources from pollution.

washouts where water flows into a stream from the adjacent land.

Water Quality versus Water Contamination

Improvement of water quality has become one of the nation's top priorities. Without water, there would be no life. Contamination of water jeopardizes all life.

In most areas, the primary contaminant of water is soil particulate matter. As compared to other agricultural land uses, growing forage crops greatly reduces erosion. If the percentage of cropland devoted to forage crops were substantially increased, there would be a considerable improvement in overall water quality.

Another primary concern regarding water quality is contamination with certain inorganic compounds. Though relatively uncommon, there have been cases where nitrates have contaminated groundwater. Over-fertilization is sometimes perceived as being a common agricultural practice, but under-fertilization is more likely to be the case. Farmers cannot afford to waste money by purchasing more fertilizer than is needed. However, many crop-lands are deficient in the primary nutrients.

Excessive quantities of nutrients, especially nitrogen or phosphorus, may contaminate surface water. On porous soils, nitrate-nitrogen can contaminate well water. In fact, because of the increased awareness of potential environmental contamination due to nitrogen fertilization associated with intensive row crop production or to concentration of large numbers of animals (such as in feedlots), much progress has been made in avoiding such problems.

When livestock are produced on pasture, the likelihood of nutrient contamination of water is much lower. When land has a thick cover of perennial forages, there is little runoff and therefore less chance for fertilizers to be washed away. Relatively few pesticides are used in forage crop

Forages play a vital role in protecting water supplies.

production, so contamination of this type is rarely a problem. Most forage crops, especially perennial grasses, form dense root systems that effectively serve as filters to remove contaminants before they can seep into the groundwater.

In pastures lacking a good forage stand, serious erosion and nutrient runoff problems can occur, particularly on steep and/or erodible land. In addition, animal wastes contain pathogenic bacteria that can contaminate water and pose a health threat to other animals as well as to humans. When animals congregate in an area for long periods of time, foot traffic may increase erosion and reduce soil water infiltration.

To reduce these hazards, animal dung and urine need to be kept away from surface water, and frequent concentration of livestock in the same area of a pasture should be discouraged. In order to minimize direct contamination of water with nutrients and pathogenic bacteria, as well as to minimize streambank degradation (as mentioned earlier), it is important to restrict animal access to streams or at least encourage them to spend as little time as possible in riparian areas.

In some situations, runoff from upland pastures flows across arable cropland areas in bottomland fields, resulting in nutrients and bacteria from pastures and particulate matter from the cropland areas reaching a stream. This problem can be reduced by planting a buffer strip containing some combination of trees, shrubs, and/or grass along the stream. A buffer strip, in essence, catches much of the material that would otherwise contribute to stream pollution.

Waste Disposal

As environmental awareness increases, waste disposal becomes an increasingly important concern. For example, millions of tons of broiler litter are produced in the Southern U.S. each year. This and other types of animal wastes require disposal in environmentally acceptable ways.

A large percentage of the animal waste produced in the region is spread on forage crops. While beef and chicken may be in competition at the grocery store, beef cattle and poultry often make highly complementary enterprises on the farm, because poultry litter can be effectively used to provide nutrients for pasture growth. Evidence of this is the fact that in many areas of the Southern U.S. where broiler production has increased in recent decades, so has the number of beef cattle.

Concern about safe disposal of municipal and industrial waste has also increased. Forages such as hybrid bermudagrasses that have a high yield potential can absorb nitrate and potentially harmful materials from applied effluent and are increasingly being used as a vegetative cover for waste disposal areas.

It is often economically feasible for livestock producers to use waste materials as a source of nutrients for pasture production. Many of the nutrients in such materials are released slowly, which is environmentally and agronomically desirable. However, they also contain some readily available nutrients, especially nitrogen and phosphorus, so application of organic waste to pastures can jeopardize water quality if not done properly.

Applying such materials at extremely high rates or in sensitive areas is an environmentally unsound practice. Research has shown that the potential for runoff from applied waste increases linearly with the amount applied. In addition, it increases sharply when waste is applied in areas that are particularly subject to erosion, and water contamination is most likely to occur when a heavy rainfall event occurs soon after application.

In many situations where waste materials are applied to pastures, the fate of nitrogen is of great interest because of concerns about environmental protection. However, increased forage production is also expected. Ammonia volatilization is an avenue of nitrogen loss from applied waste materials, the exact amounts varying with temperature, humidity, and other factors. Nitrogen volatilization estimates for various situations are provided in **Table 32.2.**

Waste application rates should be based on the availability and need for nutrients as well as the runoff and erosion potential of the field(s) in question. Various states have different guidelines for application of waste materials, and these should be strictly followed.

Management Practices

Most livestock producers want their operations to be environmentally friendly and are willing to expend effort to ensure that this is the case. The problems that occur are mostly due to a lack of understanding of the impacts of various management practices, as well as a lack of awareness that there even are problems or potential problems.

As the human population increases in rural areas, there is more concern by the general public regarding agricultural practices, including how forage/livestock enterprises are managed. Thus, it is in the best interest of livestock

Table 32.2. Approximate ammonia losses for applied animal waste under various application methods and soil conditions.

Applied method	Ammonia volatilized, % of application		
Injection		5	
Sprinkling		25	
Broadcast (fresh solids) and incorporated		see below	
Days between application and incorporation	**Ammonia volatilized, % of application**		
	Warm dry soil	Warm wet soil	Cool wet soil
1	30	10	0
4	40	20	5
7 or more	50	30	10

Source: Soil Conservation Service. National Engineering Handbook: Agricultural Waste Management Field Handbook. Part 651.

producers to minimize environmental hazards. Steps producers can take to avoid or reduce water quality problems include the following:

- When land is cleared, quickly plant a vegetative cover.
- Keep pastures healthy and vigorous by applying lime and fertilizer according to soil test recommendations.
- Use a no-till seeder as needed to thicken forage stands, especially in areas that are particularly vulnerable to erosion.
- Remove animals from steep pastures during wet weather.
- Use rotational stocking to minimize the opportunity livestock have to form trails (especially on steep slopes where the soil is vulnerable to erosion) and to minimize their access to any given part of a stream.
- Regardless of the stocking method used, keep the stocking rate low enough that a good vegetative cover is maintained throughout the pasture (this is especially important on steep slopes).
- Avoid feeding hay on steep slopes or near streams.
- Place alternate water sources and mineral feeders away from surface water and erodable areas.
- Provide shade for animals in places other than along riparian areas or near other surface water.
- If feasible, fence livestock out of streams or other surface water or at least limit their access to such areas.
- Apply waste materials in accordance with state waste disposal guidelines.
- Avoid application of waste materials in highly erodible areas.
- Apply waste materials at times of the year when high rainfall storms are less likely.
- Plant buffer vegetation strips as needed along riparian areas to filter out nutrients, bacteria, and soil sediment and to minimize development of washouts along stream banks.
- Locate new animal working facilities on a level site and at least 200 feet away from surface water.
- Minimize the number of vehicle crossings through streams or at least

Many people appreciate the beauty of a pastoral scene such as on this farm in Breckinridge County, Kentucky.

locate crossings in areas of minimum impact.

Final Thoughts

Many people find that there is something particularly restful, peaceful, and satisfying in watching animals graze. This is evidenced by the thousands of paintings and photographs that have pasture scenes as their primary focus. If animals alone created this peaceful aura, a feedlot or corral scene would serve just as well. Millions of people, many of whom may not have consciously thought about it, appreciate a pastoral scene, just as many people appreciate woodlands or other natural settings.

The key to developing a particularly keen appreciation of forage crops comes from learning more about them and from exposure to successful, positive examples. After all, this is consistent with the generally accepted idea that a person who has never been exposed to a particular type of music, art, or food is unlikely to have developed much appreciation for it.

Certainly, forage crops improve the appearance of rural settings and are appreciated by many people. However, knowledgeable persons can also develop an appreciation for such things as: productivity; high forage

What could be more noble and satisfying than spending a lifetime living on, and caring for, the land? A good farmer is a true conservationist.

quality; economy of production; low weed populations; a long grazing season; and little or no soil erosion or other environmentally unsound effects. Thus, a forage planting may be even more attractive to a person who fully realizes what it is accomplishing than to one who only sees its visible beauty.

Appreciation of forage crop aesthetics and value is a seldom-mentioned aspect of forage/livestock enterprises, but it is likely more of a source of joy and satisfaction to many producers than they admit or perhaps even realize. As knowledge of forages increases, so does this satisfaction. Producers who have an appreciation for beautiful, productive forages tend to grow beautiful, productive forages. In turn, they also tend to have efficient, profitable, and environmentally friendly livestock operations.

Agricultural production is essential, but it must also be protective of the environment. When properly managed, perennial pastures and forage crops are an especially environmentally friendly type of agricultural production. In fact, it can be argued that agriculture and nature are rarely in better harmony than with grassland/animal production. SF

List of Appendices

A.1. Common Weights and Measures.

Length
Inch = 1/12 or 0.083 foot = 2.54 centimeters = 25.4 millimeters
Foot = 12 inches = 0.3048 meters = 30.48 centimeters
Yard = 36 inches = 3 feet = 0.9144 meters
Furlong = 220 yards
Mile = 1,760 yards = 5,280 feet = 1.61 kilometers = 8 furlongs = 80 chains

Area
Square inch = 0.007 square foot = 6.45 square centimeters
Square foot = 144 square inches = 929.03 square centimeters
Square yard = 9 square feet = 0.836 square meters
Acre = 4,840 square yards = 43,560 square feet = 160 square rods = 4,047 square meters = 0.405 hectare
Hectare = 10,000 square meters = 2.47 acres
Square mile = 640 acres = 2.59 square kilometers = 1 section
Section = 1 square mile = 640 acres = 2.59 square kilometers

Liquid Measures
Teaspoon = 0.1667 fluid ounce = 60 drops = 4.93 milliliters
Tablespoon = 3 teaspoons = 0.5 fluid ounce = 14.8 milliliters
Fluid ounce = 2 tablespoons = 29.58 milliliters
Cup = 8 fluid ounces = 16 tablespoons = 236.6 milliliters
Pint = 2 cups = 16 fluid ounces = 473.2 milliliters
Quart = 4 cups = 2 pints = 32 fluid ounces = 0.946 liters
Liter = 2.113 pints = 1,000 milliliters = 1.057 quarts
Gallon = 4 quarts = 8 pints = 128 fluid ounces = 3.785 liters
Cubic foot of water = 7.5 gallons = 62.4 pounds = 28.3 liters
Acre inch of water = 27,154 gallons = 3,630 cubic feet
Imperial gallon = 4.8 quarts = 9.6 pints = 154 fluid ounces = 4.55 liters

Dry Measures
Teaspoon (level) = 0.35 cubic inch = 5.74 cubic centimeters
Tablespoon (level) = 1.05 cubic inch = 3 level teaspoons = 17.21 cubic centimeters
Cup = 16 level tablespoons = 16.8 cubic inches = 275.3 cubic centimeters
Pint = 2 cups = 32 level tablespoons = 33.6 cubic inches = 550.6 cubic centimeters
Quart = 2 pints = 64 tablespoons = 67.2 cubic inches = 1.101 liters
Peck = 8 quarts = 16 pints = 538 cubic inches = 8.8 liters
Bushel = 4 pecks = 2,150 cubic inches = 32 quarts = 35 liters

Volumes
Cubic inch = 0.00058 cubic foot = 16.4 cubic centimeters
Cubic foot = 1,728 cubic inches = 0.037 cubic yard = 0.028 cubic meter
Cubic yard = 27 cubic feet = 0.765 cubic meters

Weights
Gram = 15.43 grains = 1,000 milligrams
Ounce = 28.35 grams = 437.5 grains
Pound = 16 ounces = 7,000 grains = 454 grams
Kilogram = 1,000 grams = 2.205 pounds
Ton (short) = 2,000 pounds = 0.907 metric tons (tonnes)
Ton (long) = 2,240 pounds = 1.016 metric tons (tonnes)

A.2. Conversion Factors for U.S. and Metric Units.

To convert column 1 into column 2, multiply by	Column 1	Column 2	To convert column 2 into column 1, multiply by
	Length		
0.621	kilometer, km	mile, mi	1.609
3.281	meter, m	foot, ft	0.3048
1.094	meter, m	yard, yd	0.914
0.394	centimeter, cm	inch, in	2.54
	Area		
0.386	kilometer^2, km^2	mile^2, mi^2	2.590
247.1	kilometer^2, km^2	acre	0.00405
2.471	hectare, ha	acre	0.405
	Volume		
35.32	cubic meters, m^3	cubic feet, ft^3	0.02832
0.00973	meter^3, m^3	acre-inch	102.8
0.0284	liter, l	bushel, bu	35.24
1.057	liter, l	quart (liquid), qt	0.946
	Mass		
1.102	tonne (metric ton)	ton (short)	0.9072
2.205	quintal, q	hundredweight, cwt (short)	0.454
2.205	kilogram, kg	pound, lb	0.454
0.035	gram, g	ounce (avdp), oz	28.35
	Pressure		
14.50	bar	lb/inch^2, psi	0.06895
0.9869	bar	atmosphere, atm	1.013
0.9678	kg (weight)/cm^2	atmosphere, atm	1.013
14.22	kg (weight)/cm^2	lb/inch^2, psi	0.07031
14.70	atmosphere, atm	lb/inch^2, psi	0.06805
	Yield or Rate		
0.446	tonne (metric ton)/ha	ton (short)/acre	2.240
0.891	kg/ha	lb/acre	1.12
0.891	quintal/hectare	hundredweight/acre	1.12
1.15	hectoliter/hectare, hl/ha	bu/acre	0.87
	Temperature		
(1.8 x C) + 32	Celsius, C	Fahrenheit, F	0.56 (F-32)
	-17.8°C	0°F	
	0°C	32°F	
	20°C	68°F	
	100°C	212°F	

Metric Prefix Definitions

mega	1,000,000	deca	10	centi	0.01
kilo	1,000	basic metric unit	1	milli	0.001
hecto	100	deci	0.1	micro	0.000001

A.3. Helpful Calculations and Formulas.

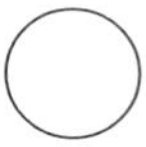

Area of circle = radius squared x 3.1416; or diameter squared x 0.7854

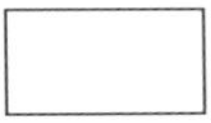

Area of rectangle or square = length x width

Area of right triangle = length x width ÷ 2

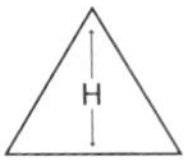

Area of other triangles = base x height at right angle to base ÷ 2 (see diagram)

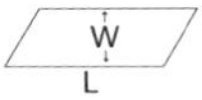

Area of parallellogram = length x width (see diagram)

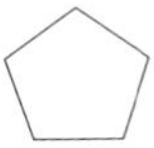

Area of pentagon (5 equal sides) = length of one side squared x 1.720.

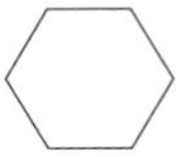

Area of hexagon (6 equal sides) = length of one side squared x 2.598.

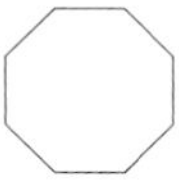

Area of octagon (8 equal sides) = length of one side squared x 4.838.

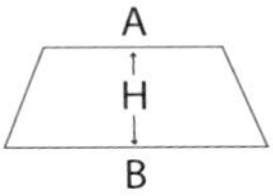

Area of trapezoid is

$$\frac{(A + B) \times H}{2}$$

(see diagram)

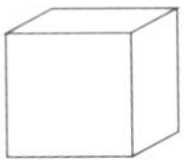

Volume of cube or rectangular box is length x width x height.

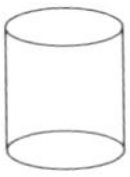

Volume of a cylinder is radius squared x 3.1416 x length of cylinder.

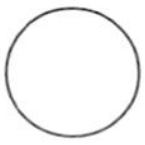

Volume of a sphere is radius cubed x 4.1888.

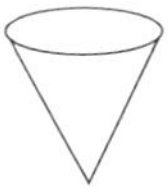

Volume of cone is radius squared x 1.0472 (e.g., round hopper bottom).

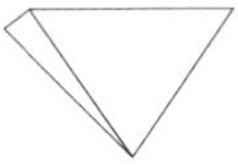

Volume of pyramid is area of base x 1/3 the height (e.g., hopper bottom).

Handy Formulas

To find circumference of a circle when diameter is known, multiply diameter by 3.1416.

To find diameter when circumference is known, divide circumference by 3.1416 or multiply by 0.3183.

Volume Conversion Factors

Cu. ft. x 0.8 equals bushels grain or shelled corn

Cu. ft. x 0.4 equals bushels ear corn

Cu. ft. x 7.48 equals gallons

Cu. ft. x 62.4 equals pounds water

Gallons x 8.34 equals pounds water

Gallons x 0.1337 equals cu. ft.

Cu. ft. x 1,728 = cu. in.

Cu. in. ÷ 1,728 = cu. ft.

Cu. yd. x 27 = cu. ft.

Cu. ft. ÷ 27 = cu. yds.

A.4. Conversions and Equivalences.

1 fluid ounce	29.5 milliliters
1 fluid ounce	2 tablespoons or 6 teaspoons
8 fluid ounces	16 tablespoons or 1 cup
16 fluid ounces	1 pint or 2 cups
32 fluid ounces	1 quart or 2 pints
128 fluid ounces	1 gallon or 4 quarts
1 gallon of water weighs 8.34 pounds	
1 gallon of fuel oil weighs 7.2 pounds	
Avoirdupois Weight	
16 drams	1 ounce or 437.5 grains
16 ounces	1 pound
2,000 pounds	1 short ton
2,240 pounds	1 long ton
Household Measure	
60 drops	1 teaspoon or 1/6 ounce
2 teaspoons	1 dessert spoon
3 teaspoons	1 tablespoon or ½ ounce
16 tablespoons	1 cup
2 cups	1 pint or 16 fluid ounces

A.5. Celsius and Fahrenheit Temperatures.

Degrees Celsius (°C)		Degrees Fahrenheit (°F)
100	Boiling point of water	212
90		194
80		176
70		158
60		140
50		122
40		104
37	Human body temperature	98.6
35		95
30		86
25		77
20		68
15		59
10		50
5		41
0	Freezing point of water	32
- 5		23
-10		14
-20		-4
-30		-22
-40		-40
(1.8 x C) + 32 = F		0.56 x (F-32) = C

A.6. Wind Chill Index.

A strong wind makes a cold day colder. This effect is called the wind chill index. The chart below gives examples of wind chill equivalents. In 2001, the U.S. National Weather Service and the Meterological Services of Canada updated the method for determining wind chill index. The formula is shown below.

To determine the wind chill temperature in the partial chart shown here, find the outside air temperature on the top line, then read down the column to the measured wind speed. For example, when the outside air temperature is 20°F and the wind speed is 15 miles per hour, the wind chill index temperature is 6°F. For more information on wind chill, check the website at: http://205.156.54.206/om/windchill

		Temperature (°F)								
Wind speed (miles per hour)	Calm	30	25	20	15	10	5	0	-5	-10
	5	25	19	13	7	1	-5	-11	-16	-22
	10	21	15	9	3	-4	-10	-16	-22	-28
	15	19	13	6	0	-7	-13	-19	-26	-32
	20	17	11	4	-2	-9	-15	-22	-29	-35
	25	16	9	3	-4	-11	-17	-24	-31	-37
	30	15	8	1	-5	-12	-19	-26	-33	-39
	35	14	7	0	-7	-14	-21	-27	-34	-41

Formula for wind chill: (°F) $= 35.74 + 0.6215T - 35.75 (V^{0.16}) + 0.4275T (V^{0.16})$
Where T = air temperature (°F) V = wind speed (mph)

A.7. Chemical Symbols for Essential Plant Nutrients and Common Forms Absorbed by Crops.

Nutrient	Symbol	Common forms absorbed by crops[1]
Nitrogen	N	Nitrate (NO_3^-); ammonium (NH_4^+)
Phosphorus	P	Primary orthophosphate ($H_2PO_4^-$); secondary orthophosphate (HPO_4^{2-})
Potassium	K	K^+
Sulfur[2]	S	Sulfate (SO_4^{2-})
Calcium	Ca	Ca^{2+}
Magnesium	Mg	Mg^{2+}
Boron	B	Borate (BO_3^{3-})
Chloride	Cl	Cl^-
Copper	Cu	Cu^+; Cu^{2+}
Iron	Fe	Fe^{2+}
Manganese	Mn	Mn^{2+}
Molybdenum	Mo	Molybdate (MoO_4^{2-})
Nickel	Ni	Ni^{2+}
Zinc	Zn	Zn^{2+}

[1]Plants get their carbon (C), hydrogen (H), and oxygen (O) from air and water.
[2]Sometimes absorbed through the leaves as SO_2 gas.

A.8. Conversion Table for Nutrient Concentrations in Compounds.

To convert column 1 to column 2, multiply by	Column 1	Column 2	To convert column 2 to column 1, multiply by
4.43	N	NO_3	0.23
1.22	N	NH_3	0.82
4.72	N	$(NH_4)_2SO_4$	0.21
2.86	N	NH_4NO_3	0.35
1.20	K	K_2O	0.83
0.63	KCl	K_2O	1.58
0.71	CaO	Ca	1.40
0.56	$CaCO_3$	CaO	1.78
0.60	MgO	Mg	1.66
2.99	MgO	$MgSO_4$	0.33
3.43	MgO	$MgSO_4 \cdot H_2O$	0.29
2.09	MgO	$MgCO_3$	0.48
0.16	$MgSO_4 \cdot 7H_2O$	MgO	6.25
2.29	P	P_2O_5	0.44
0.46	$Ca_3(PO_4)_2$	P_3O_3	2.18
2.00	S	SO_2	0.50
2.50	S	SO_3	0.40
3.00	S	SO_4	0.33
0.13	$MgSO_4 \cdot 7H_2O$	S	7.68
0.25	$(NH_4)_2SO_4$	S	4.00
0.23	$MgSO_4 \cdot H_2O$	S	4.31

A.9. Calibration Tables and Travel Speed Chart.

	Seconds required to travel:		
Miles per hour	100 ft.	200 ft.	300 ft.
1	68	136	205
2	34	68	102
3	23	46	68
4	17	34	51
5	14	27	41
6	11	23	34
7	10	20	29
8	9	17	26
9	8	15	23
10	7	14	21

1 mph = 88 feet per minute
1 mph = 1.466 feet per second
Speed in mph = Number of steps per minute/30

Source: D.E. Brann, D.L. Holshouser, and G.L. Mullins. (eds). Agronomy Handbook. Virginia Coop. Ext. Serv. Pub. 424-100.

A.10. Amount of Liquid or Dry Material Necessary to Treat a Small Area when the Recommendation Is on a per Acre Basis.

Dry Material[1]

Rate per acre	Rate per 100 square feet	Rate per 1,000 square feet
1 pound	0.037 oz.	0.37 oz.
2 pounds	0.072 oz.	0.72 oz.
3 pounds	0.11 oz.	1.1 oz.
4 pounds	0.15 oz.	1.5 oz.
5 pounds	0.19 oz.	1.9 oz.
6 pounds	0.22 oz.	2.2 oz.
8 pounds	0.30 oz.	3.0 oz.
10 pounds	0.37 oz.	3.7 oz.
50 pounds	1.85 oz.	1 lb., 3 oz.
100 pounds	3.7 oz.	2 lb., 5 oz.

Liquids[2]

Rate per acre	Rate per 100 square feet	Rate per 1,000 square feet
1 cup	1/8 tsp.	1 1/4 tsp.
1 pint	1/4 tsp.	5/6 tbsp.
1 quart	1/2 tsp.	1 2/3 tbsp.
1 gallon	2 tsp.	6 2/3 tbsp.
25 gallons	1 cup	5 pints
50 gallons	1 pint	5 quarts
75 gallons	1 1/2 pints	1 7/8 gallons
100 gallons	1 qt.	2 1/2 gallons

[1]Dry formulations vary in bulk and density. The above table provides estimates of the volume required. Always follow label directions when applying any product.

[2]One teaspoon (tsp.) equals approximately 1/6 ounce (oz.)

A.11. Calculating Fertilizer and Seed Weights for Small Areas.

lb/A	grams/sq. ft.	lb/sq. ft.	lb/A	grams/sq. ft.	lb/sq. ft.
1	.01042	.000023	75	.7815	.00172
2	.02064	.000046	100	1.042	.0023
3	.03126	.000069	150	1.563	.0035
4	.04168	.000091	200	2.084	.0046
5	.05210	.000114	300	3.126	.0069
6	.06252	.000138	400	4.168	.0092
7	.07294	.000161	500	5.210	.0115
8	.08336	.000184	600	6.252	.0138
9	.09378	.000207	700	7.294	.0141
10	.1042	.00023	800	8.336	.0184
15	.1565	.00034	900	9.378	.0207
25	.2605	.00057	1,000	10.42	.0230
50	.5210	.00115	1 sq. ft. = .00002296 acre		

A.12. Estimating Acres within a Field[1].

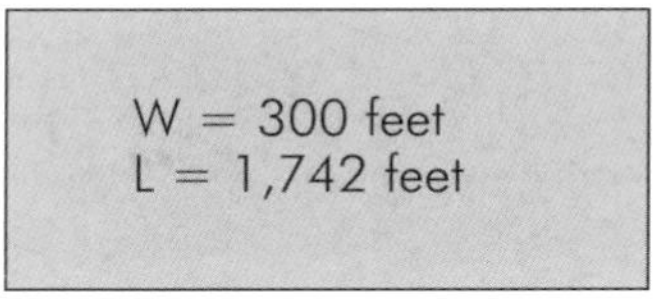

$$\text{Acres} = \frac{\text{length (L) x width (W)}}{43{,}560}$$

Example:

$$\frac{1{,}742 \times 300}{43{,}560} = 11.997 = 12 \text{ acres}$$

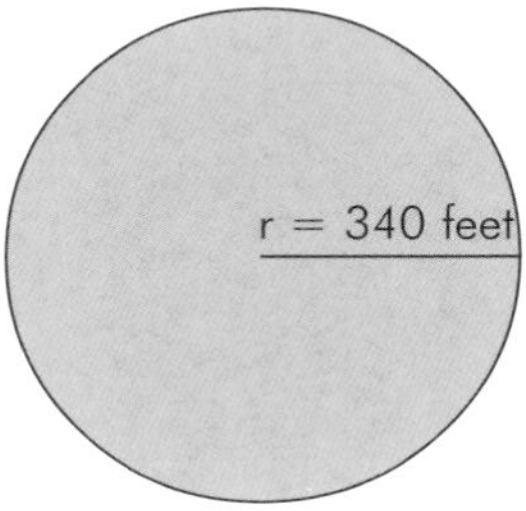

$$\text{Acres} = \pi r^2/43{,}560$$

π = 3.14

r = radius

$$\text{Example: } \frac{3.14 \times 340^2}{43{,}560} = 8.33 \text{ acres}$$

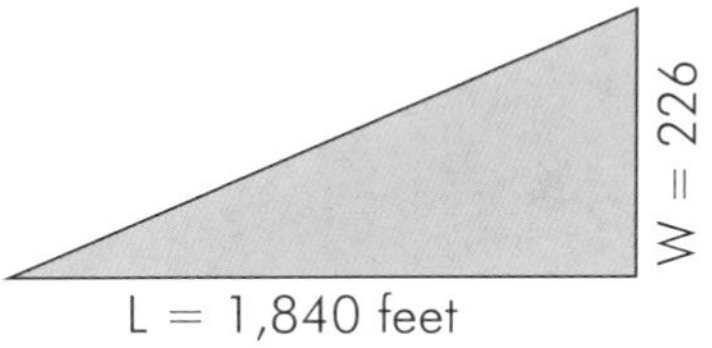

$$\text{Acres} = \frac{\frac{1}{2}\text{(length x width)}}{43{,}560}$$

Example:

$$\frac{\frac{1}{2}(1{,}840 \times 226)}{43{,}560} = 4.77 \text{ acres}$$

---

[1]Most fields will not exactly fit the above description and may require a combination of the above or use of other formulas. See **A.3** for additional formulas for shapes and sizes.

A.13. Calibrating Seeders.

To calibrate any seeding machine, two things must be known: 1) area covered, and 2) amount of seed used.

$$\text{Seeding Rate (SR)} = \frac{\text{S (amount of seed)}}{\text{A (area covered in acres)}}$$

$$A = \frac{\text{(area covered in square feet)}}{\text{43,560 (square feet in one acre)}}$$

1 pound = 16 ounces = 454 grams

1. Area Covered
   A. Drill to determine area covered
      1. Measure seeding width of machine used
      2. a) Measure distance around drive wheel or sprocket and turn a given number of times
         b) Pull the machine at the desired seeding speed for some measured distance

2. Amount of seed used.
   A. Place some type of collection device or container at seed outlet(s). Collect and weigh seed.

   Examples:
   1. A drill with a 7 foot seeding width is pulled 100 feet with 0.25 pounds of seed dispensed. What is the seeding rate?

      SR = S/A

      $$A = \frac{7 \times 100}{43{,}560} = 0.016 \text{ acres}$$

      $$SR = \frac{S}{A} = \frac{0.25}{0.016} = 15.6 \text{ lb/A}$$

   2. A cyclone seeder with a 12 foot seeding width dispenses 0.12 pounds of seed in 100 feet. Calculate the seeding rate.

      SR = S/A

      $$A = \frac{12 \times 100}{43{,}560} = 0.028 \text{ acres}$$

      $$SR = \frac{S}{A} = \frac{0.12}{0.028} = 4.3 \text{ lb/A}$$

   3. Three pounds of seed were placed in a spinner (cyclone) seeder with a 12 foot seeding width. Seed was sufficient to cover a distance of 1,000 feet. What is the seeding rate per acre?

      SR = S/A

      $$A = \frac{12 \times 1{,}000}{43{,}560} = 0.28 \text{ acres}$$

      $$SR = \frac{S}{A} = \frac{3}{0.28} = 10.7 \text{ lb/A}$$

A.14. Common and Scientific Names of Forage Grasses, Legumes, and Forbs.

Common name	Scientific name	Category[1]
Forage grasses		
Bahiagrass	*Paspalum notatum* Flugge	WSP
Barley	*Hordeum vulgare* L.	CSA
Bermudagrass	*Cynodon dactylon* (L.) Pers.	WSP
Bluegrass, Kentucky	*Poa pratensis* L.	CSP
Bluestem		
Big	*Andropogon gerardii* Vitman	WSP
Caucasian	*Bromus caucasia* (Trin.) C.E. Hubb.	WSP
Bromegrass, smooth	*Bromus inermis* Leyss.	CSP
Canarygrass, reed	*Phalaris arundinacea* L.	CSP
Crabgrass, hairy	*Digitaria sanguinalis* (L.) Scop.	WSA
Corn (maize)	*Zea mays* L.	WSA
Dallisgrass	*Paspalum dilatatum* Poir.	WSP
Fescue, tall	*Festuca arundinacea* Schreb.	CSP
Gamagrass, eastern	*Tripsacum dactyloides* (L.) L.	WSP
Hardinggrass (phalaris)	*Phalaris aquatica* L.	CSP
Johnsongrass	*Sorghum halepense* (L.) Pers.	WSP
Millet		
Browntop	*Panicum ramosum* L.	WSA
Foxtail	*Setaria italica* (L.) Beauv.	WSA
Japanese (barnyardgrass)	*Echinochloa crusgalli (L.) Beauv.*	WSA
Pearl	*Pennisetum americanum* (L.) Leeke	WSA
Oat	*Avena sativa* L.	CSA
Orchardgrass (cocksfoot)	*Dactylis glomerata* L.	CSP
Quackgrass (couchgrass)	*Elytrigia repens* (L.) Nevski	CSP
Rescuegrass	*Bromus catharticus* Vahl.	CSP*
Rye	*Secale cereale* L.	CSA
Ryegrass		
Annual (Italian)	*Lolium multiflorum* Lam.	CSA
Perennial	*Lolium perenne* L.	CSP
Sorghum	*Sorghum bicolor* (L.) Moench	WSA
Sudangrass	*Sorghum bicolor* (L.) Moench	WSA
Switchgrass	*Panicum virgatum* L.	WSP
Timothy (herdgrass)	*Phleum pratense* L.	CSP
Triticale	*X Triticosecale* Wittmack	CSA
Wheat	*Triticum aestivum* L.	CSA
Wheatgrass		
Fairway crested	*Agropyron cristatum* (L.) Gaertn.	CSP
Standard crested	*Agropyron desertorum* (Fisch. ex Link) Schultes	CSP
Legumes		
Alfalfa (lucerne)	*Medicago sativa* L.	CSP
Alyceclover	*Alysicarpus vaginalis* (L.) DC.	WSA
Big trefoil	*Lotus uliginosus* Schkuhr.	CSP
Birdsfoot trefoil	*Lotus corniculatus* L.	CSP
Black medic	*Medicago lupulina* L.	CSA
Burclover		
California	*Medicago polymorpha* L.	CSA
Spotted (manganese)	*Medicago arabica* (L.) Huds.	CSA

Legumes...Continued

Common name	Scientific name	Category[1]
Button clover	*Medicago orbicularis* (L.) Bartal.	CSA
Caleypea		
(Roughpea, Singletary pea)	*Lathyrus hirsutus* L.	CSA
Cicer milkvetch	*Astragalus cicer* L.	CSP
Clover	*Trifolium*	
Alsike	*T. hybridum* L.	CSP
Arrowleaf	*T. vesiculosum* Savi	CSA
Ball	*T. nigrescens* Viv.	CSA
Berseem (Egyptian)	*T. alexandrinum* L.	CSA
Crimson	*T. incarnatum* L.	CSA
Hop, large	*T. campestre* Schreb.	CSA
Hop, small	*T. dubium* Sibth.	CSA
Kura (caucasian)	*T. ambiguum* Bieb.	CSP
Persian	*T. resupinatum* L.	CSA
Red	*T. pratense* L.	CSP*
Rose	*T. hirtum* All.	CSA
Strawberry	*T. fragiferum* L.	CSP
Subterranean	*T. subterraneum* L.	CSA
White (ladino)	*T. repens* L.	CSP
Cowpea	*Vigna unguiculata* (L.) Walp.	WSA
Crownvetch	*Coronilla varia* L.	CSP
Jointvetch, American	*Aeschynomene americana* L.	WSA
Kudzu	*Pueraria lobata* (Willd.) Ohwi	WSP
Lespedeza		
Annual, Korean	*Kummerowia stipulacea* (Maxim.) Makino	WSA
Annual, striate	*Kummerowia striata* (Thunb.) Schindler	WSA
Sericea	*Lespedeza cuneata* (Dum.-Cours.) G. Don	WSP
Medic, black	*Medicago lupulina* L.	CSA
Perennial peanut	*Arachis glabrata* Benth.	WSP
Sainfoin	*Onobrychis vicifolia* Scop.	CSP
Soybean	*Glycine max* (L.) Merr.	WSA
Sweetclover	*Melilotus*	
Annual yellow	*M. indica* (L.) All.	CSA
White	*M. alba* Medik.	CSB
Yellow	*M. officinalis* Lam.	CSB
Vetch	*Vicia*	
Bigflower (grandiflora)	*V. grandiflora* Scop.	CSA
Common	*V. sativa* L.	CSA
Hairy	*V. villosa* Roth	CSA
Forbs		
Chicory	*Cichorium intybus* L.	CSP
Kale	*Brassica oleracea* L.	CSA
Rape (winter rape)	*Brassica napus* L.	CSA
Turnip	*Brassica rapa* L.	CSA

[1]WS = warm season, CS = cool season, A = Annual, B = Biennial, P = Perennial, *P = May act as an annual or may live for two to three years, depending on environmental conditions and management.

A.15. Common and Scientific Names and Life Cycles of Some Common Pasture Weeds.

Common name	Scientific name	Life cycle[1]
Annual foxtail	*Setaria* spp.	A
Bitter sneezeweed	*Helenium amarum*	A
Bracted plantain	*Plantago aristata*	A
Briars	*Rubus* spp.	P
Broadleaf signalgrass	*Brachiaria platyphylla*	A
Broomsedge	*Andropogon virginicus*	P
Buckhorn plantain	*Plantago lanceolata*	P
Cheat	*Bromus secalinus*	A
Common chickweed	*Stellaria media*	A
Common pokeweed	*Phytolacca americana*	P
Common ragweed	*Ambrosia artemisiifolia*	A
Curly dock	*Rumex crispus*	P
Cutleaf eveningprimrose	*Oenothera laciniata*	B
Dogfennel	*Eupatorium capillifolium*	P
Fall panicum	*Panicum dichotomiflorum*	A
Giant foxtail	*Setaria faberi*	P
Giant ragweed	*Ambrosia trifida*	A
Goldenrod	*Solidago* spp.	P
Hairy buttercup	*Ranunculus sardous*	A
Henbit	*Lamium amplexicaule*	A
Horsenettle	*Solanum carolinense*	P
Horseweed	*Conyza canadensis*	A
Little barley	*Hordeum pusilium*	A
Mouse-ear chickweed	*Cerastium vulgatum*	A
Musk thistle	*Carduus nutans*	B
Pennsylvania smartweed	*Polygonum pensylvanicum*	A
Pigweeds	*Amaranthus* spp	A
Prickly sida	*Sida spinosa*	A
Red sorrel	*Rumex acetosella*	P
Sandburs	*Cenchrus* spp	A&P
Shepherdspurse	*Capsella bursa-pastoris*	A
Sicklepod	*Cassia obtusifolia*	A
Smutgrass	*Sporobolus indicus*	P
Swinecress	*Coronopus didymus*	A
Tall ironweed	*Vernonia altissima*	P
Texas panicum	*Panicum texanum*	A
Torpedograss	*Panicum repens*	P
Vaseygrass	*Paspalum urvillei*	P
Virginia pepperweed	*Lepidium virginicum*	A
Wild garlic	*Allium vineale*	P
Wild mustard	*Brassica kaber*	A

[1]A = Annual, B = Biennial, P = Perennial

A.16. Characteristics of Forage Grasses.

Name	Climate zone adaptation[1]	Seedling vigor[2]	Tolerance[2] to			
			Soil acidity	Poor drainage	Drought	Grazing
Warm season perennial grasses						
Bahiagrass	AB	P	E	G	E	E
Bermudagrass	ABC	F	E	P	E	E
Dallisgrass	AB	P	F	E	G	G
Johnsongrass	ABCD	G	F	E	G	P
Switchgrass	BCD	P	F	F	E	P
Warm season annual grasses						
Corn	ABCD	E	F	P	P	P
Crabgrass	ABCD	G	G	P	F	E
Pearl millet	ABCD	E	E	P	E	F
Sorghum	ABCD	G	P	P	E	F
Sorghum-sudan	ABCD	E	P	F	G	F
Cool season perennial grasses						
Kentucky bluegrass	CD	P	F	F	P	E
Orchardgrass	BCD	F	F	F	F	G
Reed canarygrass	CD	F	G	E	G	F
Smooth bromegrass	CD	F	F	F	G	F
Tall fescue E+[3]	BCD	G	G	G	G	E
Tall fescue E–[3]	BCD	F	G	G	F	F
Timothy	CD	F	F	F	F	F
Cool season annual grasses						
Annual ryegrass	ABC	G	G	E	F	E
Oats	ABC	E	F	F	F	G
Rye	ABCD	E	G	F	F	G
Wheat	ABCD	E	P	P	F	G

[1]Some species are adapted only in portions of a zone.
[2]E = Excellent, G = Good, F = Fair, P = Poor
[3]E+ = Endophyte-infected (toxic or novel endophyte), E– = Endophyte-free

A.17. Characteristics of Forage Legumes.

Name	Climate zone adaptation[1]	Seedling vigor[2]	Tolerance[2] to: Soil acidity	Poor drainage	Drought	Grazing
Warm season perennial legumes						
Perennial peanut	A	NA[3]	G	P	G	F
Sericea lespedeza	ABCD	P	E	F	E	P[4]
Warm season annual legumes						
Annual lespedeza	BCD	F	E	F	G	G
Cool season perennial legumes						
Alfalfa	ABCD	G	P	P	E	P[4]
Birdsfoot trefoil	BCD	P	G	G	G	F
Red clover	ABCD	E	F	F	F	F
White clover	ABCD	F	F	G	P	E
Cool season annual legumes						
Arrowleaf clover	AB	F	F	P	F	G
Berseem clover	A	G	P	G	G	F
Caley pea	AB	G	F	G	F	F
Crimson clover	ABC	G	G	P	F	F
Hairy vetch	ABCD	E	G	P	F	F
Rose clover	A	F	P	P	G	F
Subterranean clover	A	G	F	G	F	E

[1]Some species adapted only in portions of a zone.
[2]E = Excellent, G = Good, F = Fair, P = Poor
[3]Not applicable: vegetatively propagated
[4]Grazing-tolerant varieties are rated G

A.18. Compatibility of Legumes with Grasses.

Legume	Bahiagrass or bermudagrass[1]	Dallis-grass[1]	Johnson-grass[1]	Tall fescue, orchardgrass, timothy, or Ky. bluegrass[1]	Small grain or ryegrass[1]
Perennial peanut	X				X
Sericea lespedeza					X
Annual lespedeza				X	
Alfalfa				X	
Birdsfoot trefoil				X	
Red clover		X	X	X	X
White clover		X		X	
Arrowleaf clover[2]	X				X
Berseem clover[2]	X	X	X		X
Crimson clover[2]	X				X
Hairy vetch[2]	X				X
Rose clover[2]	X				X
Subterranean clover[2]	X				X
Caleypea[2]		X	X		

[1]The X denotes compatibility under most conditions.
[2]Annual clovers and hairy vetch may be grown with tall fescue, but are less desirable than perennial clovers.

A.19. Evaluating Alfalfa Stands.

A. Plants per square foot needed for optimum yield

Age	Plants/sq. ft.
New seeding	25-40
1st year	12-20
2nd year	8-12
3rd year and beyond	3-8

B. Stems per square foot

>50	Excellent yields possible
30-50	Expect some yield reduction
<30	Significant forage yield reduction

A.20. Approximate Seed Germination Time for Selected Plants.*

Common name	Approximate germination time, days[1]	Common name	Approximate germination time, days[1]
Alfalfa	7	Indiangrass	21
Alyceclover	21	Lespedeza	
		Korean	14
Austrian winter pea	8	sericea	28
Bahiagrass	21	Millet, pearl	7
Barley	7	Oats	7
Bermudagrass	21	Orchardgrass	10
Bluegrass, Kentucky	21	Peanut	8
Bluestem, big	14	Rye	7
Bromegrass, smooth	14	Ryegrass, annual	7
Canarygrass, reed	21	Sorghum	10
Clover		Soybean	7
Alsike	7		
Arrowleaf	10	Sudangrass	7
Burclover	14		
Button	10	Sweetclover	10
Crimson	7	Switchgrass	21
Red	7		
White	7	Timothy	10
Corn	7	Trefoil, birdsfoot	7
Cowpea	8	Velvetbean	14
Crabgrass (aged)	12	Vetch, hairy	10
Dallisgrass	21	Wheat	7
Fescue, tall	10		

[1]The number of days for each species is typical. However, **germination times will vary** depending on several factors, especially age, temperature, and moisture. Fresh seed of crabgrass and some other grasses require longer periods for germination than aged seed.

*Adapted from various sources.

A.21. Inoculation Groups for Commonly-Grown Forage Legumes.

Alfalfa group
(*Rhizobium meliloti*)
Alfalfa
Black medic
Burclover
Button clover
White sweetclover
Yellow sweetclover

Clover group
(*Rhizobium trifolii*)
Alsike clover
Arrowleaf clover[1]
Ball clover
Berseem clover
Crimson clover
Hop clover
Persian clover
Red clover
Rose clover[1]
Subterranean clover[1]
White clover

Cowpea group
(*Bradyrhizobium japonicum* spp.)
Alyceclover
Cowpea
Kudzu
Peanut
Lespedeza
Jointvetch

Lupine group
(*Rhizobium lupini*)
Blue lupine
White lupine

Pea and vetch group
(*Rhizobium leguminosarum*)
Bigflower vetch
Common vetch
Hairy vetch
Roughpea
Winter pea

Other[2]
Birdsfoot trefoil (*Rhizobium loti*)
Cicermilk vetch
Crownvetch
Soybean (*Rhizobium japonicum*)
Kura clover

[1]Specially selected strains specific for this legume species are most effective.
[2]Except for legumes listed under **Other** and those that require species-specific strains, the same inoculum can be used for all the species listed within an inoculation group.

A.22. Essential Elements for Plants and Animals.

		Plant	Animal			Plant	Animal
Carbon	C	✔	✔	Copper	Cu	✔	✔
Hydrogen	H	✔	✔	Fluorine	F	—	✔
Oxygen	O	✔	✔	Iodine	I	—	✔
Nitrogen	N	✔	✔	Iron	Fe	✔	✔
Phosphorus	P	✔	✔	Lead	Pb	—	✔
Potassium	K	✔	✔	Manganese	Mn	✔	✔
Calcium	Ca	✔	✔	Molybdenum	Mo	✔	✔
Magnesium	Mg	✔	✔	Nickel	Ni	✔	✔
Sulfur	S	✔	✔	Selenium	Se	—	✔
Arsenic	As	—	✔	Silicon	Si	—	✔
Boron	B	✔	✔	Sodium	Na	—	✔
Chloride	Cl	✔	✔	Vanadium	V	—	✔
Chromium	Cr	—	✔	Zinc	Zn	✔	✔
Cobalt	Co	—	✔				

A.23. Composition of Principal Fertilizer Materials.

Material Supplying	Nitrogen (N), %	Phosphate (P_2O_5), %	Potash (K_2O), %	Sulfur (S), %
Nitrogen				
Ammonium nitrate	33.5	0	0	0
Ammonium nitrate and limestone	20.5	0	0	0
Anhydrous ammonia	82	0	0	0
Urea-ammonium nitrate solution	28 to 32	0	0	0
Ammonium sulfate	21	0	0	24
Urea	46	0	0	0
Ammonium thiosulfate	12	0	0	26
Sewage sludge (activated)	4 to 6	2.5 to 4	0	<1
Phosphorus				
Ammonium polyphosphate (APP)	10	34	0	0
Diammonium phosphate (DAP)	18	46	0	0
Monoammonium phosphate (MAP)	10 to 12	50 to 55	0	0
Triple superphosphate (TSP)	0	44 to 46	0	1
Ground rock phosphate	0	26 to 35 (Approx. 3 % available)	0	0
Basic slag	0	10 to 25	0	0
Potassium				
Potassium chloride	0	0	60 to 62	0
Potassium nitrate	13	0	44	0
Potassium sulfate	0	0	48 to 52	18
Sulfate of potash magnesia	0	0	22	22

Source: Potash & Phosphate Institute

A.24. Average Amounts (lb/ton, wet basis) of Nutrients in Manures from Various Farm Animals.

	Average content, lb/ton				
Nutrient	Dairy cattle	Beef cattle	Poultry	Swine	Sheep
Nitrogen (N)	10.0	14.0	25.0	10.0	28.0
Phosphorus (P)	2.0	4.0	11.0	2.8	4.2
Potassium (K)	8.0	9.0	10.0	7.6	20.0
Sulfur (S)	1.5	1.7	3.2	2.7	1.8
Calcium (Ca)	5.0	2.4	36.0	11.4	11.7
Iron (Fe)	0.1	0.1	2.3	0.6	0.3
Magnesium (Mg)	2.0	2.0	6.0	1.6	3.7
Boron (B)	0.01	0.03	0.01	0.09	0.02
Copper (Cu)	0.01	0.01	0.01	0.04	0.01
Manganese (Mn)	0.03	0.01	0.18	0.04	0.02
Zinc (Zn)	0.04	0.03	0.01	0.12	0.05
Moisture, %	85	85	72	82	77

Source: L.M. Walsh, and R.F. Hensler, Manage Manure for Its Value, Wis. Ext. Circ., No. 550. H.F. Miller, I.J. Ross, and G.W. Thomas. Farm Manure: Production-Value-Use, ID-19, University of Kentucky Cooperative Extension Service, Lexington, KY.

A.25. Amount of Wet Dung Produced per 1,000 Pounds Animal Live Weight per Year.

Animal	Pounds of dung
Horse	17,500
Dairy	35,000
Beef	22,000
Sheep	13,500
Swine	19,700
Poultry	8,400

Source: Nutrient Management Code 590, Natural Resources Conservation Service, KY.

A.26. Feed and Forage Composition.

<table>
<tr><th colspan="6">Analytical fractions</th><th>Chemical constituents</th><th>Other analyses</th></tr>
<tr><td rowspan="13">Percentage of feed or forage</td><td colspan="5">Moisture</td><td>Water</td><td rowspan="3"></td></tr>
<tr><td rowspan="12">Dry matter</td><td colspan="4">Ash</td><td>Various minerals plus sand</td></tr>
<tr><td rowspan="11">Organic matter</td><td rowspan="4">NDF</td><td rowspan="3">ADF</td><td>Cellulose</td></tr>
<tr><td>Lignin</td><td>ADL</td></tr>
<tr><td>Fiber-bound nitrogen[1];
Heat-damaged nitrogen[1]</td><td>ADICP,
NDICP</td></tr>
<tr><td colspan="2">Hemicellulose</td><td></td></tr>
<tr><td rowspan="7">NDS</td><td rowspan="2">NDSC</td><td>Fructans
Glucans
Pectic substances</td><td>NDSF</td></tr>
<tr><td>Sugars
Starches
Organic acids</td><td></td></tr>
<tr><td rowspan="3">Crude protein</td><td>NPN (amino acids, amines, urea)</td><td></td></tr>
<tr><td>True protein — degradable</td><td>RDP (DIP)</td></tr>
<tr><td>True protein — undegradable</td><td>RUP (UIP)</td></tr>
<tr><td rowspan="2">Ether extract</td><td>Esterfied fatty acids</td><td rowspan="2"></td></tr>
<tr><td>Pigments and waxes</td></tr>
</table>

[1]Fiber-bound nitrogen and heat-damaged nitrogen are found also in Crude Protein and RUP

NDF = Neutral Detergent Fiber (insoluble in neutral detergent reagent)
ADF = Acid Detergent Fiber (insoluble in acid detergent reagent)
ADL = Acid Detergent Lignin (lignin extracted from ADF)
ADICP = Acid Detergent Insoluble Crude Protein (from nitrogen found in ADF)
NDICP = Neutral Detergent Insoluble Crude Protein (from nitrogen found in NDF)
NDS = Neutral Detergent Solubles (all constituents soluble in neutral detergent reagent)
NDSC = Neutral Detergent Soluble Carbohydrates
NDSF = Neutral Detergent Soluble Fiber (undigestible by animal enzymes)
NPN = Non-Protein Nitrogen
RDP = Ruminally Degradable Protein (DIP = Degradable Intake Protein)
RUP = Ruminally Undegradable Protein (UIP = Undegradable Intake Protein)
Source: J.E. Moore, Professor Emeritus (retired), Animal Sciences Dept., Univ. of Florida.

A.27. Forage Quality Parameters for Selected Forage Crops[1].

Crop	CP[2]	ADF	NDF	TDN	RFV
Alfalfa					
Bud	22-26	28-32	38-47	64-67	127-164
Early flower	18-22	32-36	42-50	61-64	113-142
Mid bloom	14-18	36-40	46-55	58-61	98-123
Full bloom	9-13	41-43	56-60	50-57	90-110
Corn silage					
Well eared	7-9	23-30	48-58	66-71	105-138
Fair to poorly eared	7-9	30-39	58-67	59-66	81-105
Tall fescue, orchardgrass					
Vegetative-boot	12-16	30-36	50-56	61-66	101-122
Boot-head	8-12	36-42	56-62	56-61	84-101
Ryegrass					
Vegetative-boot	12-16	27-33	47-53	63-68	111-134
Boot-head	8-12	33-39	53-59	59-63	92-111
Switchgrass, caucasian bluestem					
Vegetative-boot	10-14	35-40	55-60	58-62	90-104
Mature, head	6-10	40-50	60-75	50-58	62-90
Bermudagrass					
4 week old	10-12	33-38	63-68	52-58	81-93
8 week old	6-8	40-45	70-75	45-50	67-77
Pearl millet, sorghum-sudangrass					
	8-12	35-40	55-70	50-58	77-104
Red clover					
Early flower	14-16	28-32	38-42	64-67	142-164
Late flower	12-14	32-38	42-50	59-64	110-142
Annual lespedeza	12-16	35-40	45-55	58-62	98-127

[1]These are estimates. Forage quality varies as a result of many factors. Except for RFV, values in these columns are expressed in terms of percent dry matter.

[2]Abbreviations over columns are: CP=crude protein; ADF=acid detergent fiber; NDF=neutral detergent fiber; TDN=total digestible nutrients; RFV=relative feed value.

Source: J.C. Henning and G.D. Lacefield, University of Kentucky.

A.28. Yield Estimates for Three Pasture Types of Various Heights.

	Pasture canopy height (inches)			
	2	4	6	8
Species	Dry matter yield, lb/A			
Fescue-clover	700	1,500	2,000	2,400
Hybrid bermuda	1,000	2,000	2,500	3,000
Rye (small grain)	300	700	1,300	1,700

Source: D.S. Chamblee and J.T. Green, Jr. (eds). Production and Utilization of Pastures and Forages in North Carolina. North Carolina State University Tech. Bull. 305.

A.29. Maturity Stages of Grasses and Legumes.

	Grasses
Vegetative	Leafy growth, few stems, no reproductive (seedhead) growth
Late vegetative	Stem is elongating
Boot	Stem elongated, top of stem swollen
Early bloom	Seed heads (flower heads) begin to emerge
Mid bloom	At least 25% of seedheads emerged, pollen beginning to shed
Full bloom	Most seed heads emerged; peak pollen shed
Milk	All seed heads emerged; seed forming, seed soft and immature
Dough	Seed becoming harder and having a doughlike consistency
Mature	Seed hard and ready for harvest
	Legumes
Vegetative	Leaf and stem growth; no buds, flowers, or seed pods
Bud	Buds begin to swell and become apparent at a few nodes
Late bud	Several nodes with buds; buds more swollen
Early flower	A few buds open, flower color apparent
Late flower	Many flowers apparent
Early seed	Green seed pods apparent on a few flowers
Late seed	Many green seed pods apparent; some seed pods turning brown
Mature	Seed pods brown to black and dry; seed ready to harvest as moisture content permits

A.30. Crude Protein and In-vitro Dry Matter Digestibility (IVDMD) of Selected Cool Season Weeds and Forages at Three Stages of Maturity.

	Vegetative		Flower/boot		Fruit/head	
	Crude protein, %	IVDMD, %	Crude protein, %	IVDMD, %	Crude protein, %	IVDMD, %
Weeds						
Carolina geranium	19	78	14	70	11	68
Cutleaf evening primrose	20	72	14	69	11	52
Virginia pepperweed	32	86	26	72	17	63
Curly dock	30	73	19	54	16	51
Virginia wildrye	23	80	19	74	7	60
Wild oats	23	75	-	-	-	-
Cheat	23	81	18	69	14	61
Little barley	24	82	18	78	14	62
Forages						
Rye	28	79	24	81	13	70
Tall fescue	22	78	17	73	13	67
White clover	27	81	22	85	23	83
Hairy vetch	30	80	29	77	26	77

Adapted from: C.S. Hoveland, G.A. Buchanan, S.C. Bosworth, and I.J. Bailey. Alabama Agric. Exp. Stn. Bull. 577.

A.31. Crude Protein and In-vitro Dry Matter Digestibility (IVDMD) of Selected Warm Season Weeds and Forages at Three Stages of Maturity.

	Vegetative		Flower/boot		Fruit/head	
	Crude protein, %	IVDMD, %	Crude protein, %	IVDMD, %	Crude protein, %	IVDMD, %
Weeds						
Sicklepod	22	84	14	76	17	71
Coffee senna	17	81	22	75	15	67
Hemp sesbania	31	70	14	66	11	52
Tall morningglory	20	82	-	-	14	76
Ivyleaf morningglory	19	80	-	-	11	78
Cypressvine morningglory	21	80	-	-	13	77
Florida beggarweed	22	74	17	65	13	56
Prickly sida	17	80	18	70	12	56
Common purslane	-	-	19	80	-	-
Bur gherkin	-	-	17	75	14	79
Redroot pigweed	24	73	17	71	11	64
Jimsonweed	25	72	21	66	17	56
Fall panicum	19	72	9	63	7	54
Texas panicum	16	74	11	62	8	52
Yellow foxtail	18	73	12	66	14	57
Crabgrass	14	79	8	72	6	63
Crowfootgrass	16	67	8	54	9	43
Forages						
Pearl millet	17	59	6	60	8	60
Bermudagrass	16	58	7	51	8	43

Adapted from: C.S. Hoveland, G.A. Buchanan, S.C. Bosworth, and I.J. Bailey. Alabama Agric. Exp. Stn. Bull. 577.

A.32. Hay Weight/Storage Volume.

Material	Pounds/cubic foot	Cubic feet/ton
Hay or straw (loose)	4	500
Hay (baled loose)	10	200[1]
Hay (baled tight)	25	80[1]
Hay (chopped long)	8	250
Hay (chopped short)	12	170
Straw (baled)	12	170[1]

[1]Rectangular or square bales

A.33. Hay Heating.

Temperature, °F	Potential for
120	Protein breakdown
140	Sugar carmalization
150-180	Combustion

Monitoring temperatures over time is advisable. Maximum temperature is usually reached about one week after baling, but can occur up to three weeks after baling.

A.34. Characteristics of Hay Bales.

Bale shape	Height or diameter, ft	Width, ft	Length, ft	Volume, ft^3	Typical weight, lb	Dry matter density, lb/ft^3	Safe baling moisture, %
Rectangular	1.2	1.5	3.2	5.5	60[1]	9	20
Rectangular	2.7	3	7	56	900	15	12-16[2]
Rectangular	4	4	8	112	1,800	15	12-16[2]
Round	4	—	4	50	500	12	18
Round	4	—	5	63	850	12	18
Round	5	—	4	79	1,000	12	18
Round	5	—	5	98	1,300	12	18
Round	6	—	5	141	1,900	12	18

[1]Bale weight varies with any package type. For example, weights of small rectangular bales range from less than 45 to over 70 pounds.
[2]The lower moisture range is preferred where low humidities allow this moisture level to be reached; the higher range is used in other regions.

Source: M. Collins, University of Kentucky.

A.35. Breakeven Barn Cost for Various Levels of Storage Loss and Varying Hay Value at Harvest. (Inputs other than storage loss and hay value are not included.)

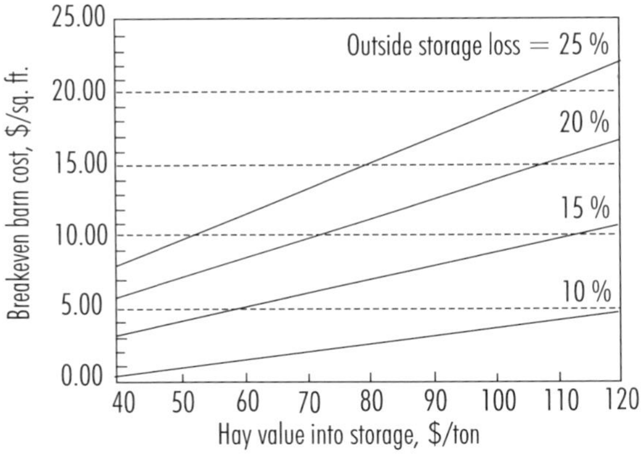

Note: This analysis includes the following assumptions: in-barn stacking height of three bales, 10-year barn life, and barn construction cost of $7.50/sq. ft.
Source: D.R. Buckmaster. Evaluator for round hay bale storage. J. Prod. Agric. 6:378-385.

A.36. Dry Matter Loss vs. Average Spoilage Depth in Round Bales of Various Diameters.

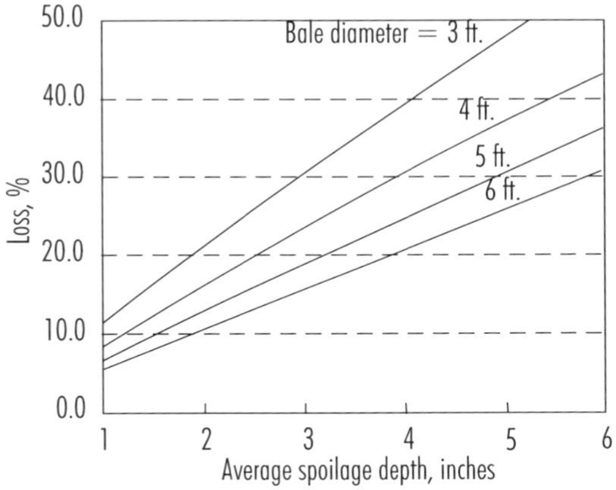

Source: D.R. Buckmaster. Evaluator for round hay bale storage. J. Prod. Agric. 6:378-385.

A.37. Determining Forage Moisture Content Using a Microwave Oven.

1. Chop fresh forage into 1 to 2 inch lengths for ease of handling.
2. Weigh out approximately 100 grams (3.5 ounces) of chopped forage.
3. Spread forage thinly on a microwave-safe dish and place into microwave.
4. Heat for two minutes and reweigh.
   a) If forage is not completely dry, reheat for 30 seconds and reweigh. (Microwaves vary considerably in drying capacity. It is better to dry for short intervals and reweigh until the last two weights are constant than to overdry and run the risk of burning the forage and damaging the oven.) Continue this process until back-to-back weights are the same or charring occurs.
   b) If charring occurs, use the previous weight.
5. Calculate moisture content using the following equation:

$$\% \text{ moisture content} = \frac{W1 - W2}{W1} \times 100$$

W1 = weight of forage before heating
W2 = weight of forage after heating
Dry Matter (DM) is the percentage of forage that is not water.
DM equals 100% minus percent water.
Example: moisture content 14%
DM = 100 - 14 = 86%

A.38. Estimate of Dry Matter (DM) Percentage in Forages at Different Stages of Growth.

Dry matter range, %	Description of forage
8 to 15	Young, green, succulent (i.e. small grains, tall fescue, ryegrass, especially in seedling stages)
15 to 20	Young, green leafy grasses in spring or when growth is rapid and succulent; white clover in mature stages; alfalfa in pre-bud stage
20 to 30	Older, slightly brown, or slow-growing plants; headed cool-season grasses; bermudagrass actively growing; alfalfa at 10% bloom
40 to 50	Growth that is more than 40% brown; stockpiled growth in winter and dormant grasses; may be stored in an airtight silo or tightly wrapped bales
40 to 80	Plants that have been cut for storage; feels slightly damp or pliable, but too wet to bale
80 to 85	Hay freshly baled; mold forms if stored below 80% DM
85 to 92	Hay stored inside after several months; in samples that are air dried in cloth bags, the leaves will break easily when crumbled or twisted

This assumes that no dew or raindrops are on the forage. Also, these are estimates that serve only as a rough guide; variations may occur with certain species, environmental conditions, or management.

Source: Adapted from: D.C. Chamblee and J.T. Green, Jr. (eds). Production and Utilization of Pastures and Forages in North Carolina. North Carolina State Univ. Tech. Bull. 305.

A.39. Nitrate in Forages.

Nitrate in feed on dry matter basis %	ppm[1]		Comments
0.0-0.25	0-2,500	SAFE	Generally considered safe.
0.25-0.50	2,500-5,000	CAUTION	Generally safe when fed with a balanced ration. For pregnant animals limit to one-half of total dry ration. Make certain water for livestock is low in nitrates. Prolonged feeding may result in Vitamin A deficiency. Do not feed with liquid feed or other non-protein nitrogen supplements. Be cautious with pregnant and young animals.
0.50-1.5	5,000-15,000	DANGER	Limit to one-fourth of ration. Should be well fortified with energy, minerals, and Vitamin A. May experience milk production loss in four to five days, possible occurrence of reproduction problems.
Over 1.5	over 15,000	TOXIC	Toxic. Do not use in free-choice feeding program. Feed containing such levels may be ground and mixed if high nitrate feed is limited to 15% of total ration.

Method of expression	Chemical designation	To convert to nitrate multiply by	To convert to nitrate nitrogen multiply by	To convert to potassium nitrate multiply by
Nitrate	NO_3	1.00	0.23	1.63
Nitrate nitrogen	NO_3-N	4.40	1.00	7.20
Potassium nitrate	KNO_3	0.61	0.14	1.00

Example: 1.0% NO_3 x 0.23 = 0.23% NO_3-N
1.0% KNO_3 x 0.14 = 0.14% NO_3-N
To convert ppm to percent, move the decimal point four places to the left, e.g. 4,400 ppm = 0.44%, 5,000 ppm = 0.5%

[1]parts per million

Note: The table above presents general guidelines that can be helpful in determining the nitrate toxicity potential of forages. However, the likelihood of toxicity can be affected by several factors including species and class of animal, degree of animal stress, animal health, extent of previous exposure to nitrate, and feeding management (see Chapter 22). In addition, sampling errors can result in misleading results. Considerable variation exists among state-to-state guidelines with regard to nitrate levels that may cause animal feeding problems.

Source: Materials compiled from several sources including: D. Miksch and G.D. Lacefield. Kentucky Agric. Ext. Ser. Herd Health memo; B.G. Ruffin, D.M. Ball, and H.A. Kjar. Alabama Agric. Ext. Ser. Cir. ANR 112.

A.40. Silo Capacities—Upright.

Tower silo capacity, wet tons
Silage at 65% moisture, wet basis. Capacities allow 1 ft. of unused depth for settling in silos up to 30 ft. high and 1 ft. more for each 10 ft. beyond 30 ft. height. Capacities rounded to nearest 5 tons.

Silo height ft.	Silo diameter, ft. 14	16	18	20	22	24	26	28	30
	- - - - - - -	- - - - -	- - - - -	wet tons	- - - - -	- - - - -	- - - - -	- - - - -	- - - - -
20	45	60	75	95	115	135	160	185	210
24	60	75	95	125	150	175	205	235	275
28	75	100	125	150	185	215	255	295	340
32	90	115	150	185	225	265	310	365	415
36	105	135	175	215	265	310	370	430	490
40	125	165	205	255	305	365	430	495	570
44	145	185	235	290	350	420	490	570	655
48	160	210	265	330	400	475	560	645	745
52	185	235	300	370	450	530	625	725	830
56	205	265	335	410	500	590	695	805	925
60	225	290	370	455	550	650	780	885	1020
64			405	500	600	715	850	970	1120
68			445	545	650	780	925	1060	1215
72						840	1000	1145	1310
76						890	1075	1220	1400
80						955	1120	1300	1485
84							1215	1385	1575
88							1285	1475	1660
92							1375	1560	1745
96							1445	1640	1830
100							1515	1730	1930

Tower silo capacity, tons dry matter
Capacities allow 1 ft. of unused depth for settling in silos up to 30 ft. high and 1 ft. more for each 10 ft. beyond 30 ft. height. To determine silo capacity in wet tons, multiply silo capacity value, dry matter, by the DMF value from **Appendix A.42.B.** Capacities rounded to nearest 5 tons.

Silo height ft.	Silo diameter, ft. 14	16	18	20	22	24	26	28	30
	- - - - - - -	- - - - -	- - - - -	wet tons	- - - - -	- - - - -	- - - - -	- - - - -	- - - - -
20	15	20	25	35	40	45	55	65	75
24	20	25	35	45	50	60	70	85	95
28	25	35	45	55	65	75	90	105	120
32	30	40	50	65	80	95	110	125	145
36	35	50	60	75	90	110	130	150	170
40	45	55	70	90	105	125	150	175	200
44	50	65	80	100	125	145	170	200	230
48	55	75	95	115	140	165	195	225	260
52	65	85	105	130	155	185	220	255	290
56	70	95	115	145	175	205	245	280	325
60	80	100	130	160	190	230	275	310	355
64			140	175	210	250	300	340	390
68			155	190	230	270	325	370	425
72						295	350	400	460
76						315	375	425	490
80						335	400	455	520
84							425	485	550
88							450	515	580
92							480	545	610
96							505	575	640
100							530	605	675

Source: Reproduced with permission from: Beef Housing and Equipment Handbook, MWPS-6, 4th Edition. Midwest Plan Service, Ames, Iowa.

A.41. Silo Capacities—Horizontal.

Horizontal silo capacity, wet tons
65% moisture; 40 lb/ft.^{3} or 50 ft.^{3} = 1 ton; 1.25 ft.^{3}/bu. Silo assumed level full. Capacities rounded to nearest 5 tons. To calculate capacity of other silo sizes: (silage depth, ft. x silo width, ft. x silo length, ft.) ÷ 50.

Depth, ft.	Silo floor width, ft. 20	30	40	50	60	70	80	90	100
	wet tons/10 ft. length								
10	40	60	80	100	120	140	160	180	200
12	50	70	95	120	145	170	190	215	240
14	55	85	110	140	170	195	225	250	280
16	65	95	130	160	190	225	255	290	320
18	70	110	145	180	215	250	290	325	360
20	80	120	160	200	240	280	320	360	400

Horizontal silo capacity, dry matter
Silo assumed level full. Capacities rounded to nearest 5 tons.

Depth, ft.	Silo floor width, ft. 20	30	40	50	60	70	80	90	100
	wet tons/10 ft. length								
10	15	20	30	35	40	50	55	65	70
12	15	25	35	40	50	60	65	75	85
14	20	30	40	50	60	70	80	90	100
16	20	35	45	55	65	80	90	100	110
18	25	40	50	65	75	90	100	115	125
20	30	40	55	70	85	100	110	125	140

Source: Reproduced with permission from: Beef Housing and Equipment Handbook, MWPS-6, 4th Edition. Midwest Plan Service, Ames, Iowa.

A.42. Silage Conversions.

A. Grain moisture factor (GMF)
To convert wet tons to tons at 15.5% moisture, divide by GMF. To convert tons at 15.5% moisture to wet tons, multiply by GMF. GMF = 84.5 ÷ (100 – % moisture).

% moisture	GMF
18	1.03
20	1.06
22	1.08
24	1.11
26	1.14
28	1.17
30	1.21
32	1.24
34	1.28
36	1.32
38	1.36
40	1.41
45	1.54
50	1.69

B. Dry matter factor (DMF)
To convert from wet tons to tons of dry matter, divide by the DMF. To convert from tons of dry matter to wet tons, multiply by the DMF. DMF = 100 ÷ (100 – % moisture).

% moisture	DMF
30	1.43
40	1.67
50	2.00
55	2.22
60	2.50
65	2.86
70	3.33
75	4.00
80	5.00

Source: Reproduced with permission from: Beef Housing and Equipment Handbook, MWPS-6, 4th Edition. Midwest Plan Service, Ames, Iowa.

A.43. Animal Unit Equivalents.

Animal class	Animal unit equivalent[1]
Cow 1,000 lb non-lactating	1.0
Pregnant heifer ≥18 months	1.0
Bull>24 months	1.5
Bull<24 months	1.2
Cow and calf	1.3
Yearling>18 months	0.9
Yearling 12-18 months	0.8
Calves<12 months	0.6
Sheep and Goats	
Non-lactating ewe or doe	0.2
Ewe or doe with young	0.3
Weaned lamb or kid	0.15
Horse	
Draft	1.5
Saddle	1.25
Others	
Deer, red	0.34
Deer, fallow	0.17
Bison, mature	1.00
Elk, mature	0.65

[1]An animal unit (AU) is considered equivalent to one mature, non-lactating cow weighing 1,000 pounds and fed at maintenance level.

A.44. Estimating Hay Needs.

Type livestock	Approximate lb hay/animal/day
Dry, pregnant cows	15-20
Cows with calves	25-28
Replacement heifers	10-12
Bred yearling heifers	18-23
Herd bull	28-30
Stocker steers	10-14
Horse	24-30
Sheep	3-6
Goat	2-5
Fallow deer	2-5

Total pounds/day x days of winter feeding = total pounds of hay needed
Total pounds needed ÷ 2,000 = tons needed

A.45. Gestation Periods.

Species	Days[1]
Cat	63
Cow	283
Coyote	63
Deer	210
Dog	63
Donkey	365
Fox	52
Goat	151
Guinea pig	68
Horse	338
Llama	342
Pig	114
Rabbit	32
Rat	22
Sheep	148
Squirrel	44

[1]These are approximate values based on information from various sources. Gestation periods may vary within species due to breed and/or environmental conditions.

A.46. Incubation Periods.

Species	Days[1]
Chicken	20-22
Duck	26-28
Goose	26-28
Ostrich	41-43
Pheasant	21-28
Pigeon	16-18
Quail	21-28
Turkey	26-28

[1]These are approximate values based on information from several sources. Incubation periods can vary within species due to breed and/or environmental conditions.

A.47. Names of Breeding Animals and Their Offspring.

Species	Bovine	Ovine	Caprine	Equine	Porcine	Feline	Canine
Common name	**Cattle**	**Sheep**	**Goat**	**Horse**	**Pig**	**Cat**	**Dog**
Male	Bull	Ram	Buck	Stallion	Boar	Tom	Dog
Female	Cow	Ewe	Doe	Mare	Sow	Queen	Bitch
Name of young	**Calf**	**Lamb**	**Kid**	**Foal**	**Pig**[1]	**Kitten**[1]	**Puppy**[1]
Young male	Bull	Ram lamb	Buckling	Colt	Boar	-	-
Young female	Heifer	Ewe lamb	Doeling	Filly	Gilt	-	-
Castrated male	Steer	Wether	Wether	Gelding	Barrow	-	-

[1]These are born in litters.

A.48. Reproduction Characteristics of Domestic Animals.

Species	Heat period	Heat cycle (days)	Gestation period (days)	Females per male (number)
Horses	6-7 days	22	336-340	15-30
Cattle	12-18 hours	19.5	283	25 average
Sheep	29-36 hours	17	142-150	25 or more
Goats	24-26 hours	20-22	151	25 or more

The age at puberty for domestic animals:

Horses	Second spring (yearling)
Cows	5 to 13 months (depending on breed and condition)
Sheep	First autumn
Goats	7 to 8 months

Source: Adapted from: National Range and Pasture Handbook, USDA/NRCS.

A.49. Estimated Water Requirements for Various Animals.

	Daily needs, gal/head[1]	
	50°F	90°F
Beef		
400 lb calf	4	10
800 lb feeder	7	15
1,000 lb feeder	8	17
Cows and bulls	8	20
Dairy		
Cows	15	30
Calves	2	12
Replacement heifers	6	15
Bulls	8	20
Horses or mules	8	12
Sheep or goats	1.5	3.5
Fallow deer	1	1.5
Swine (per 100 lb liveweight)	1	1.5
Turkeys (per 100 birds)	10	15
Chickens (per 100 birds)	6	9

[1]Water consumption varies considerably depending on animal class, overall animal health, temperature, stage of lactation, water temperature, and other environmental conditions. A rule of thumb of 1 gal of water per 100 lb of body weight is used by many cattlemen. One gal water = 8.34 lb; one cubic foot of water = 62.4 lb.

A.50. Pasture Shape/Perimeter Relationships.

Shapes[1]	Perimeter of 1 acre (feet)
Circle	744
Square	836
L = 2 x W	888
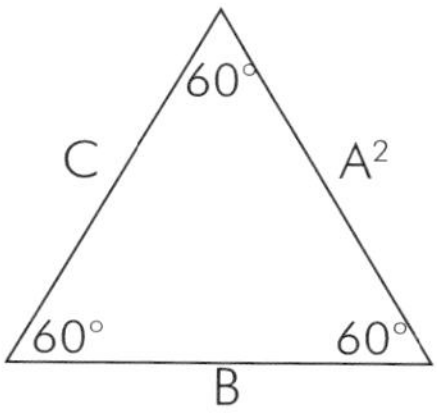	951
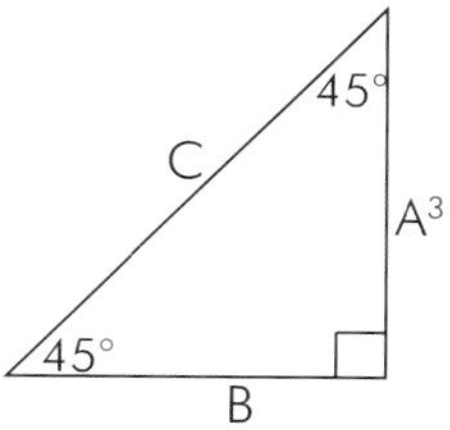	1,007
L = 4 x W	1,040
1 ft. x 43,560 ft.	87,122

L=length; W=width.

[1]Assume each figure contains the same area.

[2]Assume sides A, B, and C are of equal length.

[3]Assume sides A and B are of equal length.

A.51. Grazing Formulas.

$$\text{Number of Paddocks} = \frac{\text{Days of rest}}{\text{Days of grazing}} + 1$$

Example: Graze 4 days, rest 28 days $\frac{28}{4} + 1 = 8$

Acres Required per Paddock =

$$\frac{\text{Avg. wt. of animals to be grazed} \times \text{Dry matter consumed}^{1} \text{ per animal as \% of body weight} \times \text{Number of animals} \times \text{Days on the pasture}}{\text{Dry matter available in the area to be grazed}^{2} \times \text{\% of the dry matter utilized by grazing}^{3}}$$

Example: Forty 600 lb steers consuming 3% body weight for 4 days. Twelve inches growth, thick stand (12 x 225 lb/inch) utilizing approximately 60%.

$$\text{Acres/Paddock} = \frac{600 \times .03 \times 40 \times 4}{(12 \times 225) \times .60} = \frac{2{,}880}{1{,}620} = 1.8$$

Total Acres Required = Number of paddocks x acres required per paddock

Example: 8 x 1.8 = 14.4

$$\text{Stocking Rate} = \frac{\text{No. of animals to be grazed}}{\text{Total acres grazed}} \quad \text{Example: } \frac{40}{14.4} = 2.8$$

$$\text{Stocking Density} = \frac{\text{No. of animals grazing}}{\text{Paddock size (acres)}} \quad \text{Example: } \frac{40}{1.8} = 22$$

[1]Grazing animals will normally consume from 2 to over 3 percent of their body weight in dry matter each day. Intake varies with pasture quality and quantity and animal class. Dry beef cows will normally consume around 2 percent per day; growing steers and lactating dairy cows will normally consume around 3 percent.

[2]Dry matter available depends on species, growing conditions, and density. Although considerable variation will occur, a range of 150 to 300 pounds of dry matter for each inch of usable pasture growth is often used.

[3]Amount of dry matter utilized will depend on grazing method and grazing time. A range of 40 to 70 percent pasture utilization is common. Utilization in the upper portion of this range may occur with higher stocking rates and shorter grazing times. By comparison, forage utilization by other means might be assumed to be as follows: hay, 70 to 80 percent; strip grazing, 75 to 80 percent; silage or greenchop, 85 to 95 percent.

A.52. Approximate Pounds of Forage Available per Inch.

Species	Dry matter pounds/inch/acre	
	Average[1]	Range[2]
Alfalfa or alfalfa-grass mixture	225	75 - 400
Arrowleaf clover	200	100 - 300
Bermudagrass	260	150 - 500
Caucasian bluestem	180	75 - 350
Crimson clover	200	100 - 300
Kentucky bluegrass	160	100 - 175
Native warm season bunchgrasses	100	50 - 250
Orchardgrass	180	75 - 300
Orchardgrass-clover	200	100 - 325
Red clover	220	100 - 300
Annual ryegrass	250	75 - 400
Oats, rye, wheat	150	75 - 250
Tall fescue	210	100 - 350
Tall fescue-white clover	190	80 - 325

[1]**The values should only be used as guides.** They represent average values taken from many sources. These estimates assume reasonably thick, well fertilized, actively growing stands.

[2]Range covers thin, non-fertilized, often unmanaged stands up to fertilized, thick stands with rapid growth and high yields.

A.53. Guidelines for Rotational Stocking of Selected Forage Crops[1].

Crop	Target height, in. Begin grazing	Target height, in. End grazing[2]	Usual days rest
Alfalfa (hay types)	10-16	3-4	35-40
Alfalfa (grazing types)	10-16	2-3	15-30
Bahiagrass	6-10	1-2	10-20
Bermudagrass	4-8	1-2	7-15
Bluestem, big	15-20	10-12	30-45
Bluestem, caucasian	10-20	4-6	14-21
Bromegrass, smooth	8-12	3-4	20-30
Clover, white and subterranean[3]	6-8	1-3	7-15
Clovers, all others[3]	8-10	3-5	10-20
Dallisgrass	6-8	3-4	7-15
Eastern gamagrass	18-22	10-12	30-45
Fescue, tall	4-8	2-3	15-30
Indiangrass	12-16	6-10	30-40
Johnsongrass	16-20	8-12	30-40
Kentucky bluegrass	8-10	1-3	7-15
Lespedeza, sericea	8-15	4-6	20-30
Orchardgrass	8-12	3-6	15-30
Pearl millet	20-24	8-12	10-20
Ryegrass, annual	6-12	3-4	7-15
Small grains	8-12	3-4	7-15
Sorghum, forage	20-24	8-12	10-20
Sorghum/sudan hybrids	20-24	8-12	10-20
Switchgrass	18-22	8-12	30-45

[1]These are merely guidelines. Stocking rates and growing conditions greatly affect forage growth. Also, the more closely pastures are grazed, the longer the rest period generally needs to be for species that are sensitive to defoliation.

[2]The nutritional requirements of the livestock being grazed should be considered when deciding when to end grazing. The closer a pasture is grazed, the lower forage quality will be toward the end of that particular grazing cycle.

[3]Clovers are typically grown with pasture grasses. White clover and subterranean clover are quite tolerant of close defoliation; most other clovers are not.

Source: Information compiled from several sources including: D.M. Ball, C.S. Hoveland, and G.D. Lacefield. Southern Forages (2nd Edition), Potash & Phosphate Institute and Foundation for Agronomic Research; Natural Resources Conservation Service Conservation Practice Standard (Alabama), Code 528A; D.S. Chamblee and J.T. Green, Jr. (eds). Production and Utilization of Pastures and Forages in North Carolina, North Carolina State University, Tech. Bull. 305. In addition, advice regarding certain species was provided by V.G. Allen, Texas Tech University; R.L. Dalrymple, The Samuel Roberts Noble Foundation; and J. Gerrish, University of Missouri-Columbia.

A.54. Approximate Diet Selection of Grazing Animals when Offered in a Mixed Pasture.

Animal species	Type of diet		
	Grasses	Broadleaf weeds and legumes	Browse[1]
Cattle	65-75	20-30	5-10
Horses	70-80	15-25	0-5
Sheep	45-55	30-40	10-20
Goats	20-30	10-30	40-60
White-tail deer	10-30	30-50	30-50
Elk, red, and fallow deer	30-60	40-50	10-30

[1]Shrubs or trees.

Source: D. Forbes and G.W. Evers, Texas A&M Univ.; D.I. Bransby, Auburn Univ.; M.A. McCann, Virginia Tech Univ.; and W.R. Getz, Fort Valley State Univ.

A.55. Characteristics of Selected Plants for Wildlife.

	Tolerance to soil acidity[1]	Annual or perennial	Fertility needs[2]			Tolerance to wet soils[1]
			N	P	K	
Alfalfa	P	P	NA	H	H	P
American jointvetch	F	A	NA	M	M	F
Annual lespedeza	G	A	NA	L	L	P
Browntop millet	G	A	H	M	M	F
Chufa	G	A	M	M	M	G
Egyptian wheat	P	A	H	M	M	P
Florida beggarweed	G	A	NA	M	M	E
Foxtail millet	G	A	H	M	M	F
Japanese millet	G	A	H	M	M	E
Sorghums	P	A	H	M	M	P
Cowpea	G	A	NA	M	M	P
Partridge pea	G	A	NA	L	L	G
Proso millet	G	A	M	M	M	P
Sericea lespedeza	E	P	NA	L	L	P
Sesame	P	A	L	M	M	P
Sesbania	G	A	NA	L	L	E
Shrub lespedeza	E	P	NA	M	M	P
Sunflower	F	A	L	H	H	P
Velvetbean	F	A	NA	M	M	P
Annual ryegrass	F	A	H	H	H	G

[1]E = Excellent; G = Good; F = Fair; P = Poor

[2]NA = Not applicable; properly inoculated legumes fix N that they use for growth. H = High; M = Medium; L = Low

Index

*Numbers in color indicate a photograph or illustration.